WORLD®
AIR POWER
J O U R N A L

Aerospace Publishing Ltd

Airtime Publishing Inc.

Published quarterly by
Aerospace Publishing Ltd
179 Dalling Road
London W6 0ES
UK

Copyright © 1993 Aerospace
Publishing Ltd

Cutaway drawings
copyright © 1993 Greenborough
Associates Ltd

ISSN 0959-7050

Aerospace ISBN 1 874023 34 4
(softback)
1 874023 35 2
(hardback)
Airtime ISBN   1-880588-07-2
(hardback)

Published under licence in USA and
Canada by Airtime Publishing Inc.,
10 Bay Street, Westport,
CT 06880, USA

Editorial Offices:
WORLD AIR POWER JOURNAL
Aerospace Publishing Ltd
179 Dalling Road
London W6 0ES
UK

Publisher: Stan Morse
Managing Editor: David Donald
Editor: Jon Lake
Production Editors:
   Karen Leverington
   Trisha Palmer
Design: Barry Savage
        Robert Hewson
Typesetting: SX Composing Ltd
Origination and printing by
   Imago Publishing Ltd
Printed in Singapore

Europe Correspondent:
   Paul Jackson
Washington Correspondent:
   Robert F. Dorr
USA West Coast Correspondent:
   René J. Francillon
Asia Correspondent:
   Pushpindar Singh

The editors of WORLD AIR
POWER JOURNAL welcome
photographs for possible
publication, but cannot accept any
responsibility for loss or damage to
unsolicited material.

The publishers gratefully acknowledge
the assistance given by the following
people:
Mr Tom Pollard, Commander Doug
Caie, Captain Tony White, Captain
Jan Thomson, Major D. Everett,
Major Marty Tate, Captain Jane
McDonald, Captain John Blakely for
their help with the Air Power
Analysis.

World Air Power Journal is a
registered trademark in the
United States of America of
Airtime Publishing Inc.

World Air Power Journal
is published quarterly
and is available by
subscription

**SUBSCRIPTION AND BACK
NUMBERS:**

UK and World (except USA and
Canada) write to:
Aerospace Publishing Ltd
FREEPOST
PO Box 2822
London
W6 0BR
UK

(No stamp required if posted
within the UK)

USA and Canada, write to:
Airtime Publishing Inc.
Subscription Dept
10 Bay Street
Westport, CT 06880
USA

Prevailing subscription rates are
available on request.
For single and back issues of the
soft-cover edition (subject to
availability):
$17.95 each for delivery within
mainland USA, Alaska and
Hawaii. $22 (Can) each for
delivery to Canada. $22 (US)
each for delivery overseas.
Please enclose payment with
your order. Visa, MasterCard
and American Express accepted.
Include your card number,
expiration date and signature.
Hard-cover subscription rates
available on request.

Publisher, North America:
   Melvyn Williams
Subscription Director:
   Linda DeAngelis
Charter Member Services
Manager:
   Jill Brooks

WORLD AIR POWER®

JOURNAL

CONTENTS

Military Aviation Review

Western Europe

BELGIUM:

MIRSIP contract cut short

Having been ordered to retire its Mirage 5s at the end of 1993, the FAB/BLu limited its Mirage Safety Improvement Programme (MIRSIP) to the 10 aircraft on which work had already begun. In addition to the prototype, BA60, flown on 28 December, they are Mirage 5BAs BA04, 11, 46 and 62 and Mirage 5BD trainers BD01, 03, 13, 14 and 15. The programme was originally intended to comprise 15 BAs and five BDs. With delivery of the last MIRSIP aircraft due a few weeks before the disbandment of 42 Squadron in December 1993, Belgium was attempting to find a new home for its surplus Mirages, also including 27 BAs, 18 reconnaissance BRs and five BDs, none of which has been upgraded.

FRANCE:

Last Mirage III overhaul

Impending retirement of the Mirage IIIE and IIIBE was marked on 25 February by the roll-out at Nancy of the 897th and last Mirage IIIE/IIIBE to receive a major overhaul by the support groups at Dijon, Luxeuil, Colmar and Nancy. The final aircraft, IIIE No. 539 '3-XO' of EC 3/3, was finished in a highly original air defence grey and blue colour scheme, in contrast to the normal green and dark grey. EC 1/3 will begin conversion to Mirage 2000Ns in February 1994, in preparation for which the first of this sub-variant was handed over to the Armée de l'Air on 9 April to begin trials at Mont-de-Marsan.

Mirage 2000C for EC 2/12

EC 2/12, the second of three Mirage F1C squadrons in 12 Wing to receive Mirage 2000Cs, was returned to flying on 23 April, having stood down on 1 November 1992 to begin conversion. It was due to be redeclared operational on 1 September 1993.

The Aérospatiale Alouette II is becoming something of a rarity in ALAT service, but a number are retained for regional defence force work and for training.

First Tucanos received

EMBRAER was expecting to display the first pair of Tucanos for France at the Paris air show in June. The aircraft are assigned the designation EMB-312F to reflect their high proportion of French avionics. French requirements are for 50 Tucanos to replace the ageing Fouga Magisters at the Ecole de l'Air (GI 312) at Salon de Provence, plus a further 30 (unlikely to be ordered) for various base flights also operating Magisters. The Brazilian manufacturer expects to produce 14 Tucanos in 1993, including the two Super Tucanos for the USAF's JPATS competition.

Rafale carrier trials

Naval Rafale prototype M01 completed its second series of catapult trials in the USA during January and February in preparation for an initial sea landing aboard the carrier *Foch* in the Mediterranean. Arriving in the US by sea on 7 January, M01 began its month of trials, including 28 take-offs, on the dummy deck at NAWC Lakehurst on 14 January as a follow-up to an earlier series in July-August 1992. The first real deck landing aboard the *Foch* was made on 19 April while operating from Istres. For take-offs, of which about 30 were made, the *Foch* was fitted with a temporary 1.5° ski-jump. M01 will return to America in 1994 for further testing. Rafale Ms are to enter service in 1998 although it will be 2000 before the new, nuclear-powered *Charles de Gaulle* is commissioned.

Mirage IV keeps going on

Prospects were revealed early in the year for further life extension for Mirage IVP strategic bombers, 18 of which serve two squadrons of 91 Wing following their conversion from IVA standard. It is now proposed that, after replacement as carriers of the ASMP nuclear stand-off weapon by Mirage 2000Ns in 1995, they will be assigned to strategic reconnaissance at least until 1998.

Hawkeye order

The navy's search for an airborne early warning aircraft to operate from the new aircraft-carriers *Charles de Gaulle* and *Richelieu* – the first of which is now under construction – ended with the expected decision in favour of Grumman's E-2C Hawkeye. The US Congress has been formally notified of a French request for four aircraft.

Fouga fraternity festivity

A reunion of former Fouga CM.170 Magister personnel at Salon-de-Provence on 19 May marked the 2 millionth flying hour in French service of this venerable trainer. Salon is the base of Groupement d'Instruction 312, the last major operator of the aircraft, and also the first, when deliveries began in 1956. In all, 437 Magisters were delivered to the Armée de l'Air.

GERMANY:

New structure for Luftwaffe

Details were published in the spring of the fourth air force structure plan (Luftwaffenstruktur 4) due to come into force at the end of 1994. In its new guise, the Luftwaffe will be divided into Northern and Southern Commands, each with two Divisions. Formerly, Divisions were wholly devoted to either air defence or strike/attack/reconnaissance; in future, they will contain a variety of units. Transport wings are controlled from a higher level of the command chain. As part of the restructuring process, Lw personnel will fall from 105,000 to 83,400 or less.

As before, the General Staff (Führungsstab der Luftwaffe) will control three principal commands, all at Köln-Wahn: Luftwaffenamt, Luftwaffen Führungskommando (formerly known as Luftflottenkommando) and Luftwaffen Logistikskommando (previously LwUnterstützungsKdo). **Luftwaffenamt** (Air Force General Office) will administer the German element of the Trinational Tornado Training Establishment at RAF Cottesmore; Amt für Wehrgeophysik (military mapping unit, including two BAC Canberras); 1 and 3 Technische Schulen (technical schools, including some instructional airframes); two training academies, three training regiments, four musical corps, security service and medical service. The training command in the USA also reports to LwAmt. **Luftwaffen Logistikskommando** (LwLogKdo – Air Force Logistics Command) will control the Air Materiel Office, six supply regiments and the German section of NATO HQ at Glons, Belgium.

Luftwaffen Führungskommando (LwFührungs-Kdo – Air Force Central Command) in fact is to comprise four subordinate commands: LwFührungsdienstkommando (Service Command at Köln-Wahn) with two radar regiments and three reporting centres; Lufttransportskommando (Air Transport Command at Münster) with three mixed transport wings (LTG 61-63) of Transall C.160Ds and Bell UH-1Ds, plus the VIP transport unit (Flugbereitschaftstaffel) and various SAR flights of UH-1s; Luftwaffenkommando Süd and Luftwaffenkommando Nord with the majority of combat aircraft.

LwKdo Süd at Messtetten will have two divisions: 1 and 2 Luftwaffendivision, the former including JBG 32 (Tornado IDS), JG 74 (F-4F Phantom), FlaRakGruppen 5 and 6 (SAMs), Radar Control Regiment 2 and the tactical training command on Crete (TaktAusbKdo GR). In 2 Division at Birkenfeld will be JBG 31, 33 and 34, all with Tornado IDS; FlaRakG 4 (SAM); tactical training command in Sardinia (TaktAusbKdo IT) and a radar training group.

LwKdo Nord at Kalkar also divides assets between two divisions. 3 LwDiv at Gatow is to control JG 72 (F-4F), JG 73 (F-4F and MiG-29), AG 51 Tornado IDS (recce), FlaRakG 1 and 2 (SAM) and tactical training command USA (TaktAusbKdo USA). 4 LwDiv at Aurich has JBG 38 (Tornado IDS), JG 71 (F-4F), FlaRakG 3 (SAM), Radar Control Regiment 1, the German contingent flying NATO Sentries (DtA NATO E3A) and tactical training command at Goose Bay (TaktAusbKdo CA).

The Belgian army has ordered 28 of the A 109BA anti-tank helicopter. Each carries eight TOW missiles.

Luftwaffe in Eastern Germany

Presently known as 5 LwDivision, the air component in former East Germany will become 3 Division in the new structure. The Luftwaffe has decided which units will be retained. Listed by base, these are:

Berlin: 3 Staffel/Flugbereitschaftstaffel (Mi-8 and L-410 at Schönefeld); Lw Museum (presumably relocated from Uetersen); Fernmeldesektoren 121 (Radar Reporting Sector 121);

Döbern: Abgesetzter Technischer Zug 253 (Technical Disposals Platoon);

Elmenhorst: Abgesetzter Technischer Zug 164 (Technical Disposals Platoon);

Gleina: Abgesetzter Technischer Zug 254 (Technical Disposals Platoon);

Holzdorf: Lufttransportgeschwader 62 (C.160D and UH-1D); Radarführungsabteilung 25 (Radar Control Section); Radarführungskompanie 251 (Radar Control Company); Technische Kompanie 252 (Technical Company);

Krugau: Luftwaffenmaterialdepot 51 (Material Depot); Luftwaffenkraftfahrzeugtransportstaffel 52 (Road Transport Squadron);

Laage: Jagdgeschwader 73 (MiG-29 and F-4F);

Ladeburg: Stab FlaRak Geschwader 2 (HQ of SAM Wing); Stab FlaRak Gruppe 24 (HQ of SAM Group); Versorgungsstaffel and 1-6 Staffeln of FlaRak Gruppe 24 (Supply Squadron and Nos 1-6 Squadrons of 24 SAM Group with Patriot SAMs from 1997);

Putgarten: Abgesetzter Technischer Zug 163 (Technical Disposals Platoon);

Sanitz: FlaRak Gruppe 31 Stab, Versorgungsstaffel and 1-6 Staffeln (HQ, Supply Squadron and 1-6 Squadrons of SAM Group with Hawk SAMs – first two squadrons began moving in on 1 July 1993);

Schneeberg: LwMunitionsdepot 51 (Ammunition Depot);

Trollenhagen: LwVersorgungsregiment 5 (Supply Regiment); Luftwaffenwerft 51 (Workshops); Luftwaffenkraftfahrzeugtransportstaffel 53 (Road Transport Squadron); Radarführungsabteilung 16 (Radar Control Section); Radarführungskompanie 161 (Radar Control Company); Fernmeldesektor 110 (Radar Sector); Fliegerhorststaffel (Air Base Squadron); Luftwaffensicherungsstaffel (Security Squadron);

Utzedel: LwBetriebsstoffdepot 51 (Fuel depot);

Wittstock: HQ and 20-25 Staffeln of LwAusbildungsregiment (Training Regiment);

Wusterwitz: Abgesetzter Technische Zug 255 (Technical Disposals Platoon).

Heeresfliegerstaffel 11 of the German army celebrated 25 years of accident-free flying with special marks on this Alouette II.

The list reflects early 1993 reversal of plans to transfer more units to the east, notably one of the two fighter wings scheduled for the former GDR. Immediate post-unification intentions were for JBG 35 and 36 to re-role from attack to air defence and relocate their Phantoms to the east, becoming JG 73 at Holzdorf and JG 75 (JG 72 in the interim) at Laage. The destination of Holzdorf was switched to Falkenberg (a few miles away, although still in the south-east), but the cost of upgrading either base has proved prohibitive. Instead, JG 35 will replace one of its two F-4F ICE Phantom squadrons with the entire German MiG-29 inventory and relocate to Laage, south of Rostock, in the north-east, from where it will be responsible for covering all of eastern Germany. The other wings remain in the west as JG 71 at Wittmundhafen, JG 72 at Hopsten and JG 74 at Neuburg. Holzdorf will now become the base of transport wing LTG 62, which is to move in from Wunsdorf, having previously been earmarked for Neubrandenburg. LTG 62 is to augment its C.160s with two squadrons of UH-1Ds when HTG 64 disbands later in 1993.

Tornado ECR consolidation

382 Squadron (2/JBG 38) at Jever is expected to relinquish its Tornado ECR (Electronic Combat and Reconnaissance) aircraft in favour of the IDS model as part of a plan to concentrate the ECR force of 35 aircraft at Lechfeld. The latter currently houses 321 Squadron (1/JBG 32) operating ECRs and 322 Squadron operating IDSs

This special scheme was applied to commemorate the end of Mi-8 flying at Cottbus. Only LTG 65 remains with the type.

which are earmarked for Jever (Jever's 1/JBG 38 is the Tornado weapons training unit). German ECRs have been operating in air defence suppression roles with up to four AGM-88 HARM anti-radar missiles, but their full capabilities will not be achieved until late in 1993. This is the consequence of development delays with the Texas Instruments emitter-locator system (ELS), which enables the aircraft to detect and pinpoint a radar transmitter before launching a missile towards it. Five aircraft had previously been fitted with an ELS for trials, but the first production units did not begin arriving until April 1993.

Last call for AG 52

Disbandment of the second and last remaining German RF-4E Phantom wing was foreshadowed in plans announced by AG 52 at Leck early in 1993 to hold a final beer-call on 26 August. The wing, which was then training Turkish personnel on its aircraft (including some from disbanded AG 51), intended to begin running down in September. Its badge, a panther (interpreted as a 'tiger' for NATO purposes), will be transferred to AG 51 at Schleswig/Jagel. The latter reformed on 1 April and began receiving Tornados transferred from co-located naval wing MFG 1, which will run down to disbandment early in 1994. Despite being assigned some 40 ex-navy Tornados, AG 51 will have only nine camera pods (six of them from Italy) with which to conduct its reconnaissance duties. A new recce system will be acquired for the late 1990s.

Elint Atlantic upgrade

Following cancellation of the Grob D-500 Egrett high-altitude reconnaissance aircraft in February, Germany launched a priority upgrading programme for its five specially-modified Elint Atlantic 1s of MFG 3 at Nordholz. The aircraft differ from the 14 remaining maritime patrol Atlantics in having a large, black ventral radome.

Base closures

Air bases at Husum (ex JBG 41) and Bremgarten (ex AG 51) were closed at the end of January following disbandment of their resident units the previous month. A few JBG 41 Alpha Jets continued to operate from Schleswig until their pilots were able to begin conversion to other types of aircraft. The Flugbereitschaftstaffel (VIP Squadron) at Köln-Wahn withdrew its last Do 28D Skyservant in December 1992, one example (5903) being among a further batch of 25 Skyservants (including four naval) offered for sale early in 1993.

GREECE:
Starfighter farewell

F-104G Starfighters were withdrawn from Greek service at the end of March when Nos 335 and 336 Squadrons at Araxos began re-equipping with newly arrived US-surplus A-7 Corsairs. Only these two units have operated the F-104, although Greece received 135 aircraft since 1963, comprising 43 F-104Gs, two RF-104Gs and

Another KLu squadron celebrating 40 years was No. 316.

six TF-104Gs from original MAP production; 10 F-104Gs and two TF-104Gs from Spain in 1972; two more trainers from Germany in 1977; 10 F-104Gs from the Netherlands in 1982; and 47 F-104Gs and 13 TF-104Gs from Germany through the 1980s. Not even the Starfighter's allegedly high attrition accounts for such a large number of aircraft with just two squadrons, for many of the late deliveries were used for spares breakdown.

New equipment

As well as receiving A-7s, Greece was assimilating other newly arrived aircraft in the spring of 1993. These included three ex-USAF C-130B Hercules serving alongside C-130Hs of 356 Mira at Elefsis and an unknown number of ex-German RF-4E Phantoms with 348 Mira at Larissa.

ITALY:
Further air force cuts

Italy's worsening financial crisis early in 1993 prompted another defence review which, if implemented, will result in further deep cuts in the armed forces. The AMI is expected to be worst hit and will suffer a manpower reduction from 75,000 to 60,000, closure of 12 of its 25 principal air bases and a Eurofighter 2000 programme trimmed from 130 aircraft to between 90 and 110. Also at risk is the AMX programme. Of 187 single-seat and 51 trainer versions planned, only 110 and 26 are on firm order, and some of these may be cancelled or else built and stored. Naval

aviation is more fortunate: its 18 ordered Harrier IIs will be delivered and a further eight obtained later. Production of the single-seat AMX had reached the 72nd when MM7160 was delivered to 103° Gruppo on 1 February 1993.

5 Wing run-down

The AMI will not re-equip 101° Gruppo of 8° Stormo at Cervia with the AMX when its Aeritalia G91Ys are retired next year. Instead, 8 Wing will gain the Starfighter-equipped 23° Gruppo from nearby Rimini, where 5° Stormo is being disbanded. The 5th's other squadron, No. 102 which moved to reinforce the 6° Stormo at Ghedi in October 1992, began to receive the first of 19 Tornados there in August 1993. In future, Rimini's only flying unit will be 83° Centro of 15° Stormo flying SAR HH-3F Pelicans.

Reconnaissance reorganised

As the result of development problems with the pallet-mounted recce equipment intended for its AMX fighter-bombers, the AMI is planning to repackage the Martin Marietta ATARS (Advanced Tactical Air Reconnaissance System) for internal stowage. This will be issued to four squadrons: 28° and 132° Gruppi of 3° Stormo at Villafranca; 13° Gruppo/32° Stormo at Brindisi; and 103° Gruppo/51° Stormo at Istrana. The Villafranca squadrons will be dedicated recce units, additionally equipped with Delft Instruments Orpheus

pods formerly carried by F-104G Starfighters. Furthermore, 102° Gruppo's new Tornados are to have a dual recce/attack tasking, perhaps using the podded version of ATARS together with a synthetic aperture radar. These modifications will be incorporated at the type's mid-life update.

Upgraded G222

Trials were conducted during the Italian contribution to the relief operation in Somalia of an Alenia G222 (believed to be MM62105) with upgraded avionics. The new kit, now expected to be incorporated in all 31 aircraft of the 46ª Brigata Aerea, comprises SMA-710 weather radar (as in HH-3F Pelicans), a Litton LTN-92 INS and an Elmer five-channel GPS.

NETHERLANDS:
Helicopter force reorganised

In preparation for the arrival of new combat and support helicopters, the KLu's Groep Helikopters began expansion from three to five squadrons. 302 Squadron formed on 1 January within the existing 300 Squadron at Deelen and, although currently assigned to training, it will eventually go to Gilze-Rijen as a combat unit. The other combat squadron will be No. 301, also to form at Gilze. Of the existing squadrons, No. 298 will move from Soesterberg to Eindhoven and replace its Alouette IIIs with transport helicopters for airlift and medevac; No. 299 moves from Deelen to Gilze with its BO 105s in support of 11 Air Mobile Brigade; and No. 300 replaces Alouette IIIs with new helicopters for training, ECM, medevac and other incidental tasks and transfers from Deelen to Eindhoven.

Naval Lynx force standardised

The MLD's standardisation programme for the Westland Lynx was drawing to a conclusion in mid-1993. Naval aviation has converted five utility UH-14As, nine sonar-equipped SH-14Bs and eight MAD-equipped SH-14Cs to SH-14D standard (although the SH-14Cs underwent interim modification to SH-14Bs when their MAD was replaced by sonar). Fleet equipment now includes 'dunking' sonar, FLIR, radar warning receivers, GPS, uprated (Mk 42) versions of Rolls-Royce Gem engines and composite-materials rotor blades. Only 16 of the helicopters carry their sonar, but the other six have provisions for its installation.

F-16 squadron changes announced

316 Squadron, flying F-16As from Eindhoven, is to be disbanded on 1 April 1994, its 41st birthday. The OCU task previously performed by No. 316 will pass to No. 313 at Twenthe on the date the former disbands. No. 314 at Gilze-Rijen will become the OCU on 1 January 1996, allowing No. 313 also to disappear. From 1994, Eindhoven will replace de Peel as the reserve base for Volkel.

The KLu workshop at Woensdrecht, DMVS, redelivered the last of 55 early-production F-16s (J-638) retrofitted with a tail parachute housing under the Pacer Tail programme. A further 45 were modified by Fokker. Tail parachutes, which were on Norwegian F-16s from the outset, were introduced to air force aircraft on the production line from 85-0135 (J-135).

NORWAY:
Falcon 20s upgrade

The three Dassault Falcon 20s of Skvadron 335 at Gardemoen, two of them outfitted for ECM training, were being converted to -5 configuration during 1993 by Allied Signal at Springfield, Illinois, with Garrett TFE731-5BR engines. Work was

scheduled for completion in September and consists principally of the installation of the new turbofans.

PORTUGAL:
More Aviocars

Two CASA C.212 Srs 300 Aviocars were ordered for coastal pollution control and fisheries protection duties early in 1993, to be equipped with SLAR and IR/UV scanners. The FAP operates the survivors of 24 earlier Aviocars in transport, ECM training and geographical survey roles, two of them currently assigned to the roles to be assumed by the new aircraft.

F-16 plans

The first of Portugal's F-16s will be delivered to 201 Esquadra of Grupo 51 at Monte Real in June or July 1994 and the last of the 17 F-16As (serials 6101-6117) and three F-16Bs (6118-6120) will have been received by January 1995. Despite their designations, the aircraft have most of the capabilities of the current production standard of F-16C/D. When Portugal receives ex-German Alpha Jets – late in 1993, it is hoped – they will be operated from Beja by 301 Esquadra, which is currently at Montijo with G91Rs. Built by Germany as a fair-weather training base, Beja is to be transferred to Portuguese control. Tancos is to be closed by the end of 1993.

SPAIN:
Mirages congregate at Albacete

Mirage F1EEs formerly with Esc 462/Ala 46 at Gando, Canary Islands, returned to the mainland early in the year to be repainted with the insignia of Ala 14, the operator of Mirage F1CEs. From its base at Albacete, 14 Wing now provides detachments of both Mirage sub-variants to Gando and Manises. At the latter, Ala 11 retired its Mirage IIIEEs on 1 October 1992, replaced by 12 F-1s.

F-5 changes

Ala 21, the SF-5 wing at Morón, is shortly to re-equip with 18 CASA C.101 Aviojets taken from Esc 411/412 at Matacán. The SF-5As and SRF-5As of Esc 211 and 212 will be passed to Ala 23 at Talavera, which currently flies just SF-5B trainers, although only a few will remain operational, the remainder being scrapped for spares.

Harrier order confirmed

Spain's confirmation of its follow-on order for Harriers was received on 8 March when McDonnell Douglas revealed a commitment to eight AV-8B Harrier II Plus aircraft to be delivered from 1996 onwards. Assembled locally by CASA from US/ UK-supplied kits, these radar-equipped aircraft will augment the 11 survivors of 12 standard AV-8Bs which are also earmarked for upgrading to the same configuration. Spain has also ordered a TAV-8B trainer.

UNITED KINGDOM:
RAF's 75th anniversary

Torrential rain forced cancellation of a 148-aircraft flypast to mark the 75th anniversary of the Royal Air Force in a ceremony held at Marham on 1 April. In spite of the weather's cruel joke, HM The Queen and other members of the Royal Family reviewed a line-up of 70 aircraft representing most Europe-based flying units of the RAF and a further eight which formed part of an indoor display of RAF history since its formation from the Royal Flying Corps and Royal Naval Air Service in 1918.

Tornado GR.Mk 4 troubles

Delays of up to 18 months in the Tornado GR.Mk 1 to GR.Mk 4 mid-life upgrade (MLU) programme which had accumulated by the spring resulted in Treasury pressure on the RAF for its abandonment. Concerns that the number of aircraft to be modified will be reduced to about 80 and some of the intended new equipment will be deleted were partly realised on 4 May when the Chief of Air Staff, Sir Michael Graydon, announced that the GEC-Marconi Spartan terrain-referenced navigation system (for stealthy, low-level penetration) and FLIR would be omitted, although the Mk 4 will still receive a digital databus (providing an improved avionics/ weapons interface), new information displays and upgraded ECM equipment. The MLU prototype is one of the oldest Tornados remaining: XZ631 (P15), which was due to fly in May or June, has been outfitted with some of the appropriate avionics. It will be joined soon afterwards by two full conversions, ZD708 and ZG773, the latter having seen no RAF service as a GR.Mk 1.

Modification of Tornado GR.Mk 1s to maritime attack GR.Mk 1Bs is to be a two-phase programme. The aircraft concerned are those of Nos 27 and 617 Squadrons at Marham, which are due to move to Lossiemouth. Under the original plans, No. 27 was to have transferred on 1 April 1993 and become No. 12 Squadron on 1 October. However, as the infrastructure for the Tornado was not completed in time, No. 12 Squadron (Buccaneer) is to disband on 1 October and transfer its number plate to No. 27. The new No. 12 Squadron (Tornado) will relocate to Lossiemouth on 1 January 1994. No. 208 Squadron is to disband on 1 April 1994, ending the Buccaneer's career with the RAF, and be replaced by No. 617. The initial phase of the GR.Mk 1B conversion will enable the Tornado to carry an 'austere optional' fit of four Sea Eagle anti-ship missiles (or two, plus two tanks). At a later stage the aircraft will be able to fly with five missiles (or four, plus one tank). Candidate prototype Mk 1B ZA407 arrived at BAe, Warton for rework on 20 January.

The RAF is working on a baseline specification for the Tornado GR.Mk 1/4 replacement, Air Staff Target 425. One possible solution being examined is the Eurofighter 2000, a further 100 of which could be bought (increasing the UK's share to 350) to replace some Harrier GR.Mk 7s and, possibly, part of the Tornado fleet. However, that would severely diminish prospects for a supersonic STOVL replacement for the Harrier.

Airborne stand-off radar

Also under study is Staff Requirement (Land/Air) 925 which defines the need for at least six aircraft to undertake stand-off radar reconnaissance for the UK armed forces. The system will be a parallel to the USAF's E-8C J-STARS and French Horizon radar beneath a Eurocopter Cougar (Super Puma). An air platform has yet to be selected, but may be a large business jet. Radar trials have been under way for several years in a Canberra and bulbous-nosed B-N Islander. NATO is looking for a similar capability and the RAF may wish (or be forced) to join that venture.

Chinook HC.Mk 2 arrives

Delayed from March, delivery to the UK of the first Chinook HC.Mk 2 upgrade (ZA718) was rescheduled for 10 May,

On its return from service at Incirlik on Operation Warden, this Jaguar sported new nose-art.

when its transporting ship was due at Liverpool docks. Belated arrival was understood to be the result of repairs following damage caused by an Allen key left in a gearbox.

Flight-checking civilianised

Hunting Aviation Services was selected on 1 April to calibrate RAF air traffic control and landing aids throughout the UK, Germany and Mediterranean. The firm will take over four Andover E.Mk 3s of No. 115 Squadron and operate them from East Midlands Airport, providing crews, operations management and technical support. In view of the fact that the Andover is not certified for civil operations, it is possible that the aircraft will retain their military markings.

Squadron moves

A May announcement revealed that No. 39 (No. 1 PRU) Squadron is to move its Canberra PR.Mk 9s to Marham in December, while No. 51 Squadron's three Elint Nimrod R.Mk 1s are to go to Waddington in January 1995. Logically, the Electronic Warfare Operational Support Establishment will also transfer to Waddington during the autumn of 1995. The moves, together with the previously revealed relocation of No. 100 Squadron's Hawks to Finningley in the late summer, will divest Wyton of its flying units, as No. 360 Squadron (Canberra T.Mk 17/17A) will disband in October 1994 when its electronic warfare training roles are taken over by a civilian firm. Wyton will become a satellite of RAF Logistic Command when it forms at nearby Brampton on 1 April 1994, its units including elements from Swanton Morley and Harrogate. Personnel and Training Command is to be established at Innsworth on 1 April 1994, its responsibilities including all flying training units. The present Support Command is to disappear.

Auf Wiedersehen, RAFG

As planned, RAF Germany became No. 2 Group of Strike Command on 1 April, commanded by Air Vice Marshal 'Black' Robertson. Demotion from Command to Group status as a result of halving aircraft strength has been accompanied by NATO-related command changes. The officer commanding RAF Germany has always had the dual position of OC 2nd Allied Tactical Air Force at Rheindahlen. However, on 7 April, 48 NATO aircraft flew a mass mission to mark the transfer of 2nd ATAF command from the UK (ACM Sir Andrew Wilson) to Germany (Major General Friedrich Busch).

Flying units of No. 2 Group on its reformation comprised Nos 3 and IV Squadrons with Harrier GR.Mk 7s at Laarbruch, Nos IX, 14, 17 and 31 with Tornado GR.Mk 1s at Brüggen, and No. 18 with Chinooks and Pumas at Laarbruch. No. 431 MU at Brüggen was closed on 31 March and RAF Gütersloh held its closing ceremony (final aircraft movements) the same day.

Aircraft of the RAF's 2nd Tactical Air Force (Nos 2, 83, 84 and 85 Groups) arrived in Europe in June 1944 and became the British Air Force of Occupation on 15 July 1945. The 2nd TAF re-emerged in September 1951 and was assigned to NATO in February 1952, becoming RAFG on the first day of 1959, shortly after the last of the Groups (No. 2) had disbanded.

Women join AAC

The Army Air Corps gained its first women pilots on 30 April when Captain Rose Ashkenazi and Sergeant Alison Jenkins received their wings after training at Middle Wallop. Both have been posted to Gazelle squadrons in Germany and may progress to Lynx later in their careers.

The former Czech and Slovak air force is splitting between the two now-separate republics. This is a MiG-21MF visiting Cambrai.

Base closures

Despite the comparatively recent (May 1992) arrival of USAF Special Forces aircraft, RAF Alconbury is to close as a flying station, it was officially announced on 7 May. The Hercules and MH-53Js of the 352nd SOG will transfer by the end of March 1995 to Mildenhall, where new accommodation is being built, but the U-2Rs were all due to have returned to the US before the end of September 1993.

The same announcement confirmed that Upper Heyford is to be returned to the UK MoD, the US Navy presence at Brawdy is to end by September 1996, and the US Army is to close its munitions storage base at RAF Caerwent by December 1993, instead of mid-1995. Heyford was scheduled for relegation to a stand-by base at the end of 1993, but the USAF will now withdraw completely by 30 September 1994. In addition, RAF Greenham Common, the former USAF base and previous home of the International Air Tattoo, is to be sold. RAF Hullavington was closed on 31 March and handed over to the army the following day. In spite of the change, the airfield remained active and was due to receive two Volunteer Gliding Schools later in 1993: No. 621 from Weston-super-Mare and No. 625 from South Cerney.

First 'production' Sea Harrier FRS.Mk 2

Delayed by development problems, delivery of the Royal Navy's first 'production' rebuilt Sea Harrier (XZ497) took place on 2 April. The aircraft was assigned to the A&AEE at Boscombe Down for trials work, augmenting the two prototypes. Of the latter, XZ439 made the type's first launch of a Hughes AIM-120 AMRAAM on 29 March while flying from Eglin AFB, Florida.

In addition to the 29 'production' Mk 2s on order, the Royal Navy is expecting to acquire at least 18 more from new manufacture. A commitment to 10 was made early in 1990, then increased to between 18 and 22, deliveries to start in 1995. The RN received 57 Mk 1 versions of the Sea Harrier. BAe delivered the last of 23 Mk 51s to India in April 1992, leaving the aircraft temporarily out of production.

DRA retirements

Withdrawal of Defence Research Agency aircraft from Farnborough has continued with transfers to Boscombe Down and retirements of some older equipment. DRA's Comet 4(Mod) XV814 has been withdrawn from service after 27,000 hours and relegated to a spares source at Boscombe Down to keep the A&AEE's XS235 flying. The latter, first flown on 26 September 1963, is the world's last airworthy Comet. Pre-dating it by a considerable margin, Douglas Dakota ZA947 was withdrawn from the DRA Transport Flight, which disbanded at Farnborough on 1 April, and was presented to the RAF Battle of Britain Memorial Flight at Coningsby, with which it will fly in World War II colours for a trial period.

Record-breaking OCU disbands

A ceremony at Wyton on 23 April marked disbandment for No. 231 OCU after 41 years with the same type of aircraft. Formed at Bassingbourn on 1 December 1951 to train crews on the new English Electric Canberra, No. 231 accepted its initial aircraft in February 1952 to become the world's first jet bomber OCU. Since then it has trained over 8,000 aircrew from 17 countries. It is believed that no other unit has operated the same type of aircraft for such a length of time, although the record is slightly blemished by a temporary disbandment on 15 December 1990, following which the unit became the Canberra Standardisation & Training Flight until it reclaimed the No. 231 number plate shortly afterwards.

Sea King training to St Mawgan

Two Westland Sea King HAR.Mk 3s of the Sea King Training Unit officially transferred from RNAS Culdrose to RAF St Mawgan on 2 April, having spent the years

since 1978 attached to the Royal Navy. There, the unit is being built up to OCU standard with more helicopters and its own simulator in preparation for the conversion of RAF Wessex SAR flights with six Sea King HAR.Mk 3As on order. Previously, it had been producing six new crews per year.

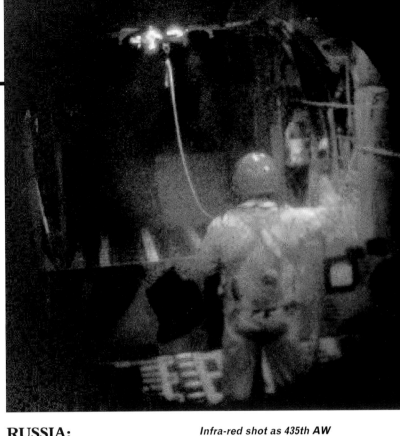

Eastern Europe

BALTIC STATES:
Air force expansion

Deliveries to the newly founded Lithuanian air force early in 1993 included a pair of ex-German military L-410UVP(T) light transports. These have joined at least 16 ex-civil (LY- prefix) An-2 'Colts', some ex-aero club Yak-52s and the four L-39C trainers recently obtained from Kyrgyzstan. The L-39s officially began operations from Panevezys on 16 February, wearing the national marking of a two-armed crucifix within a shield. An-2s have been reported operating from Prociunai. To show lack of bias, Germany has also delivered pairs of L-410s to Latvia (joining seven An-2s) and Estonia. The latter's allocation was given civil registrations (ES- prefix), although a civil Mil Mi-2 was recently given a military tactical code, implying formation of an air arm.

CROATIA:
Air force strengthened

Several ex-Aeroflot Mil Mi-8TV-1s appear to have entered service with the new air force of Croatia in recent months. Five in the airline's markings (H-103, H-203, H-211, H-213 and one other) were noted at Divulje barracks in April, together with camouflaged H-101, H-205, H-207 and H-210, plus H-201 and H-204 in red, white and blue.

Use of microlight aircraft in Croatian insignia was revealed in spectacular fashion on 4 February when a two-seat machine was brought down by small-arms fire near Deletovci, within a Serb-held enclave of Croatia. The unidentified aircraft was alleged to have been dropping hand grenades and taking photographs.

GEORGIA:
Russian aircraft downed

Georgian forces claimed to have shot down a Russian Sukhoi on 19 March as the aircraft was attempting to intercept Su-25s operated by Georgian military units in the breakaway region of Abkhazia. Russia claimed that the Georgians were about to attack its positions, but a counter allegation stated that Russian aircraft had previously been used in bombing raids in support of Abkhaz separatists. The aircraft type was reported as an Su-27 'Flanker'.

Georgia currently has an air force comprising a helicopter regiment (including Mi-8 'Hips') at Novo Alexeevka. Its share of the former Soviet air forces should comprise 100 aeroplanes and 50 helicopters, few of which appear to be operational, with the exception of any new Su-25 'Frogfoots' which may be built at Tbilisi.

HUNGARY:
Orlik order

The first known export order for Poland's PZL-130TB Orlik basic trainer was revealed to be Hungary, which is to acquire 12. This may presage a change in Hungarian pilot training procedure, which used to train in former Czechoslovakia after grading in Zlin 43 light aircraft.

MACEDONIA:
UN recognition

Over a year after declaring its independence from Yugoslavia, Macedonia was accepted as a sovereign state by the UN Security Council on 7 April. Its national flag, a brilliant sun on a red field, has yet to appear on any aircraft. This leaves Serbia as the sole remnant of 'new' Yugoslavia, and it is unlikely that Macedonia will be allowed to split peaceably from the federation.

POLAND:
K-15 power for Iryda

Rejecting the 2,425-lb st (10.8-kN) PZL-5 turbojet which powered the first five PZL I-22 Iryda prototypes, the Polish air force has specified a pair of PZL K-15s rated at 3,300 lb st (14.7 kN) for its production version. Flight trials began in the spring with a re-engined aircraft (fourth prototype, SP-PWD) designated I-22 Model 92, and these engines were earmarked for the sixth prototype, which was due to fly later in 1993.

One of many aircraft to appear in Bosnia in the all-white United Nations scheme is this Il-76 from Russia.

RUSSIA:
Disbandments and scrapping

Russian withdrawals from Germany continued in March with departure of three combat regiments in two days. It was the turn of the MiG-27 fighter-bomber to suffer as 296 Regiment left Grossenhain and 55 Regiment departed Finsterwalde, both on 22 March, followed by 19 Regiment from Mirow the next day. Each unit had an establishment of 31 MiG-27s, plus seven or eight tandem-seat MiG-23 versions for operational training. Grossenhain and Mirow hosted the MiG-27M and MiG-27D respectively and Finsterwalde the later model MiG-27K unofficially known as 'Flogger-J2'.

The MiG-27s may be among the 2,000 aircraft which Russia expects to scrap from 1993. All MiG-21s, Su-7s, older Su-17s and Aero L-29s have already been withdrawn from use (in Russia, not necessarily in other CIS members), and will eventually be joined by Su-17Ms, MiG-23s and MiG-27s. This move will leave only the MiG-29, Su-24, Su-25 and Su-27 in tactical service. Unfortunately for the air force, planned 1993 deliveries of MiG-29s and Su-27s have been halted because of funding shortages.

Infra-red shot as 435th AW crewmen drop supplies into Bosnia from a C-130E.

Strategic forces of Long-Range Aviation are shortly to scrap their last Tu-16 bombers, Tu-95Ks, Tu-95Ms and original Tu-22s, leaving only Tu-95MS, Tu-22M and Tu-160, plus Il-78 tankers. Military Transport Aviation will standardise on the Il-76 and a small force of 26 An-124s, augmented by the new An-70T. Most An-12s have gone from this branch of the air force, as has apparently the An-22 (most of which always seem to have been with Aeroflot).

(former) YUGOSLAVIA:
Air drops over Bosnia

USAF Hercules from the 37th ALS/435th AW based at Rhein Main, Germany, embarked on a programme of aid drops to besieged communities in Bosnia-Herzegovina as the danger of mass starvation increased in the face of Serbian advances on Muslim-held territory. Augmented by detached C-130Es from Pope AFB's 317th AW and MC-130H Combat Talon IIs from the 7th SOS/352nd SOG at Alconbury, UK, Operation Provide Promise began on the night of 27/28 February with

a drop by two aircraft of 600,000 leaflets which, it was hoped, would dissuade the several warring factions from opening fire on the aid aircraft. As a further security measure, this and subsequent flights were at 10,000 ft (3050 m) and under cover of darkness.

The initial food drop was made over Cerska on the night 28 February/1 March, three aircraft delivering 23 tons (21 tonnes), of which about 1.6 tons (1.5 tonnes) was medical supplies. Aid was said to have fallen within 195 ft (60 m) of the aiming point, but the nearest of the nine pallets dropped proved to be 0.75 mile (1.2 km) in error and were not retrieved by their intended recipients. The second night's operation, over Zepa, was reported to have enjoyed greater success. Following a review after the third night's mission, the US government decided to continue with the drops. The main food item was the US armed forces' MRE (Meal Ready to Eat) ration pack – hardly renowned as *cordon bleu*, but nutritious and sufficiently compact for up to 8,000 to be carried by each Hercules.

The Provide Promise operation was soon joined by Transall C.160s flown by French and German crews from all operating wings in both countries. The first French mission was flown on 27 March using as a forward base Frankfurt/Main, to where two aircraft had deployed on 21 March as Operation Courlis. Supported by E-3B/C Sentries and USN E-2C Hawkeyes keeping watch for any fighter activity, nightly missions normally comprised eight transport aircraft: six US and one each from the other two participants. In the first six weeks, 2,000 tons (1815 tonnes) of food and 50 tons (45 tonnes) of medical supplies were delivered with increasing accuracy, the average being a 125-ft (38-m) error, thanks to GPS updates of the Hercules' Adverse Weather Delivery Systems. Three drop zones were visited each night. The USAF operation was later joined by Hercules from several ANG and AFRes units.

It had been expected that the RAF would join the airlift, using the two Sarajevo-airlift Hercules which had been transferred from Zagreb to Ancona, Italy, in mid-February. Support would have been provided by Tornado F.Mk 3s and Jaguars which the RAF had on stand-by in the event of the UN enforcing its 'No-Fly Zone' over Bosnia. However, with the re-opening of Sarajevo airport on 23 February after a break in the air bridge, the aircraft returned to their normal duties and Britain decided not to participate in parachute drops. In contrast, France and Germany

joined the USAF effort and regularly attached one of their Transall C.160s to the Hercules formations. The Netherlands offered a squadron of F-16s (drawn from Nos 306 Squadron at Volkel in the recce role and No. 315 at Twenthe) to escort the USAF Hercules missions, but this was not taken up.

In anticipation of a general ceasefire, NATO was planning during March to lead a 32,000-man UN force to keep the peace in Bosnia, supported by US Army AH-64A Apache combat helicopters and fixed-wing aircraft based on carriers and at Italian air bases. Major vessels in the area then included USS *Kennedy*, USS *Guam*, HMS *Ark Royal* and FNS *Clemenceau*. Westland Lynx were well represented, apart from two each aboard HMS *Coventry* and HMS *Brilliant*, including those aboard the Royal Netherlands navy frigate HrMs *Abraham Crijnssen* and FNS *De Grasse* and *Jean Bart*. RN forces were strengthened late in January with the addition of four Sea King HAS.Mk 6s shipped out by RFA *Fort Grange*.

As Serbian forces closed in on the Muslim enclave of Srebrenica in Bosnia-Herzegovina during late March, international calls intensified for a UN-approved campaign of precision bombing raids on Serbian military targets and implementation of the long-declared but unenforced 'No-Fly Zone' over Bosnia (Resolution 816). A Security Council trade-off on 31 March secured Russian approval for the zone at the expense of sanction for bombing. By 31 March, E-3 Sentries had logged 450 violations of the zone over six months, one of the most flagrant occurring early in March when three Serbian 'propeller-driven trainers' dropped bombs on two villages close to Srebrenica.

NATO approved deployment of 50-100 aircraft for the purpose of zone patrol on 2 April, control to be exercised by HQ 5th ATAF at Vicenza. This represented the first occasion on which NATO had operated outside its defined area of responsibility. Final authorisation to proceed was given by the NATO North Atlantic Council on 8 April and assembly of forces began. When complete, the NATO force totalled 74 aircraft: 10 French Mirage 2000Cs at Cervia, 18 Netherlands F-16As at Villafranca, 18 Turkish F-16Cs at Ghedi, eight RAF Tornado F.Mk 3s at Gioia, 12 USAF F-15Cs at Aviano, and 12 USN F/A-18s from USS *Theodore Roosevelt* in the Adriatic. French Mirage F1CRs at Istrana and USN F-14s also took part, apparently in the reconnaissance role to obtain intelligence for bombing raids, should they be sanctioned.

Fuji T-3s are flown by the 11th Air Wing at Shizuhama. Another wing of T-3s is based at Hofu.

EGYPT:
L-59 deliveries begun

It became evident with the first deliveries on 29 January that the 48 Aero Albatros jet trainers ordered by Egypt are of the upgraded L-59E variety, rather then L-39s. Locally-assembled EMBRAER Tucanos were supposedly the replacement for Egypt's ageing L-29 Delfins, but the Albatros order closely followed a gift from Libya in March 1990 of 10 L-39s. Production of the L-39 continues at Vodochody to meet a Thai order for up to 36 and, to date, 2,800 have been built for service in 14 countries.

IRAQ:
Strikes from both sides

Iranian fighter-bombers breached the UN 'No-Fly Zone' in northern Iraq to bomb a French-run hospital at Raniya on 15 March, killing at least six Kurdish civilians. On 9 April, three USAF F-16s and an F-4G dropped four cluster bombs on a AAA site near the Saddam Hussein Dam in northern Iraq after they had been fired upon – the first Iraqi hostile act since Mirage F1CRs were attacked on 3 February. In a further incident on 18 April an Iraqi radar site was attacked by a USAF aircraft which it had attempted to track.

ISRAEL:
Hornet prospects

Israeli interest in McDonnell Douglas F/A-18 Hornet acquisition increased to the extent of evaluating a pair of two-seat aircraft on home ground between 15 March and 2 April. The IDF/AF requires 40–48 aircraft for procurement between 1995 and 1997 and has shown interest in the night attack version of F/A-18D used by the US

Marine Corps. Also in contention, however, is the General Dynamics F-16C (already in the inventory) equipped with Martin Marietta LANTIRN navigation/targeting pods.

CH-53 upgrades begin

Hand-over of the first Sikorsky CH-53 upgraded by IAI's Mata plant at Jerusalem took place on 2 February, launching a programme which is expected to involve about 30 Stallions. Initial aircraft (serial number 044) arrived for re-work to Yas'ur 2000 (Albatross) standard in June 1990 and began flight testing in May 1992. A second prototype began modification in September 1991 and others are following as they fall due for major overhaul. Upgrading involves structural changes, new avionics (rewiring, two multi-function displays, new autopilot and mission computer), an Elisra-built electronic warfare system, external fuel tanks, refuelling boom and SAR winch. In all, 72 of the CH-53's 138 systems have been upgraded, 42 have been replaced and 24 are entirely new.

JORDAN:
Equipment disposals

Funding shortages, presumably stemming from a cut-off of Saudi Arabian aid following Jordan's moral support of Iraq in the Gulf War, were the cause of the RJAF offering for sale all nine remaining Sikorsky S-76s, the two Lockheed C-130B Hercules (leaving four C-130Hs) and five Northrop F-5As. Still in service, however, is the venerable de Havilland Dove Mk 8 light transport, which spent the early part of 1993 on overhaul in the UK.

Middle East

ABU DHABI:
Hawk 100 hand-over

Following a delay caused by dispute over power levels required by the aircraft's air-conditioning system, hand-over began at BAe's Warton plant in April of the first of 18 Hawk Mk 102s ordered in 1989. The aircraft, fitted with wingtip missile rails, laser noses and radar warning receivers, are the

first Srs 100 Hawks to be delivered to a customer. In addition, 15 survivors of 16 earlier Hawk Mk 63s have recently been upgraded to Mk 63A standard and interest has been expressed in a small number of Mk 63Cs.

In addition to transport missions within Chile and to Antarctica, the C-130s of Grupo 10 also fly overseas to collect spares and other military equipment.

Far East

HONG KONG:

RHKAAF changes

In preparation for the return of the UK colony to China in 1997, the Royal Hong Kong Auxiliary Air Force was transformed into the Government Flying Service on 1 April and its aircraft given civil registrations to replace their military serials (beginning HKG1). At the time of transition the RHKAAF/GFS possessed two Beech Super King Airs, four Slingsby Firefly trainers, eight Sikorsky S-76s and the first two of an anticipated six S-70A Black Hawks. Formed on 1 May 1949, the HKAAF became 'Royal' in 1951 and operated Spitfires before becoming a liaison and support force in 1955.

JAPAN:

FS-X go-ahead

Contracts placed during April covered the three essential elements of the first prototype FS-X fighter-bomber, a considerably modified version of the General Dynamics F-16 Fighting Falcon. Mitsubishi Heavy Industries is to provide the airframe, Mitsubishi Electric the radar and EW systems, and Mitsui the F110-GE-129 powerplant in time for a first flight in July 1995 and delivery for military trials in March 1996. Prototypes nos 2 to 6 were due to be ordered later in 1993.

Fewer Russian incursions

Data released by the ASDF for 1992 showed that there were 331 scramble sorties flown to intercept Russian aircraft transiting the Japanese air defence zone, compared with 488 in 1991 and a peak of 879 in 1988. Fighter sorties far exceed the number of incursions (which was not disclosed) as lack of refuelling probes on ASDF interceptors requires multiple launches to escort a single intruder. Reconnaissance flights by the Russians appear not to have declined to any great degree, the reductions recently noted being principally attributable to cuts in training, fish spotting and other types of mission. This is in contrast to the United Kingdom, whose Air Defence Region has not been graced by a single uninvited Russian since 6 September 1991.

Cobra replacement plans

The Ground Self-Defence Force announced its intention of terminating orders for the Fuji/Bell AH-1S Cobra attack helicopter at the 94th example, having ordered 84 up to and including the FY 5 (1993) defence budget. The type serves five attack squadrons at Tokashi, Hachinoe, Metabaru, Obihiro and Kisarazu, but will need replacement from 2005 when the aircraft's 5,500-hour airframe lives begin to be exhausted. Selection of a replacement is to be completed by 1998 from contenders including the McDonnell Douglas AH-64 Apache, Eurocopter Panther and Tiger and an improved AH-1.

ASDF future requirements

A new attack helicopter is but one of several programmes which the Japan Defence Agency intends to launch in order to replace current equipment. Some will be among the 473 new aircraft which it is intended to buy in the 1996-2000 defence plan, although the prospects for achieving that number in the current financial climate are remote in the extreme. New aircraft under consideration include **AT-X**, an advanced trainer to replace 72 Mitsubishi T-2s; a **C-X** follow-on to 27 Kawasaki C-1 transports; **KC-X**, which will be a tanker version of the last-mentioned; **U-X** to supplant five Beech B65 Queen Airs (for selection in 1994); **LR-X**, a replacement for the GSDF's Mitsubishi LR-1s (MU-2s) used in reconnaissance and liaison roles; **AH-X**, the AH-1S replacement; and **UH-X** for replacement of some Fuji/Bell HU-1s (UH-1s).

In the last-mentioned connection, the GSDF is converting some of its 122 HU-1B/Hs to uprated HU-1J standard but plans to replace others with a new helicopter which will almost certainly be the Mitsubishi/Sikorsky UH-60J. Kawasaki was awarded a contract in February for preliminary design of the OH-X light scout helicopter which will be powered by an equally new 800-shp (596-kW) engine from Mitsubishi.

More Eagles and Orions

The Hyakuri-based 7 Air Wing completed conversion to Mitsubishi-built McDonnell Douglas F-15J Eagles in April when 305 Squadron replaced the last of its F-4EJ Phantoms. The ASDF now has seven Eagle squadrons, comprising Nos 201 and 203 in 2 Wing at Chitose; No. 202 in 5 Wing at Nyutabaru; No. 303 in 6 Wing at Komatsu; No. 304 in 8 Wing at Tsuiki; and Nos 204 and 305 at Hyakuri. The Aggressor Squadron at Nyutabaru has F-15DJs.

Maritime SDF 7 Squadron at Kanoya also completed its transition from Lockheed P-2J Neptunes to P-3C Orions in April. Orion squadrons are now Nos 1 and 7 at Kanoya (1 Group); Nos 2 and 4 at Hachinoe (2 Group); Nos 3 and 6 at Atsugi (4 Group); No. 5 at Naha (5 Group); and No. 8 at Iwakuni (31 Group). The last-mentioned also has two UP-3D Elint aircraft of 81 Squadron, while P-3Cs are used for training by 206 Squadron at Shimofusa.

Two commemorative schemes have emerged from South Africa. Above is a C-130B of No. 28 Sqn, which celebrates its 50th anniversary and 30 years flying the Hercules. Shown below is a No. 85 Air Combat School Impala Mk 2, painted as a huge gannet (the unit badge) for the September 1992 celebration of the unit's 25th. The national insignia has undergone change, with the SAAF eagle (right) replacing the springbok in the centre of the star.

SINGAPORE:

Training in Australia

Plans have been announced for the transfer of RSAF basic pilot training (to wings standard) from the island's crowded airspace to Australia. RAAFB Pearce will host the 29 SIAI S.211 jet trainers of Nos 130 'Eagle' and No. 131 'Harrier' Squadrons and 250 personnel from Paya Lebar under a 25-year agreement. Primary training on SIAI SF.260s of No. 150 'Falcon' Squadron remains at Seletar.

Australasia

AUSTRALIA:

M.B.326 problems

With the abandonment of plans to repair the fatigued wings of its 69 Aermacchi M.B.326 basic jet trainers, the RAAF has resorted to a fall-back position of ordering 19 wing sets from Italy and also returning to service about 11 aircraft unaffected by cracking. With careful use and regular rotation through storage pools, the resultant 30 serviceable aircraft should last until 2000, but it may be necessary for time to be bought on the RNZAF's M.B.339s in order to keep to training schedules. Plans for a direct M.B.326 replacement may be modified in order to accommodate a new light fighter with trainer derivative which could be ordered for the RAAF. One leading contender would be the BAe Hawk 200/100.

NEW ZEALAND:

Training changes

An announcement of 11 March confirmed that the main training base at Wigram is to close before 31 December 1995 as part of a 1991 plan to transfer flying instruction to Ohakea. The Pilot Training Squadron and Central Flying School are the main units involved, their equipment comprising 19 NZAI Airtrainers (following the February sale of the four similar AESL Airtourers) and loaned Bell 47Gs and UH-1D/Hs of the Light Rotary Wing Flight. The helicopters will go to Hobsonville, the home of No. 3 Squadron. Nos 2 and 3 Technical Training Schools and the Command Training School are destined for Woodbourne.

Africa

MOROCCO:

French arms requirements

Fresh interest was shown early in the year in the purchase of 15-20 Dassault Mirage 2000E multi-role fighters, reportedly after the United Arab Emirates promised financial assistance. Meanwhile, Dassault was awarded a contract to refurbish the remaining 40 of 50 Mirage F1CH/EH fighters.

SOMALIA:

UN takes over

Operation Restore Hope, the US humanitarian initiative in Somalia, officially ended on 4 May when American forces handed over the peacekeeping effort to the UN, which has deployed 30,800 troops. The food airlift into refugee camps ended on 28 February when both the USAF and RAF ceased Hercules operations, road convoys by then having become a safe method of transporting aid. US contributions to Somali relief cost $750 million. The RAF carried 3,300 tons (3000 tonnes) of food in its two Hercules between 12 December 1992 and 28 February.

South American news: Chile has received the P-3 Orions (below) from US Navy stocks to patrol its extensive coastline, while Brazil has introduced ACC-style tailcodes. The A-1 (bottom left) has 'SC' for Santa Cruz, while the T-27 (complete with new two-tone grey scheme) wears 'PV' for Porto Velho.

SOUTH AFRICA:

Nuclear bombs dismantled

First official acknowledgement of a nuclear capability was made on 24 March when President de Klerk announced that the RSA had ended its atomic weapons programme in 1990. This had been established in 1974 with the intention of building seven bombs, but only six had been produced by the time the armoury was dismantled. The intended delivery aircraft is not known, but there is a strong correlation between weapon numbers and the quantity of BAe Buccaneer S.Mk 50s in SAAF service. The Buccaneers were withdrawn from operations on 31 March 1991 when No. 24 Squadron disbanded at Waterkloof.

Rooivalk reprieve

Shortly before the cut-off of development funding due on 31 March, the two Atlas Rooivalk helicopter gunships gained a reprieve when the army allocated funds for a further two years of trials. Although initially intended for the SAAF, the Rooivalk will now be angled towards army requirements, notably close support of Olifant and Rooikat armoured vehicles used by mechanised divisions. The first prototype had completed type testing by early 1993 and was earmarked for trials of the nose cannon. At the same time, the second helicopter had completed 56 hours of tests and was being prepared for the start of electronic warfare and weapons trials in June. Efforts will be made to reduce the Rooivalk's weight and development is to be undertaken of a new avionics system with simpler cockpit displays.

South America

ARGENTINA:

Surplus aircraft deliveries

Crew conversion was proceeding under Grumman guidance early in the year on the first of a batch of 12 Grumman OV-1D Mohawk battlefield reconnaissance aircraft delivered to the Comando de Aviación del Ejercito (Army Aviation Command) from 19 December from US Army surplus stocks. A further eight are expected to complete the transaction.

The US offer of up to 54 McDonnell Douglas A-4 Skyhawk fighter-bombers was finalised in April for 36 aircraft costing $125 million. They are intended to replace the surviving 16 A-4B/Cs of V Brigada Aérea at Villa Reynolds, restoring the I and II Escuadrones de Caza-Bombardeo of Grupo 5 de Caza to their established strength of 16 aircraft each. The Skyhawks are reported to have enhanced air-to-air combat capabilities.

BOLIVIA:

Sabres withdrawn

Retirement in February of three North American F-86F Sabres from Grupo Aéreo de Caza 32 at Santa Cruz appears to have marked the end the Sabre's long and illustrious career in military aviation. The Bolivian aircraft are believed to have outlived the six (including some from Canadair and Fiat licence-production) used until recently by Honduras. First flown on 1 October 1947, the Sabre entered service in 1950 and achieved fame in the Korean War; notably, the world's first jet versus jet air combat (with MiG-15s) on 17 December the same year.

CHILE:

Orions received

Delivery was begun in February of the first of two Lockheed P-3A and six UP-3A Orions supplied from USN surplus to the Servicio de Aviación de la Armada. The P-3As will assist two Dassault Gardians and six EMBRAER EMB-111s in the patrol of Chile's extensive coastline.

MEXICO:

New turboprop trainers

Mexico emerged as the first export customer for Finland's Valmet L.90TP Redigo when two aircraft from an unannounced order were delivered as air freight at the end of April. They are presumed to be for the Escuela Militar de Aviación at Zapopán.

PERU:

New aircraft

FAP light transport requirements are to be met by a recent order for three EMBRAER EMB-110 Bandeirantes (from 'white-tail' stock) and an EMB-120 Brasilia. Naval aviation was expanded on 19 January with the air freight (Antonov An-124 Ruslan) delivery of three Mil Mi-8 'Hips', while the air force has put into service the 12 Mil Mi-17 'Hips' and seven Mi-25 'Hinds' bought from Nicaragua in August 1992.

URUGUAY:

More T-33s

Six Lockheed T-33As retired from Portuguese service have found a new lease of life with the FAU's Grupo de Aviación 2 at Santa Bernardina, Durazno, where they have reinforced three AT-33As.

VENEZUELA:

F-5 upgrade

Redelivery was due in May of a Canadair/Northrop VF-5A and two-seat VF-5B following upgrading in the Far East by Singa-

pore Aerospace. The aircraft were among the 13 VF-5As and single VF-5B operated by Escuadron 36 of Grupo Aéreo de Caza 12 at Barquisimeto when grounded in May 1990 by fatigue problems. Local refurbishment of a further seven VF-5As is due for completion by May 1994 but, in the meantime, 36 Squadron is continuing operations with ex-Netherlands aircraft (five NF-5Bs and one NF-5A), all of which had been delivered by mid-1993.

Grupo 13 reforms

Disbanded on 14 September 1990 on retirement of its veteran BAC Canberras, Grupo 13 reformed with EMBRAER A-27 Tucanos at its old base of Barcelona. The armed Tucanos have been acquired from Grupo 15 at Maracaibo following an injection of 18 ex-USAF OV-10 Broncos to boost the dwindling original force of 11. Grupo 13 and the A-27s are no longer regarded as front-line equipment, now training COIN instructors.

Above: The 138th FS, NY ANG, aka 'The Boys from Syracuse', have recently converted from F-16A/Bs to F-16C/Ds.

The final ANG unit to give up its A-7D/Ks (for F-16C/Ds) is the 162nd Fighter Squadron, Ohio ANG, at Springfield.

North America

CANADA:

Aircraft upgrades

The air force's venerable Canadair CT-133 Silver Stars (Lockheed T-33s) could receive a further lease of life as part of a wide-ranging programme of avionics upgrades for Canadian military aircraft. It is intended to give the CT-133s new cockpit instrumentation, communications and navigation equipment (including TACAN) while Canadair CT-114 Tutors are also earmarked for similar treatment. Plans are being formulated for improvements to the McDonnell Douglas CF-18 force, to include new mission computers, digital display indicators and modified radar, plus the ability to carry reconnaissance sensors and precision-guided weapons. Submissions have also been made for the Lockheed CP-140 Aurora which, subject to funding, is to gain a synthetic aperture radar, modified acoustics system, 99-channel sonobuoy receiver and new ESM.

Other upgrades are already under way, the latest at Edmonton, where CAE Aviation is adding radar warning receivers, missile approach warners and chaff dispensers to 31 Lockheed CC-130 Hercules. In April, Lockheed Canada at Ottawa was contracted to fit three Canadair Challenger 600s with electronic warfare training systems. At a later stage, Hercules will be fitted with a standard package of upgraded avionics including EFIS 'glass cockpit', global positioning system, flight management system, INS and new communications.

ECM Challenger go-ahead

Modification of three Challenger 600s for ECM will be additional to the three EC-114s already providing No. 434 Squadron with a limited communications jamming capability, I-band radar jamming and provision for chaff sowing. The full Challenger EST (Electronic Support Training) conversion of transport-configured aircraft already in CAF service involves Cross Systems ULQ-21/23 radar jammers, IBM AN/ALR-76 ESM receiver, Lucas Zeta ZS 1910 communications jammer and D/F and a Lundy ALE-502 chaff dispenser. Challengers will be supported by 10 CT-133 Silver Stars carrying new podded jammers, of which 19 are on order, including an unspecified number of Ericsson Erijammers.

The Erijammer A100 has received a recent boost to sales with orders from Switzerland for use on Pilatus PC-9s and Northrop F-5F Tiger IIs, and from Sweden for fitment to Saab Sk 37 Viggens and J 32E Lansens.

UNITED STATES:

European navy air logistics reorganised

Two of the three air logistics squadrons located in the Mediterranean to support the US Sixth Fleet are in the process of disestablishing. VR-24 at NAS Sigonella, Sicily was disbanded on 31 January 1993 following the return to the USA of their C-2A Greyhounds which have been transferred to VRC-40 at NAS Norfolk, Virginia. For more than 20 years the C-2s have provided carrier onboard delivery (COD) resupply to the aircraft-carriers located in the Mediterranean with the US Sixth Fleet. This role will now be performed by two aircraft detachments from VRC-40 which will accompany the carriers for the duration of their cruise. The first such deployment commenced in October 1992. The final carrier logistics flight by a VR-24 C-2A took place on 27 October to USS Saratoga in the Adriatic Sea while on UN peacekeeping support. The three CT-39Gs formerly operated by VR-24 have been transferred to the Sigonella base flight, joining a small number of UC-12Ms.

VR-24 was established at RAF Hendon, England as VRU-4 on 3 December 1946 before being redesignated as VR-24 on 1 September 1949, having moved to Port Lyautey, Morocco one month earlier. VR-24 assumed responsibility for the C-130Fs and KC-130Fs at NAS Rota,

Spain in 1962, until 15 October 1984 when VR-22 was established to operate the Hercules as an independent unit. The latter squadron disestablished in April 1993 with the Hercules returning to the USA for reassignment or retirement. VR-24 was stationed at NAS Rota from August 1964 until 1966, when it relocated to Naples airport. The move to NAS Sigonella was completed in 1976. The distribution of personnel and cargo within the Mediterranean region will now be performed by Naval Air Reserve C-9Bs and C-130Ts on detachment from the USA.

The only European squadron which is not affected by the changes is HC-4, which operates the CH-53E Super Stallion for vertical onboard delivery (VOD) to ships at sea. Although the area of operations of the three air logistics squadrons was primarily within the Mediterranean region, they frequently supported ships in the waters around the Middle East and the eastern Atlantic.

Electronic warfare aggressor unit changes

The Navy announced recently that active-duty electronic warfare aggressor training squadrons are to be disestablished by the end of 1993, with the role being transferred to the reserves. At present three squadrons perform this function, consisting of VAQ-33 at NAS Key West, Florida employing the EA-6A and EP-3J; VAQ-34 at NAS Lemoore, California flying the F/A-18A and F/A-18B; and VAQ-35 at NAS Whidbey Island, Washington with the EA-6B. The three squadrons are under the operational control of the Fleet Tactical Readiness Group with headquarters at Norfolk, Virginia.

The elderly EA-6As will be retired and the F/A-18s and EA-6Bs transferred to the appropriate reserve squadron. The electronic warfare role will be incorporated into the duties of existing squadrons, rather than activating new units to conduct this speciality. Consideration is being given to the continued usage of the EP-3Js and a likely squadron assignment. Large-scale EW exercises are frequently accompanied by a pair of highly modified NKC-135As and an EC-24A which are operated under contract by Chrysler Industries at TSTI Airport, Waco, Texas on behalf of the Fleet Electronic Warfare Support Group (FEWSG). The three aircraft are packed with receivers, sensors and antennas to probe the communications of friendly forces and make life as difficult as possible to test the participants under controlled conditions.

Much of the electronic warfare aggressor training is conducted by VAQ squadrons deploying to Navy attack and fighter bases for exercises. The primary duty of the EW aircraft is to provide a realistic threat to the naval pilots by jamming frequencies and broadcasting spurious communications in a similar manner to that likely to be encountered in combat.

Base closure and realignment

The Pentagon announced on 12 March a further round of installations to be considered for closure or realignment. Among the major facilities to be evaluated for closure are MCAS El Toro, California; NAS Alameda, California and its naval air depot, NAS Cecil Field, Florida; NAS Barbers Point, Hawaii; NAS Meridian, Mississippi; NAS South Weymouth, Mas-

On 18 April, McDonnell Douglas delivered the first AV-8B Harrier II Plus to the USMC. The aircraft's first flight was on 17 March.

sachusetts; NAS Dallas, Texas; Homestead AFB, Florida; K. I. Sawyer AFB, Michigan; and the air reserve facility at O'Hare International Airport, Chicago, Illinois. In addition, the giant naval air depots at NAS Norfolk, Virginia and Pensacola, Florida are on the closure list. Four facilities which will be realigned are March AFB, California; McGuire AFB, New Jersey; Griffiss AFB, New York; and NAS Memphis, Tennessee. Numerous smaller installations without flying activities are also included on the Pentagon list. The Base Closure and Re-alignment Commission will conduct a review of the facilities before making their recommendations to the President for approval in July and presenting their final report to Congress during September.

NAS Alameda: Alameda is currently a Naval Air Reserve facility housing VA-304 with the A-6E/KA-6D; HM-15 and HM-19 flying the MH-53E and RH-53D respectively; HS-85 operating the SH-3H; and VR-56 with the C-9B. A small Marine Corps reserve element consists of VMA-133 flying the A-4M; MALS-42 with a pair of TA-4Js; and HMH-772 with the RH-53D. Some of these squadrons will disband, while others will move elsewhere. Alameda also has a large naval air depot (NAD) overhauling the A-6 Intruder, P-3 Orion and S-3 Viking which will be consolidated within the other NADs.

NAS Barbers Point: The possible closure of Barbers Point will radically alter patrol operations within the Pacific Fleet, as the Navy is in the process of closing its other major P-3 Orion base at NAS Moffett Field. Patrol Wing Two is the resident

unit at Barbers Point, composed of six Patrol Squadrons operating the P-3C and a single specialist unit equipped with a mix of UP-3A, P-3B and P-3C models for 'unconventional' maritime operations. The seven P-3 squadrons will be moved to MCAS Kaneohe Bay, Hawaii and NAS Whidbey Island, Washington, which may require additional facilities being constructed at both bases. Anti-submarine warfare squadron HSL-37 equipped with the SH-2F is shore-based at Barbers Point but may well join the remaining Pacific Fleet ASW units at NAS North Island. VC-1 was stationed at Barbers Point performing VIP and aggressor support role until decommissioned in September 1992. VQ-3 was also a resident, operating the E-6A for submarine communication relay duties, but had relocated to Tinker AFB, Oklahoma by September 1992. The Coast Guard facility at Barbers Point, which operates the HC-130H and HH-65A, will also move to Kaneohe Bay. The amalgamation of active-duty Navy and Marine Corps flying squadrons at the same shore station will be in marked contrast to the previous policy of clearly defined segregation.

NAS Cecil Field: Cecil Field currently has 14 Navy Hornet squadrons in residence, including VFA-106 which is the East Coast Replacement Air Group, and VFA-203 of the Naval Reserve. The remainder are active-duty fleet squadrons which deploy aboard the aircraft-carriers CV-60/USS *Saratoga*, CV-66/USS *America*, CV-67/USS *John F. Kennedy*, CVN-69/USS *Dwight D. Eisenhower*, CVN-71/USS *Theodore Roosevelt* and CVN-73/USS *George Washington*. The sole Marine Corps reserve presence is

VMFA-142 operating the F/A-18A. Apart from being the shore station for the Hornet, Cecil Field houses the Atlantic Fleet fixed-wing deployable ASW operation composed of six squadrons flying the S-3, plus VS-27 (the Viking RAG) and VQ-6 with the ES-3A for Elint duties. The facility is home to more than 200 aircraft although several squadrons are deployed aboard aircraft-carriers at any one time. The Navy will move the Hornet squadrons to MCAS Beaufort, South Carolina, while the Vikings will be stationed at MCAS Cherry Point.

NAS Dallas: Dallas is a major reservist station with seven flying units assigned: VMFA-112 with the F/A-18A, VF-201 and VF-202 both flying the F-14A, VR-59 with the C-9B, a NARU operating a trio of A-4Ms, HMH-772 flying the CH-53D, and the Texas ANG's 181st AS flying the C-130H. The majority of these squadrons will move to nearby Carswell AFB, which was itself earmarked for closure on an earlier round of cuts. The possible expansion of Carswell has caused some politicians to question the rundown of the base in the first place. Across the runway from NAS Dallas is the large Vought Corporation facility, which recently has conducted the overhaul of A-7s and some subcontract work. The lack of direct involvement with aircraft at NAS Dallas may enable the facility to continue to operate unhindered by the closure.

NAS Meridian: Meridian is the home of Training Wing 1, formed into VT-7 and VT-19 operating the TA-4J and T-2C respectively. The closure comes hard on the heels of NAS Chase Field, which shut on 1 February 1993 following the disestablish-

ment of TW 3 on 31 August 1992. The closures will see the advanced strike training role of VT-7 transferred to NAS Kingsville, Texas, and the intermediate strike training function of VT-19 to NAS Pensacola, Florida. The elimination of two of the three intermediate/advanced flying training wings reflects the anticipated large-scale reduction in the need for naval fighter pilots by the middle of the decade.

NAS South Weymouth: South Weymouth is a small reservist station whose closure will result in its three squadrons being disbanded or transferred elsewhere. Unit assignment has already been reduced with the inactivation of VMA-322 during 1992, its A-4Ms being retired or transferred to the aggressor role. Currently at South Weymouth are HSL-74 with the SH-2F, VP-92 flying the P-3C and HML-771 operating the UH-1N. VP-92 will move to NAS Brunswick, Maine and HML-771 will relocate to NAS New Orleans, Louisiana. HSL-74 has already been given notice that it will be disestablished.

MCAS El Toro: The closure of El Toro follows hard on the heels of nearby MCAS Tustin and effectively eliminates the Marine Corps aviation presence in the Los Angeles region. El Toro is the main West Coast F/A-18 facility with seven Hornet squadrons in residence: VMFA-314 and VMFA-323, both of which are front-line units operating the F/A-18A; VMFA(AW)-121, VMFA(AW)-225 and VMFA(AW)-242, which are all former A-6E all-weather attack role employing the two-seater F/A-18D; VMFAT-101 with the F/A-18A/C/D conducting pilot training for the entire Marine Corps; and Reserve squadron VMFA-134 flying the F/A-18A. The station is home base for VMGR-352 equipped with the KC-130F/R versions of

the Hercules for inflight refuelling and transportation duties.

More than 100 aircraft are stationed at the base although overseas deployments, peacekeeping commitments and large-scale exercises ensure that not all the squadrons are in residence at the same time. The majority of El Toro's squadrons would relocate to NAS Miramar, although the Marine facility at Twentynine Palms to the east of Los Angeles is being enlarged to accommodate a number of permanently assigned flying units. To facilitate the displaced Marine Corps squadrons, the current residents at NAS Miramar would move elsewhere, with the E-2 and F-14 squadrons relocating to NAS Lemoore while the aggressor role and the Naval Fighter Weapons School will move to NAS Fallon.

Griffiss AFB: Griffiss is administered by ACC with B-52Hs of the 668th BS/416th Wg in residence, along with AMC KC-135Rs operated by the 509th ARS/380th Wg. The B-52s will relocate to the 2nd Wg at Barksdale AFB, Louisiana and the 5th Wg at Minot AFB, North Dakota, which will necessitate the latter activating a second squadron. The KC-135s will move to Grand Forks AFB, North Dakota with a second squadron activated under control of the 305th Wg. AFMC's Rome Air Development Center conducts aviation research and will remain at Griffiss AFB, along with an unspecified ANG unit. The New York Guard has five squadrons located within the state at present, flying a variety of types including the C-5A, C-130H/LC-130H, HC-130P/HH-60G and F-16A.

Homestead AFB: It comes as no surprise that Homestead will close following the devastation caused by Hurricane Andrew during August 1992. The resident flying units were evacuated prior to the arrival of the hurricane to the following locations: 31st FW (ACC) F-16Cs to Shaw AFB, South Carolina and Moody AFB, Georgia; 93rd FS (AFRes) F-16As to Wright-Patterson AFB, Ohio initially and subsequently to MacDill AFB; and 301st RQS (AFRes) HC-130s and HH-60Gs to Patrick AFB, Florida. The units will remain at these facilities indefinitely. The Inter-American Air Force Academy (ATC), which operates approximately a dozen airframes for technical training, will reform at Lackland AFB, Texas.

K. I. Sawyer AFB: ACC's B-52H-equipped 410th Wg is the major unit at K. I. Sawyer, with AMC's tenant 46th ARS flying KC-135As. The closure will permit both types to be transferred to other units, although some of the tankers will probably be retired. Sawyer AFB was to have become the last bomber base to operate the B-52G model, although these plans have been changed and the type will be completely retired from service apart from the six assigned to the 366th Wing.

March AFB: March is to lose its active status under AMC and become a reserve facility. The 22nd Wg is currently the major unit, with two squadrons of KC-10As in residence and responsibility for two further Extender squadrons stationed at Barksdale AFB, Louisiana. The March-based KC-10As will relocate upstate to Travis AFB. The Air Force Reserve is moving the 445th Airlift Wing (Associate) from nearby Norton AFB to

March AFB and will switch from associate status to a direct flying role with the assignment of a number of former 63rd AW C-141Bs. The 445th AW has already become the parent organisation for the 303rd AS operating C-130B/Es at March.

In addition, the 452nd ARW is stationed at March with the 336th ARS operating KC-135Es and two KC-10A associate refuelling squadrons augmenting 22nd Wg personnel flying Extenders. The KC-135E unit will remain at March AFB while the KC-10 associate squadrons will transfer to Travis along with their front-line counterparts. The 196th RS, California ANG currently operates the RF-4C at March AFB but is due to convert to the KC-135R during 1994.

McClellan AFB: McClellan AFB was originally included on the list of closures but was given a reprieve when Defence Secretary Les Aspin reviewed the large number of sites in California affected by the drawdown; however, the base was placed back on the list by the chairman of the commission. McClellan currently houses the Sacramento Air Logistics Center which performs the overhaul of A-10s, F-111s and F-117s. As yet no details have been made available concerning the dispersal of these functions to other centres. Flying units at McClellan are confined to approximately six WC-135Bs of the 55th WRS, which are the operational element of the Air Weather Service, and four HC-130Hs of the Coast Guard. These will be relocated locally.

McGuire AFB: This is another AMC base which will change to a reserve facility, following the inactivation of the 438th AW and the transfer of its C-141Bs to Plattsburgh AFB. The 514th Airlift Wing (Associate) will also become an operational unit with 14 C-141Bs assigned. The 327th AS

will move from NAS Willow Grove, Pennsylvania to McGuire AFB along with its eight C-130Es joining the 514th AW. The 141st and 150th ARSs of the New Jersey ANG, both flying the KC-135E, will remain at McGuire.

O'Hare ARFF: The Air Reserve Facility at Chicago's O'Hare International Airport has the 108th ARS/Illinois ANG operating the KC-135E and the 64th AS/928th AG flying the C-130H. Both units will be rehoused at Greater Rockford Airport, Illinois where new facilities are being constructed. The move will enable expansion at O'Hare to satisfy the demand of the civilian market.

USAF unit news

The activation of Air Education and Training Command (AETC) in July 1993 will result in a change of plan for the units performing B-52 and KC-135 aircrew conversion. Initially the role was to be transferred from the 93rd Wg at Castle AFB, California to the 92nd Wg at Fairchild AFB, Washington. AETC will amalgamate the training of KC-135 aircrew with that of the C-5 and C-141 at Altus AFB, Oklahoma

by the 97th Air Mobility Wing. The training of B-52H aircrew will continue to be an ACC function for the time being with operations transferring to the 2nd Wg at Barksdale AFB.

The USAF does not anticipate retiring any of its 90 B-52Hs at present but will amalgamate them at just three bases by the middle of the decade. The 2nd, 5th and 92nd Wings stationed at Barksdale AFB, Minot AFB and Fairchild AFB respectively are the three units selected to continue Stratofortress operations, each with a complement of approximately 30 aircraft within two squadrons. No mention of the B-52G has been made, although it would seem likely these will be progressively retired apart from those assigned to the 366th Wing. The possibility of reservist crews flying B-1s and B-52s has been suggested, with the Kansas ANG at McConnell AFB operating the Lancer and the Washington ANG at Fairchild AFB being allocated B-52s.

F-16 aircrew training is to be centralised at Luke AFB, Arizona once AETC is formed. The resident unit at Luke is the 58th FW with three squadrons of F-16Cs to train front-line Falcon pilots, joined recently by the 63rd FS from MacDill AFB,

Reflecting its new gaining command (Air Combat Command), the 128th FS, Georgia ANG, now decorates its F-15A/Bs with 'GA' tailcodes.

Florida. The 425th FS has been reactivated at Luke AFB to undertake the training of F-16 pilots from overseas with a number of F-16Cs transferred from the 184th FG/Kansas ANG. Consideration is being given to Air Force Reserve and Air National Guard pilots receiving their training at Luke instead of at three ANG sites, as is the current practice. Reservists destined to fly the F-16C are trained at McConnell AFB, Kansas, while F-16A aircrew receive tuition at Tucson IAP, Arizona. F-16A pilots transitioning to the air defence role are trained at Kingsley Field, Oregon.

The Air Force Reserve has changed its plan to move the KC-135Es of the 314th ARS/940th ARG from Mather AFB, California to McClellan AFB in view of the possible closure of the latter base; instead, the tankers will be located at Beale AFB. Despite active-duty Air Force units vacating Carswell AFB, Texas, the AFRes will continue operations at the base with the F-16As of 457th FS/301st FW in residence. These will be joined by Falcons of the 704th FS from Bergstrom AFB, Texas, enabling the latter facility to close. The decision to move the two Ohio ANG air refuelling squadrons from Rickenbacker ANGB to Wright-Patterson AFB has been reversed, and the 145th and 166th ARSs will remain and occupy a small part of the facility which is being transformed from a military complex to become the new Columbus International Airport. The C-141Bs of the 356th AS/907th AG have completed their move to Wright-Patterson AFB as scheduled.

AMC airlift reorganisation

Air Mobility Command has announced that it is to establish two major gateways into the United States with airlift operations centred on two air force bases. The Pacific region will be served by Travis

Prior to receiving the full MH-47E special forces variant, the US Army's 160th SOAR modified some standard Chinooks to MH-47Ds, with nose FLIR turret.

AFB, California, while the Atlantic gateway will be through Plattsburgh AFB, New York. Travis AFB currently has two squadrons of C-5A/Bs and a further two equipped with the C-141B, all assigned to the 60th Airlift Wing. These will be joined by 13 KC-10As from March AFB which will probably result in a change of designation to the 60th Air Mobility Wing. The base already has much of the infrastructure required to handle the vast amount of cargo and the number of passengers who will pass through each month.

Plattsburgh AFB is currently a tanker base with the 380th ARW in residence operating two squadrons of KC-135Qs, but is in the process of switching to the KC-135R model. These will be joined by 17 KC-10As of the 458th Operations Group which are currently stationed at Barksdale AFB. Thirty-six C-141Bs displaced by the inactivation of the 438th AW will be relocated to Plattsburgh AFB, enabling the unit to become the 380th AMW. Of the remaining airlift bases, Charleston AFB, South Carolina will commence conversion to the C-17A towards the end of 1993, while the 62nd AW at McChord AFB, Washington will probably become the second Globemaster III unit. The 436th AW at Dover AFB, Delaware will remain unchanged, equipped with three squadrons of C-5 Galaxies.

The C-141B fleet is experiencing serious technical and structural fatigue problems which will result in some aircraft being withdrawn from service during 1993. Several StarLifters are approaching their limit of 45,000 'damage hours' which are calculated by multiplying the actual number of flight hours by a factor reflecting the severity of stress placed upon the aircraft during flight operations. The deterioration of the fleet combined with the slow pace of the Service Life Extension Program (SLEP) is expected to seriously affect airlift capabilities by the middle/end of the current decade. The Air Force had hoped to keep the StarLifter in service until at least the year 2010, but this may only be possible if severe constraints are imposed. Eighteen C-141Bs will be withdrawn from service this year, with more than 240 of the 265 in service retired by the year 2000. Lockheed has proposed a SLEP involving new inner and outer wing components which will extend the damage hours to 85,000, exceeding the 2010 target by five years.

USAFE base closures, changes and updates

In a release dated 7 May the US Department of Defense announced another round of closures and changes to United States facilities in the UK. The fighter base at RAF Upper Heyford was to have become a standby facility once the last examples of the F-111E were withdrawn at the end of 1993; instead, the US Air Force will withdraw completely by the end of September 1994 with the base being returned to the Ministry of Defence. The resident 20th FW has commenced returning their F-111Es to the USA, with the 79th FS inactivating on 23 April and their final four aircraft departing on 10 May. The 77th and 55th FSs will also inactivate, followed by the 20th FW in December 1993. USAFE announced that the wing and its three squadrons were to have been moved to Spangdahlem at the beginning of 1994 to replace the 52nd FW, although objections by personnel of the latter unit have seen this plan revoked.

The US Air Force is to withdraw the majority of flying activities from Alconbury. The number of aircraft stationed at Alconbury has been reduced considerably since the base switched from fighter operations to that of special forces and reconnaissance. In particular, the 95th RS had shrunk from approximately a dozen U-2Rs to just two by early 1993, although the number in residence varies according to the operational requirements. U-2Rs also transit Alconbury while deploying to and from Saudi Arabia. The squadron anticipates withdrawal of these aircraft by 1 July with inactivation due to take place in October 1993. The two resident U-2Rs had both received the 9th Wing's 'BB' tailcode during the early part of 1993 and were joined in January by an additional aircraft from duty in Saudi Arabia. A fourth example arrived in early April to monitor events over Bosnia and Serbia.

The Special Operations element consists of the 352nd SOG and its three squadrons, the 7th SOS, 21st SOS and 67th SOS. The latter two relocated to Alconbury from Woodbridge during May 1992, with their MH-53Js and HC-130N/Ps operating from the north side of the base. The 67th SOS has seven Hercules assigned, consisting of three HC-130Ps and four HC-130Ns. The squadron maintains a single aircraft detachment at Keflavik, Iceland and Incirlik, Turkey, although exercises and humanitarian commitments elsewhere in southern Europe ensure the aircraft are frequently away from Alconbury for lengthy periods.

The complement of the 21st SOS varies as its helicopters are also frequently away and are ferried to the USA for maintenance inside C-5 Galaxies. Seven MH-53Js were stationed at Alconbury during the latter half of 1992, although at least two are believed to have left inside a C-5B during October 1992 as the unit should only have a complement of five helicopters. Apart from a detachment in eastern Turkey for Operation Provide Comfort the squadron has deployed helicopters to Italy for Operation Provide Promise.

The 7th SOS operates four MC-130Hs, with a fifth example due imminently. In addition, a C-130E is employed as a base hack for proficiency training and support. The unit is also heavily committed to Provide Promise, having deployed three aircraft to Rhein Main AB, Germany by early March to perform nightly leaflet drops over Bosnia.

Prior to Alconbury closing the three Special Forces squadrons will be rehoused at Mildenhall commencing in 1994, with completion of the move scheduled for March 1995. The withdrawal of U-2 operations from Alconbury will still require a facility to support aircraft on detachment to Europe for monitoring duties as well as those in transit from Beale AFB to the Saudi detachment at Taif. It is possible Alconbury may still perform this role, as it is the north side of the base which is closing. The runway and south side will remain active to enable communications aircraft to visit in connection with the huge complex at Molesworth.

Mildenhall is to become the entry point for military inspectors working under the Intermediate-Range Nuclear Forces Treaty. Inspection teams have previously flown into Greenham Common under Operation Zarnich; the last flight took place on 17 April 1992 by an Aeroflot Tu-154 and the ongoing operation will involve periodic visits by CIS aircraft. 58th AS UH-1Ns have been flown to the UK to ferry officials between the sites to be inspected, which may well account for the trial deployment of the two helicopters to Mildenhall during the first half of 1992. Under the treaty, CIS inspectors are permitted to visit appropriate bases to verify the number of weapons available and to oversee the periodic destruction.

The 48th FW at Lakenheath has received the majority of its F-15Es, with 41 delivered by mid-May and approximately 10 more due for delivery by the end of 1993. The 492nd FS commenced familiarisation sorties during May with aircraft carrying a pair of GBU-15 2,000-lb precision-guided bombs fitted to the underwing hardpoints. The wing has been conducting flying training for any contingency which the USAF may authorise to enforce United Nations resolutions. In particular, there is a strong possibility the 48th FW could be involved in any combat sortie launched against Serbians in Bosnia. The wing is also believed to be preparing for participation in Operation Provide Comfort at Incirlik AB, Turkey to replace the 27th FW F-111Fs. Prior to any commitment which could involve combat sorties the wing would need to be declared to NATO as a fully operational, and a tactical evaluation is scheduled for August.

Christi, Texas changed to a primary training squadron after three years as an instructor training squadron for the Beech T-44A Pegasus. The squadron began converting to the Beech T-34C Turbo Mentor on 16 February 1993, leaving Corpus Christi-based VT-31 'Wise Owls' as the US Navy's only T-44A squadron.

All US Navy active-duty operators of the Kaman SH-2F Seasprite LAMPS Mk I helicopter are scheduled to be disestablished by 31 March 1994. These squadrons are HSL-30 'Scooters', HSL-32 'Tridents', and HSL-34 'Professionals', all at NAS Norfolk, Virginia, plus HSL-33 'Sea Snakes' at NAS North Island, California

HS-9 'Sea Griffins' at NAS Jacksonville, Florida, operating the Sikorsky SH-3H Sea King, was disestablished on 31 May 1993.

VMFA(AW)-224 'Bengals' at MCAS Cherry Point, North Carolina received their current designation, changed from VMA(AW)-224, on 5 March 1993. The squadron is transitioning from the Grumman A-6E Intruder to the McDonnell F/A-18D(RC) Lot 14 Hornet and is scheduled to move to MCAS Beaufort, South Carolina by 1 July 1993.

VMO-1 'Yazoo' at MCAS New River, North Carolina and VMO-2 'Broncos' at Camp Pendleton, California, equipped with the Rockwell OV-10D(Plus) Bronco, were scheduled to be deactivated on 30 June 1993. This step leaves VMO-4, a Reserve OV-10D(Plus) squadron in Atlanta, Georgia, as the only remaining American military operator of the Bronco. VMO-4 is scheduled to deactivate on 31 March 1994.

HMH-769 was reactivated at NAS Alameda, California on 1 April 1993 as a Reserve operator of the Sikorsky RH-53D Sea Stallion. The squadron had previously been deactivated in 1980.

F/A-18D Hornets evaluated in Israel

Two McDonnell F/A-18D Hornets (BuNos 164690, 164717) were evaluated in Israel 15 March-2 April 1993 in connection with that country's requirement for 40-48 aircraft with multi-role, all-weather/night attack capability. The tests reportedly included assessment of Israel's Elbit DASH (display and sight helmet) targeting and

display system as well as standard American night-vision goggles. The helmet-mounted system is similar in weight and function to the Kaiser Agile Eye tested by the US Navy several years ago.

Israel was also expected to evaluate the Lockheed F-16C Fighting Falcon Block 50/52 in May 1993. An Israeli purchase of Hornets would include an upgraded version of Hughes APG-65 radar and General Electric F404 engines.

X-31 tests make progress

A Rockwell X-31 research aircraft completed a post-stall, minimum-radius 180° turn known as the Wolfgang Herbst manoeuvre in April 1993 during tests at Edwards AFB. The manoeuvre is made in a post-stall situation and is an abrupt method of gaining the edge in air combat.

German test pilot Karl Lang was at the controls of the no. 2 X-31 (BuNo. 164585) on 29 April 1993 when the manoeuvre was carried out at 19,400 ft (5900 m) by pitching the aircraft up to a 74° maximum angle of attack, in effect using the aircraft as a giant speed brake to decelerate from 200 kt (230 mph; 369 km/h), or Mach 0.5. The X-31's thrust vectoring system was employed to initiate a rapid roll around the velocity vector, after which Lang pitched the nose down and accelerated in the opposite direction. The total turn radius was 475 ft (145 m).

F-16C Block 50D delivered

Lockheed Fort Worth Company delivered the first F-16C Fighting Falcon Block 50D/52D aircraft to the US Air Force on 7 May 1993, three months ahead of schedule. Block 50D/52D differs from the baseline Block 50/52 aircraft in having a horizontal situation display format on its cockpit multifunction displays, an upgraded programmable display generator, and improved AGM-88 HARM capability. This series also introduces software compatible with the AGM-65G Maverick and the PGU-28/B 20-mm cannon round. Block 50D changes will be introduced on the F-16 production from late 1993.

CH-54 Tarhes retired from US Army service during 1993.

The sight of F-14 'Bombcats' is increasingly common. This VF-41 machine releases Mk 83 LDGPs.

C-141 loads limited by structural problems

The USAF's Air Mobility Command has restricted its C-141B StarLifter fleet to about 74 per cent of normal payload because of structural cracking that could lead to fuel leaks and weakened wings. AMC chief General Ronald R. Fogleman ordered on 14 April 1993 that all 260 StarLifters used by active and Reserve forces be restricted to carrying about 55,000 lb (24950 kg) of payload, or about 14,000 lb (6350 kg) less than the normal maximum. The restriction also curbs low-level flying and air refuelling, which will be limited to training flights with no cargo aboard.

Fogleman's decision is the latest in a series of problems caused by cracks in weep holes, centre wing boxes, wing joints, main frames, pressure bulkheads and windshield posts. The windshield post cracks had previously caused several dozen C-141Bs to be limited to an uneconomical altitude of 26,000 ft (7925 m). The restrictions are a major hindrance to the US airlift fleet at a time when the future of the Douglas C-17A Globemaster III is in doubt and Lockheed has proposed a SLEP (Service Life Extension Program) for the C-141B.

Lockheed proposes that 178 of Air Mobility Command's 260 C-141Bs undergo SLEP. Aircraft which emerge from this modification programme would have 40,000 flying hours added to their current lifetime of 45,000. The SLEP would include replacing the C-141B's inner and outer wings and would also involve replacements for the fuselage cab top and portions of several main frames. The vertical stabiliser would receive modifications to reduce stress during low-altitude missions. The total of 178 aircraft was chosen to meet the current Department of Defense strategic airlift capability goal of 57 million ton-miles per day, taking into account plans to acquire 120 C-17As. Pentagon officials have been reluctant to support a C-141B SLEP because they see it competing for scarce funds with the C-17.

US Navy, Marine Corps squadron changes

The US Navy continues to disestablish squadrons as it reduces its overall size to 12 carrier battle groups. Several units have also been lost by the Marine Corps, which deactivates its units rather than disestablishing them.

VA-65 'Tigers' at NAS Oceana, Virginia was disestablished on 31 March 1993. The squadron operated the Grumman A-6E Intruder.

VA-155 'Silver Foxes' at NAS Whidbey Island, Washington was disestablished on 30 April 1993. The 'Foxes' also flew the A-6E.

The US Navy's three electronic warfare and electronic aggressor squadrons – VAQ-33 'Firebirds' at NAS Key West, Florida, VAQ-34 'Electric Horsemen' at NAS Lemoore, California and VAQ-35 'Greywolves' at Whidbey Island – were scheduled to be disestablished on 30 October 1993. Grumman EA-6A Intruders will be retired from service; EP-3J Orions will be transferred to Reserve squadron VP-66 'Liberty Bell' at NAS Willow Grove, Pennsylvania; and F/A-18A Hornets and EA-6B Prowlers will be distributed among active-duty units.

VF-114 'Aardvarks' at NAS Miramar, California was disestablished on 30 April 1993 after 48 years of service. The squadron flew Grumman F-14A Tomcats.

VP-6 'Blue Sharks' at NAS Barbers Point, Hawaii was disestablished on 31 May 1993. The squadron operated Lockheed P-3C Orion Update II.5s.

VQ-4 'Shadows', one of two Navy Boeing E-6A Mercury squadrons, completed its relocation from NAS Patuxent River, Maryland to Tinker AFB, Oklahoma on 31 March 1993, marking the consolidation of the Navy's two strategic communications squadrons at one base. VQ-3 'Iron Men' from Barbers Point had moved to Tinker earlier.

VR-22 'Med Riders' at NAS Rota, Spain was disestablished 31 May 1993. The squadron operated Lockheed KC-130F Hercules.

VT-28 'Rangers' at NAS Corpus

BRIEFING

Mitsubishi F-4EJ Kai

Upgraded Phantoms for the JASDF

Japan received its first Phantoms during 1971, purchasing 140 examples of the simplified F-4EJ interceptor and 14 RF-4EJ recce platforms. The first four F-4EJs were built by McDonnell Douglas at St Louis, the first one flying on 14 January 1971. Eleven more were assembled from St Louis-supplied kits at Mitsubishi's Nagoya facility, and two further aircraft were built around St Louis-supplied forward fuselages, before the Japanese factory began outright production.

The F-4EJ bears a close external resemblance to the basic USAF F-4E, but differs in several important respects. Japan's constitution limited the aircraft to a defensive role, so all multi-role capability was deleted and the aircraft were delivered without in-flight-refuelling capability, although this was later retrofitted. The wings were unslatted and the stabilisers are unslotted, to save weight and reduce complexity.

The F-4EJ incorporated a significant amount of indigenous equipment, although it retained Westinghouse AN/APQ-120 radar. A datalink, camera gun and RHAW system of indigenous manufacture were added. Japanese F-4 serials consist of a two-digit prefix whose first numeral is the final digit of the year of delivery, with the second digit always being 7 (indicating the Phantom). The four-digit suffix starts with a numeral designating role (8 for fighter, 6 for reconnaissance), with a three digit numerical identifier following this. A handful of F-4EJs were operated in the ECM aggressor role during exercises, carrying AN/ALQ-6 ECM pods, under the probably unofficial designation EF-4EJ.

The basic F-4EJ equipped six interceptor squadrons (Hikotai), two squadrons serving with each of the three Air Defence Forces (Northern, Central and Western). Two squadrons converted to the F-15J during 1986-1989 and another began F-15J conversion during 1992, leaving three Hikotai (plus the reconaissance squadron). The operational capability of these remaining F-4 units has been enhanced by increasing their aircraft establishment, and by re-equipping them with upgraded aircraft.

It was apparent from an early stage that Japan would not be able to procure sufficient F-15s to entirely re-equip its F-4EJ force, and the Phantom's excellent performance and long remaining airframe life prompted the upgrading of these aircraft for service into the 21st century. It was therefore decided to upgrade 110 of the 125 surviving F-4EJs to F-4EJ Kai standards, although this total has since been reduced to 96 aircraft. The Kai (a Japanese character used as an abbreviation for 'plus' or 'improved') programme includes a major refurbishing which extends airframe life from 3,000 to 5,000 hours and also incorporates many new systems and equipment items.

True look-down/shoot-down capability is endowed by the newly added Westinghouse AN/APG-66J pulse-Doppler radar (as fitted to the F-16) and limited BVR combat is possible, but only by using the ancient AIM-7 Sparrow since there is no provision for AMRAAM. The new radar uses a new radome which incorporates what are variously described as strengthening strips or lightning conductors running fore and aft. The F-4EJ Kai has a new central computer, a Kaiser HUD, Hazeltine AN/

Left: Two 306 Hikotai F-4EJ Kais get airborne from their base at Komatsu. This smart air defence grey colour scheme is standard, although many variations exist.

Above: This 301st Hikotai F-4EJ Kai is one of at least two painted in this grey/green colour scheme, reminiscent of the RF-4EJ colour scheme and perhaps indicating future assignment to the ground attack role to replace or augment Mitsubishi F1s. The indigenous ASM-1 anti-ship missile has been cleared for use by the F-4EJ Kai, but has not been issued to operational squadrons yet.

Below: Several 301st Hikotai F-4EJ Kais have received a toned-down air-superiority grey colour scheme. On this aircraft even the traditional rising sun national insignia has been lightly oversprayed. The aircraft carries exercise kill markings on its intake splitter plates, applied during the annual JASDF gunnery meet. The updated and upgraded F-4EJ Kai is much more competitive than its predecessor.

Mitsubishi (McDonnell Douglas) F-4EJ Kai

Conversion programme
Ninety-six of Japan's surviving 125 F-4EJs are being converted to F-4EJ Kai configuration and 17 more will be converted for recce duties. The F-4EJ Kai prototype made its maiden flight on 17 July 1984 and full conversions began to be redelivered from 24 November 1990. The third squadron had started re-equipment by early 1993.

The 306th Hikotai at Komatsu was the last Japanese Phantom squadron to form, but became the first JASDF Phantom unit to re-equip with the F-4EJ Kai, receiving its 22 aircraft between August 1989 and March 1991. This aircraft was painted up to commemorate the unit's 10th anniversary on 30th June 1991. It was the first F-4EJ Kai to be so colourfully painted, but continued a longstanding JASDF tradition of very eye-catching Phantom colour schemes.

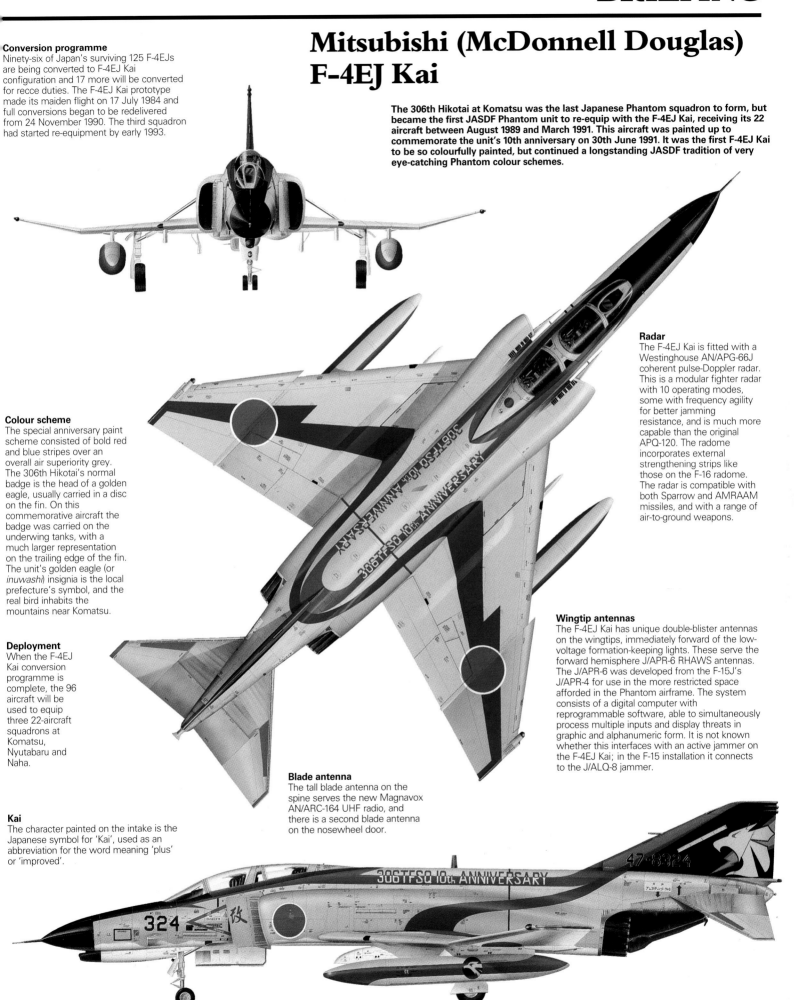

Colour scheme
The special anniversary paint scheme consisted of bold red and blue stripes over an overall air superiority grey. The 306th Hikotai's normal badge is the head of a golden eagle, usually carried in a disc on the fin. On this commemorative aircraft the badge was carried on the underwing tanks, with a much larger representation on the trailing edge of the fin. The unit's golden eagle (or *inuwashi*) insignia is the local prefecture's symbol, and the real bird inhabits the mountains near Komatsu.

Deployment
When the F-4EJ Kai conversion programme is complete, the 96 aircraft will be used to equip three 22-aircraft squadrons at Komatsu, Nyutabaru and Naha.

Kai
The character painted on the intake is the Japanese symbol for 'Kai', used as an abbreviation for the word meaning 'plus' or 'improved'.

Radar
The F-4EJ Kai is fitted with a Westinghouse AN/APG-66J coherent pulse-Doppler radar. This is a modular fighter radar with 10 operating modes, some with frequency agility for better jamming resistance, and is much more capable than the original APQ-120. The radome incorporates external strengthening strips like those on the F-16 radome. The radar is compatible with both Sparrow and AMRAAM missiles, and with a range of air-to-ground weapons.

Wingtip antennas
The F-4EJ Kai has unique double-blister antennas on the wingtips, immediately forward of the low-voltage formation-keeping lights. These serve the forward hemisphere J/APR-6 RHAWS antennas. The J/APR-6 was developed from the F-15J's J/APR-4 for use in the more restricted space afforded in the Phantom airframe. The system consists of a digital computer with reprogrammable software, able to simultaneously process multiple inputs and display threats in graphic and alphanumeric form. It is not known whether this interfaces with an active jammer on the F-4EJ Kai; in the F-15 installation it connects to the J/ALQ-8 jammer.

Blade antenna
The tall blade antenna on the spine serves the new Magnavox AN/ARC-164 UHF radio, and there is a second blade antenna on the nosewheel door.

Mitsubishi F-4EJ Kai

Above: The F-4EJ Kai can be recognised by the strips on its radome, the distinctive double RWR fairings and the increased-height blade antennas. This aircraft was on charge with the APW for tests and trials.

APZ-79A IFF and a licence-built Litton LN-39 INS. The new indigenous J/APR-6 RWR necessitates the provision of new twin radomes on the fin-tip trailing edge and wingtips, while AN/AC-164 UHF requires new, taller UHF blade antennas on the spine and below the nose.

The F-4EJ Kai usually carries an AN/ALQ-131 ECM pod in the forward port Sparrow recess, and can carry a 610-US gal (2310-litre) F-15 fuel tank, which is stressed to higher *g* loads than the standard F-4 tank. The F-4EJ Kai is compatible with the indigenous ASM-1 anti-ship missile, and it is believed that at least one F-4EJ Kai unit will assume a close air support role. Some F-4EJ Kais have already been seen wearing a gaudy tan and two-tone green colour scheme

Right: The prototype RF-4EJ Kai conversion retains fighter-type nose contours (including the gun) and carries a variety of reconnaissance pods. This one is a SLAR pod based on the Raphael SLAR-2000.

similar to that worn by the Mitsubishi F1.

A partial F-4EJ Kai was flown for the first time on 17 July 1984, and 'production' conversions were redelivered from 24 November 1990, initially to the 6th Air Wing (Kokudan) at Komatsu. Here they re-equipped the 306th Hikotai from August 1989 (22 were on strength by March 1991) and then the 301st Hikotai. The 302nd Hikotai (part of the Southwest Composite Air Wing at Naha) began re-equipment with the F-4EJ Kai during late 1992. Twelve of the unconverted survivors will be retired, but 17 are being converted for reconnaissance duties, retaining their cannon but with provision for a variety of centreline recce pods, including a Mitsubishi Melco derivative of the Thomson-CSF ASTAC Elint pod, the Raphael SLAR-2000 and a LOROP pod. These aircraft will receive digital avionics including an AN/APQ-172 radar and are confusingly designated

Above: The F-4EJ Kais of the 306 Hikotai wear a stylised golden eagle fin badge. The Kai modernisation transforms the aircraft's combat capabilities, and will allow it to serve into the next century.

RF-4EJ Kai, a designation already used by RF-4EJs upgraded with AN/APQ-172 radar, new INS, an IR recce set, digital cockpit displays and the same defensive systems as those fitted to the F-4EJ Kai.

Seychelles Coastguard

Naval and air forces combined

Last December, in a reorganisation of the defence forces following changes to the national constitution, the Seychelles People's Navy and Air Force were amalgamated to form the Seychelles Coastguard. The air element was renamed the Air Wing of the Coastguard although it continued to operate on the same lines as previously.

Currently the Air Wing operates two aircraft: a Britten-Norman BN-2A Maritime Defender and a Cessna A-150 Aerobat trainer. There is also an incomplete Hindustan Aviation Chetak helicopter (an SA 316

Alouette III manufactured under licence in India) that had been cannibalised to provide parts for two other machines of this type that have since been destroyed in separate accidents. It is doubtful whether the remaining machine will be restored to an airworthy condition.

The Defender was donated by the British government in 1980 and has given several years of good service. Its main role is to patrol the economic exploitation zone extending over an area of almost 390,000 sq miles (1 million km²), surrounding the Indian Ocean republic's 92 larger and many smaller

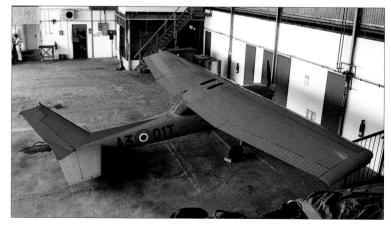

This Cessna 150 Aerobat is used by the Seychelles Coastguard Air Wing for pilot training and wears the same blue and red colour scheme as the unit's Defender.

This Pilatus Britten Norman BN-2A Defender was donated to the Seychelles Coastguard by the British government during 1980, and is the unit's primary operational aircraft. Pilots then generally move on to fly Islanders with the national airline.

islands. The radar-equipped aircraft flies regular patrols lasting up to nine hours, searching for vessels carrying out illegal fishing and other activities in the economic exploitation zone. The Defender has no provision to carry armament, and such operations are usually mounted in conjunction with patrol boats of the Coastguard's Naval Wing. The aircraft also operates in the light transport and SAR roles, and when required it flies medevac missions to bring patients from outlying islands to the main island, Mahé, for hospital treatment.

On 3 March the Air Wing's crews had a rare burst of excitement when the Defender assisted in the apprehension of a coaster, the *Ma Lo*, which had been seen behaving suspiciously near one of the islands. A Naval Wing patrol boat was ordered to the area and when members of the crew boarded the coaster they found that it was carrying about 400 tons (363000 kg) of ammunition that was apparently intended for one of the warring factions in Somalia. The vessel was taken to Mahé and is currently in the custody of the Seychelles police. It is expected that the government will take legal action to confiscate both the *Ma Lo* and her cargo.

All Air Wing pilots receive their training in the Cessna A-150, before moving to the right-hand seat of the Defender. After they have become qualified to captain the Defender, built up the requisite number of flying hours and secured the necessary commercial licences, most pilots are then

Below: This Reims Cessna Caravan II is operated by the state-owned Island Development Company, and is flown by seconded Air Wing pilots.

seconded to the national airline, Air Seychelles. There they fly Twin Otter and Islander aircraft employed on the company's domestic air services, before moving on to the Boeing 757 or the Boeing 767 used on its international routes.

The Seychelles government owns two aircraft which it operates in the passenger and light transport roles. One, a Cessna Citation V, also serves

Below: The government's VIP and Presidential aircraft, again flown by seconded Coastguard Air Wing pilots, is this Cessna Citation V.

in the VIP role as Presidential aircraft when required. The other is a Reims-Cessna Caravan II of the Island Development Company, a state-controlled organisation tasked with opening up a number of outlying islands in the group for commercial exploitation. These aircraft, too, are flown by pilots that have been seconded from the Air Wing.

The aircraft carry the following registrations: Britten-Norman BN-2A Maritime Defender – A2-01M; Cessna A 150 Aerobat – A3-01T; Cessna Citation V – SY 001; Riems Cessna Caravan II – SY 006.

British Aerospace Harrier GR.Mk 7

RAF Harrier force regains recce capability

The cancellation of the undernose MIRLS (Miniature Infra-Red Linescan System) intended for the Harrier GR.Mk 5 altered the nose profile of subsequent variants (which lost their undernose fairing) and deprived the Harrier force of its secondary tactical reconnaissance role. In an effort to regain some degree of recce capability the RAF evaluated the Vinten Vicon 18 Series 403 recce pod and the multi-sensor Vinten Vicon 57. Tentative plans also existed to procure a US Navy podded system for the Harrier, possibly based on the Martin-Marietta ATARS. The need to replace the RAF's Jaguars (ostensibly to give their oft-rotated crews a much-needed break, but perhaps to free them for possible use in Bosnia) led to the decision to send RAF Harriers to replace them in providing armed reconnaissance support to the United Nations forces enforcing the exclusion zone in northern Iraq. This consisted of the area above the 36th Parallel and was designed to protect the Kurds. The UK commitment is

One of the Harrier GR.Mk 7s modified for participation in Operation Warden will replace the Jaguars previously in use. The aircraft have been adapted to carry the Vinten optical camera pod on the centreline. This was originally used by the Harrier GR.Mk 3.

BAe Harrier GR.Mk 7

Above: The GR.Mk 3 recce pod contains a fan of four F95 cameras, and a forward oblique F135 camera. The Harrier GR.Mk 5 and GR.Mk 7 were originally intended to have had an internal IR recce system.

known as Operation Warden.

To replace the eight-aircraft Jaguar detachment at Incirlik in Turkey the RAF rewired at least nine early GR.Mk 7s (all with the original 65 per cent LERX) to enable them to carry stored Vinten reconnaissance pods previously used by RAF Harrier GR.Mk 3s, and now used only by the four-aircraft detachment in Belize. The conversion took some 600 man-hours per aircraft. This was far from an ideal solution, since the original Harrier GR.Mk 3 pod contained only conventional optical cameras, requiring normal wet-film processing. The RICs (Reconnaissance Interpretation Centres) of the Harrier GR.Mk 3 squadrons had been disestablished, and a new RIC had to be formed using equipment withdrawn from storage and personnel from Wyton and Coltishall, whose Canberras and Jaguars still use similar cameras.

The pods actually contain a fan of four F95 cameras, each with a 70-mm lens, providing panoramic horizon-to-horizon coverage plus a single forward oblique F135 camera with a 127-mm lens. The nine modified aircraft were repainted medium grey overall, with no unit markings and with reduced-size serials. The first four aircraft departed Laarbruch on 2 April, and the second group of four left on 8 April. The aircraft were drawn from both No. 3 and No. IV Squadron, although the latter unit provided all the aircrew for the first two-month detachment. Pilots from No. 3 will take over in June, and from No. 1 at Wittering in August.

The detachment will fly three two-aircraft missions each day, with each pair flying low-level recce sorties to photograph between 12 and 18 targets, which can include troop concentrations, barracks, dispersal and holding areas, EW and SAM sites, airfields and known military facilities.

Elsewhere in the Harrier Force No. 1 Squadron has already taken delivery of six aircraft equipped with an upgraded Ferranti FIN.1075G INAS

with a GPS receiver incorporated, and have begun night attack training in earnest. The aircraft's weapons options (of 1,000-lb bombs, BL-755 CBUs and 68-mm SNEB rocket pods) are being expanded by the addition of CRV-7 rockets and CBU-87 cluster bombs, both used by RAF Jaguars during the Gulf War. When the aircraft eventually receive their 25-mm Royal Ordnance Factory ADEN cannon and Plessey missile approach warning system, and are able to use their dedicated Sidewinder missile launch rails, they will be extremely versatile and effective.

Above: The pod seen in position below the centreline of one of the Warden Harriers, flanked by an empty gun pod. Use of the old-style recce pod has necessitated the establishment of a new Reconnaissance Interpretation Centre at Incirlik.

Below: The Operation Warden Harriers will be armed with CBU-87 cluster bombs and Sidewinders, in addition to a pair of underwing fuel tanks. These give the GR.Mk 7 a longer range than the Jaguars they replaced.

Lockheed EC-130E(CL)

Mystery Hercules antenna configuration photographed at last

While the Volant Solo mission of the 193rd Special Operations Group is openly admitted and can be discussed (to a certain level), the unit's other Senior Scout mission remains more highly classified; little more than the Senior Scout codename and the fact that the mission is flown on behalf of the USAF's Electronic Security Command can be released. Aircraft are not permanently configured, and until now photographs of the 'Comfy Levis' with antennas fitted have not been published.

Reports suggest that the aircraft (known as Senior Hunter C-130Es) are normally without any mission equipment, which is especially put together and installed by specialists from the NSA at Fort Meade before a mission, and removed afterwards.

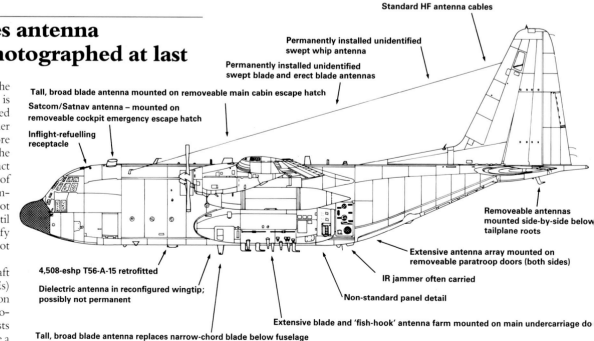

Standard HF antenna cables

Permanently installed unidentified swept whip antenna

Permanently installed unidentified swept blade and erect blade antennas

Tall, broad blade antenna mounted on removeable main cabin escape hatch

Satcom/Satnav antenna – mounted on removeable cockpit emergency escape hatch

Inflight-refuelling receptacle

4,508-eshp T56-A-15 retrofitted

Dielectric antenna in reconfigured wingtip; possibly not permanent

Tall, broad blade antenna replaces narrow-chord blade below fuselage

Removeable antennas mounted side-by-side below tailplane roots

Extensive antenna array mounted on removeable paratroop doors (both sides)

IR jammer often carried

Non-standard panel detail

Extensive blade and 'fish-hook' antenna farm mounted on main undercarriage do

EC-130E (CL) Senior Hunter (in operational Senior Scout configuration)

Left: This close-up photograph is believed to be the first published of the full 'Senior Scout' antenna configuration. These are mounted on removeable hatches and doors, and are only fitted for operational missions. The role remains highly sensitive.

Above: An EC-130E(CL) on the ramp in Japan. At the 1993 Paris Air Salon a model of 'Senior Scout' was shown (without aerials) and was coyly described as a Sigint platform, with a slide-in/slide-out equipment package.

There are suggestions that Fort Meade also provides the mission crew (apart from those on the flight deck) and that aircraft are flown to Andrews AFB for modification and demodification. This is probably a very quick and 'painless' procedure, since the mission kit is almost certainly trailer- (or at least pallet-) mounted and the antennas are almost inevitably fitted to easily removeable (replaceable) items like landing gear and crew doors and even escape hatches. This helps to explain why the EC-130E(CL)s seen at the unit's Harrisburg base are never seen with antennas. The Senior Scout designation refers only to the mission, and thus applies only to modded-up aircraft.

Five C-130Es were originally converted to EC-130E(CL) configuration by Lockheed Aircraft Services. One (63-7783) was later modified to 'Rivet Rider' configuration. The four survivors (63-7815, 63-7816, 63-7828 and 63-9816) remain in use with the 193rd SOG in a variety of colour schemes, and have all been brought up to virtual C-130H configuration with 4,508-eshp (3363-kW) T56-A-15 engines, inflight-refuelling receptacles and other improvements. 63-7816 has modified wingtips incorporating dielectric antennas, although these may be temporary. Recent photographs of this aircraft accompany this briefing.

If funding permits, two Senior Hunter aircraft are to be converted to upgraded Volant Solo configuration. This will presumably leave a shortfall of aircraft for the Senior Scout mission, which may go some of the way towards explaining why a Tennessee ANG C-130H has recently been observed (at a Green Flag EW exercise at Nellis AFB) in virtually full Senior Scout configuration. The USAF may be preparing to pass on the mission to the Tennesseee Guard, or for the 193rd SOG to absorb aircraft currently operated by Tennessee's 105th Airlift Squadron (118th Airlift Wing) to replace aircraft being upgraded to Volant Solo standards. The aircraft may already be on charge with the 193rd, and may have retained the markings of its former unit for expediency.

Above: A front view of the same EC-130E(CL) which visited Japan. Extra 'T'-shaped Satnav antennas are visible above the forward fuselage and port wingroot.

Below: 'Senior Scout' aircraft frequently taxi with their ramps down, reportedly to help cool the electronic equipment inside the hold.

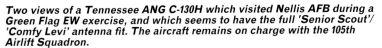

Two views of a Tennessee ANG C-130H which visited Nellis AFB during a Green Flag EW exercise, and which seems to have the full 'Senior Scout'/'Comfy Levi' antenna fit. The aircraft remains on charge with the 105th Airlift Squadron.

BRIEFING

Lockheed EC-130E(RR)

Volant Solo upgraded with 'Worldwide Colour TV'

The EC-130E(RR) is a dedicated airborne radio/TV relay and broadcast station intended for use in national emergencies and for special operations, conducting psychological warfare (Psywar or Psyops) to demoralise an enemy. It is used only by the 193rd Special Operations Squadron of the 193rd Special Operations Group, Pennsylvania ANG, based at Harrisburg International Airport (previously Olmstead State Airport). The unit's role is unique, and is not conducted by any other Guard or active-duty squadron.

The Pennsylvania ANG's connection with the Psyop mission began on 17 September 1967, when the 140th MAS became the 193rd Tactical Electronic Warfare Squadron, flying the former unit's C-121Cs. This role change was made in response to a perceived lack of Psyop capability following the 1965 Dominican crisis. The first of four or five squadron Constellations to be converted to EC-121S standard as a radio/TV station entered service during the summer of 1968, for the new Coronet Solo mission. Two aircraft subsequently saw service in South East Asia, operating from Korat in Thailand.

Conversion to the C-130 began during August 1977, and the last EC-121S was finally retired on 14 May 1979, following delivery of the first EC-130E(RR) on 16 March. The primary mission of these aircraft was

Below: A dramatic head-on view emphasises the scope of the recent changes to the 'Rivet Rider' configuration necessitated by the provision of Worldwide Colour TV broadcast capability.

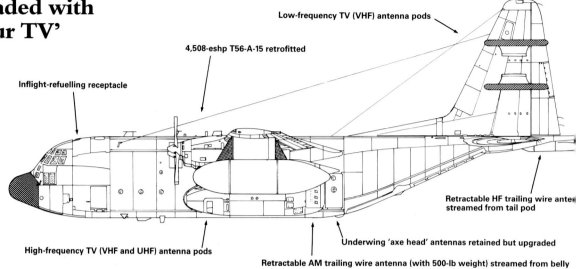

Inflight-refuelling receptacle

4,508-eshp T56-A-15 retrofitted

Low-frequency TV (VHF) antenna pods

Retractable HF trailing wire antenna streamed from tail pod

Underwing 'axe head' antennas retained but upgraded

Retractable AM trailing wire antenna (with 500-lb weight) streamed from belly

High-frequency TV (VHF and UHF) antenna pods

EC-130E (RR) Volant Solo upgrade

defined as 'the conducting of psychological operations, using electromagnetic transmissions, covering commercial AM and FM radio bands, VHF and UHF television bands, and military VHF, HF and FM frequencies'. The aircraft's systems can burn through or overpower existing transmissions if necessary.

A secondary mission was aid to the civil power during disaster relief operations, during which the aircraft can substitute for disabled ground radio or TV stations, broadcasting emergency information or instructions, or can act as flying rebroadcasting stations. The aircraft have a palletised mission fit, allowing transmitters to be installed or replaced quickly and easily. Like the EC-121Ss they replaced, the Hercules were festooned with antennas. A huge blade extended forward from the leading edge of the fin, and large axe-heads were suspended below the outer wings. Underwing pods, and a pod below the beaver tail, contain trailing

wire antennas. The very high empty weight of the aircraft necessitated re-engining with the C-130H's 4,508-eshp (3363-kW) T56-A-15 powerplant.

Three aircraft (63-7773, 63-7869 and 63-9817) were converted from C-130Es and a fourth was produced by conversion of one of the squadron's EC-130E(CL)s. The EC-130E(RR) operates with a flight crew of five, comprising two pilots, a flight engineer, a navigator and a loadmaster, with extra flight crew carried

as reliefs during very long-duration missions. The basic mission crew consists of an electronic warfare officer and five electronic communications system operators who act as programme directors or 'disc jockeys', controlling the broadcast of pre-recorded audio and video tape, re-

A very early photo of an EC-130E(RR) shows the original 'Rivet Rider' configuration, with prominent antenna at the base of the fin, and with small underwing pods outboard.

broadcasting signals from ground stations or using broadcast microphones for live transmissions. Linguists and professionally trained broadcasters are provided by the US Army, often including native speakers, who have proved more effective in propaganda broadcasts.

The unit transferred from TAC to MAC in March 1983. The mission codename was changed to Volant Solo to reflect this, the squadron redesignating as the 193rd ECS the following November. The squadron saw active service during Operation Urgent Fury (the invasion of Grenada) and Operation Just Cause (the invasion of Panama) before transferring to Special Operations Command on its formation in May 1990. Unconfirmed reports suggest that the mission codename has subsequently changed again to reflect this, to Commando Solo.

During late 1990 and early 1991 three of the squadron's aircraft operated in support of Operations Desert Shield and Desert Storm. The aircraft's long endurance (10 hours even without inflight refuelling) and standoff capability allowed the squadron to safely broadcast around the clock when necessary. This had a material effect on the crumbling of Iraqi morale, which in turn led to the surrender of thousands of enemy troops. The aircraft usually operated with fighter and AWACS support. During Desert Storm, one crew clocked up a 21-hour mission, a C-130 record for refuelled time aloft.

To conduct their operations in the Gulf War, the EC-130Es had to undergo an urgent modification programme to install a TV broadcast system compatible with the format used in Kuwait and Iraq. The modifications were undertaken by teams from Lockheed Ontario, Rockwell-Collins, Det. 4 of the 2762nd Logistics Squadron (Special) and the 193rd Special Operations Group. This experience led directly to the development of a new Worldwide Colour TV broadcast system compatible with all known TV formats in use today.

All four existing EC-130E(RR)s are to be upgraded to the new standard, together with two of the unit's Senior Hunter EC-130E(CL)s if funding permits. The new equipment necessitates a major change in external configuration, with the provision of a variety of new antennas and equipment fairings. Most obviously, four streamlined VHF low-frequency TV antenna pods are pylon-mounted on the sides of the vertical tailfin, and the old leading-edge blade antenna is removed. Huge (23-ft/7-m long, 6-ft/1.8-m diameter) pods are suspended below the outer wings. These accommodate VHF and UHF antennas dedicated to

Right and above: The basic 'Rivet Rider' saw active service during Desert Storm, some aircraft returning to Pennsylvania with mission logs.

high-frequency TV signals, and can be rotated to change their polarities. The vast pods are significantly larger than standard C-130 underwing fuel tanks and are braced by diagonal struts.

The aircraft retains a retractable trailing-wire HF antenna which is streamed horizontally from a pod under the beaver tail, and also has a new retractable 1,000-ft (305-m) AM trailing wire antenna. This is extended from the belly, and is held almost vertical by a 500-lb (227-kg) weight. The existing 'axe-head' blade antennas under the wings are increased in capability, and transmitters are similarly upgraded, with transmitter power soaring from 1 kW to 10 kW.

The first upgraded aircraft (63-9817) was modified by Lockheed Ontario and underwent flutter and handling tests at Palmdale at the hands

Right and below: The first 'Rivet Rider' upgraded to the new configuration has already travelled extensively, having been photographed in the US Virgin Islands and the UK. Sources close to the programme have expressed great satisfaction with the new equipment.

of a Lockheed/USAF/National Test Pilot's School team. Range performance, equipment and broadcast tests were carried out over the Pacific and were completed during June 1992. The first aircraft then lost its 'forehead'-mounted test boom and was flown back to Harrisburg by Colonel Walter R. Ernst, the unit's commanding officer, arriving at 9.55 a.m. on 29 July 1992.

The aircraft is "doing very well, doing exactly what it's supposed to," according to Ernst, and has impressed the 193rd with its reliability and per-

formance. Handling is not significantly affected, although drag is obviously increased, and one pilot reported that the aircraft lands 'crabwise'. The overriding judgement is that the 18-month modification programme has been a great success, and the squadron is eager to receive further modified aircraft. The first aircraft has already travelled extensively, having visited RAF Mildenhall, England during early 1992, and having operated from St Croix in the US Virgin Islands during late April/early May 1993.

Kiowa Warrior

Bell's OH-58A/C has been the US Army's standard scout since Vietnam. In the form of the OH-58D, a radical reworking of the design has breathed new life into the Kiowa, producing a light helicopter that is vital to the management of the battlefield.

The Bell OH-58D Kiowa Warrior has wrought dramatic success from its humble start as the US Army's AHIP (Advanced Helicopter Improvement Program) of 1979, which was purposely launched with modest goals. In that era of cautious spending, predating the profligate Reagan era, the Army was anxious to safeguard its high-priority AH-64 Apache attack fleet and deliberately took a 'no frills' approach to improving its less glamorous aeroscout force. In a scout, the Army wanted not a new aircraft but a cautious 'upgrade' to look and aim for others on the battlefield. This would be accomplished, the Army decided, by improving its existing Bell OH-58A/C Kiowa.

The OH-58A/C was the unpretentious Bell 206 Jet Ranger, a satisfying design with two-bladed rotors, employed in other US military guises as the Navy TH-57A/B/C Sea Ranger primary trainer, and (only recently) Army TH-67 Creek primary trainer. Well-known to police forces and corporate users, the JetRanger has also been delivered to Austria as the OH-58B and to the Canadian Armed Forces as the CH-136. Some version of the Bell 206 can be found just about anywhere. As with all Bell rotary-wing aircraft, the first digit in its company model number signifies its number of rotor blades.

As it turned out, AHIP gave the world the OH-58D, or Bell 406, distinguishable at a glance by its four-bladed rotors. More importantly, the AHIP programme resulted not just in an unarmed scout but, later, in an armed reconnaissance helicopter with formidable capability to fight and kill on the battlefield.

As the 1980s began, the Army had 3,000 Hughes OH-6 Cayuse and Bell OH-58 Kiowa light observation helicopters (those OH-58A/C models), and plenty of experience using them to scout for attack helicopters, artillery, ground troops, and even fighter-bombers. Its job performed, once, by a brave man on foot or horseback, the scout aircraft is now integral to US Army aviation. The scouting mission dates to the aerial balloons of the American Civil War and to World War II observation planes like the Piper L-4 Cub which served as the Army's eyes above the killing ground.

Left: The OH-58D Aeroscout was vital to the success of the US Army during Desert Storm. In addition to spotting for ground units, the aircraft designated targets for Apaches.

An OH-58D Kiowa Warrior lets fly with Hydra-70 rockets. These weapons provide capability against soft targets, and are often used in conjunction with a gun pod.

Using the AHIP OH-58D, the scout ventures ahead of ground columns, serves as a flank guard and ferrets out enemy positions. In the 1990s, the scout sees with FLIR, both to find his way and to find the adversary, the trademark of an Army which stakes its fortune on moving and fighting at night.

In addition to supporting the ground commander, the aeroscout today becomes a teammate to the AH-64 Apache, for whom the scout can autonomously designate targets for laser-guided weapons. Thus, the scout combines the forward air control mission of 'calling' targets with setting them up for laser-guided attack, employing the laser spot-tracker on the mast of the armed OH-58D Kiowa Warrior. The costlier and less nimble Apache can hide behind a sand dune (or ridge line, or office building), and can 'launch and loft' a Hellfire missile without ever rising above the horizon to expose itself. The 'lofted' missile can then find its way into a laser 'basket' laid down by the scout. The scout helicopter also can laser designate a target for the 155-mm laser-seeking artillery round known as Copperhead, usually fired by an M109 tracked

The Royal Saudi Land Forces were the first export customers for the Bell 406CS Combat Scout. Of the 15 aircraft purchased, five are equipped with TOW anti-tank missiles.

Right: The US Army is to receive 351 Kiowa Warriors, all to full Armed OH-58D standard. Prominent above and below the cockpit are cable cutters, necessary at the altitude at which the OH-58D is normally flown.

howitzer. Today, as one Pentagon expert sums up the scout role, it would be 'entirely normal' for the commander of an Apache or artillery battalion to find himself in the air over the battlefield in the left-hand seat of the OH-58D scout helicopter. "It's survivable and it's a good platform, with good avionics and communications. It's the best perch from which to direct the course of a battle."

When the AHIP got under way, the scout mission translated into a strong need for a manoeuvrable aircraft able to operate in NOE (nap-of-the-earth), frequently lurking behind terrain features at survivable, stand-off distance. Popping up from its 'hide' or defilade, the scout would locate, identify and hand off targets to attack helicopters, artillery, or fighter-bombers. Bringing with him new ways to navigate and communicate while in NOE, the aeroscout team leader would orchestrate the battle. During the 1970s, binoculars gave way to day/night vision equipment and tests proved the feasibility of adding a day TV and laser designator above the helicopter rotor.

Bell 406/OH-58D family

69-16139 was the third OH-58A converted to D-model standard, and was the first to feature an operative mast-mounted sight. The rear seat area was occupied with test instrumentation.

OH-58D Aeroscout

The AHIP design competition pitted Bell's design against an improved version of the Hughes OH-6A Cayuse, the familiar Loach. On 21 September 1981 the Army selected the Bell 406 the winner. The OH-58D Aeroscout (not yet, at the time, called Kiowa, the name long associated with the OH-58A/C) was powered by an uprated 650-shp (485-kW) Allison T703-A-720 turboshaft engine, identical to the civil 250-C30R powering Bell's commercial LongRanger III. The OH-58D Aeroscout was to have four-bladed main rotors, with a 33-ft 4-in (10.15-m) diameter, a new composite tail rotor, and an improved transmission. Above all, the OH-58D was to have a mast-mounted observation and target designation system.

To prepare for the OH-58D, Bell started flight tests in March 1983 of a LongRanger III, designated Bell 406LM, modified with 250-C30 engine, four-bladed rotor, and a new tail rotor. The first of five OH-58D Aeroscout prototypes (68-16748 c/n 43001), all OH-58A conversions, flew at Bell's Arlington, Texas facility on 1 September 1983. The first production OH-58D was delivered in March 1986, a time when the Army had plenty of dollars and wanted (then) to obtain 578 aircraft by 1991. All OH-58Ds are remanufactured OH-58As, but the notion of a mere 're-build' is misleading and the term 'upgrade' became insufficient. "We take the old helicopter and reduce it to a bare shell," says Bell's Orson Hurwell. "Then we chop off the tail boom and build a completely new one. We throw out the rotor and install a new rotor. We put in a different drive train, a different engine, a different tail rotor. It's a 90 per cent new aircraft." Because the transformation from OH-58A to OH-58D is so exhaustive, every ship except the five prototypes gets a new Army serial number. (The five prototypes are 68-16748, 68-16754, 69-16139, 69-16285, 69-16322; c/ns 43001/43005.)

The MMS (mast-mounted sight) is the heart of the OH-58D Aeroscout and of the later US Army OH-58D Kiowa Warrior. The first functional MMS was installed on the third OH-58D prototype (69-16139, c/n 43003) and the first

Combat Scout was the name given to a reduced-capability version of the Armed OH-58D, featuring TOW and roof-mounted sight in place of Hellfire and MMS.

flight with a functional MMS was accomplished on 6 October 1983. The MMS is a package of sensors and integrated circuitry enclosed in a sphere situated high above the rotor blades. Manufactured by McDonnell Douglas in Santa Ana, California and never given a military designation, the MMS is the core item among several scouting tools – important among them are advanced visionics, such as the ANVIS-6 night-vision system – used to pinpoint an adversary's forces in battlefield smoke and haze, day and night, in good and bad weather.

The mast-mounted sight enables the helicopter to locate targets with a TIS (thermal imaging sensor) and, furthermore, to illuminate them for attack using the all-important laser rangefinder/designator. "During the war with Iraq, everybody talked about the number of shooters out there on the desert," says Washington analyst John Gresham. "What really matters is the capability to designate targets for laser-guided weapons. This is critical in an air-land battle. In Operation Desert Storm, the Army had more laser designators than anybody else."

The mast-mounted sight traces its origins to stabilised electro-optical and camera platform work done by McDonnell Douglas in the late 1970s. Mounted above the rotor system in its 25.5-in (65-cm) diameter ball and able to be rotated through 360° in azimuth and +/−30° in

The second, third and fourth OH-58Ds seen during AHIP testing at Yuma. The early Aeroscouts all had glazing in the rear cabin door, dispensed with on Armed OH-58Ds.

elevation, the MMS contains a day TV, the TIS, a laser rangefinder/designator, and an optical boresight system (OBS). The OBS aligns the TV, TIS and laser beam, either in flight or on the ground. This sensor package is mounted on a lightweight beryllium sensor support structure that provides long-term thermal stability. Surprisingly, the MMS holds up well when helicopters, as they are prone to do, shake and shudder. The assembly is isolated from aircraft-induced vibration, pitch and yaw motion by a low-friction spherical bearing isolation system.

Glass cockpit

Beginning in the late 1980s, Bell delivered OH-58D Aeroscouts (as well as subsequent OH-58D Kiowa Warriors) with a Honeywell multiplex integrated cockpit, loosely termed a 'glass cockpit'. This is in fact a partly glass cockpit with two high-resolution (875-line) multi-function displays and compatibility with night-vision goggles. In addition to multifunction displays, the cockpit offers keyboard unit, helmet-mounted display, and improved APN-209 radar altimeter.

The right-seat pilot's display helps with flight attitude, heading, air speed and so on, and has some non-digital instruments such as a vertical tape scale. The observer in the left seat, a non-rated enlisted man or warrant officer, lacks full flight controls but has a cyclic between his legs (disconnected during normal flight operations) and is trained to safely operate the aircraft in an emergency. The observer's multifunctional display, giving him MMS imagery, is his principal tool in sighting, identifying and designating targets; his controls for the MMS are on the cyclic. In an emergency, the observer can engage a lever which will restore his cyclic to the flight control system. Full flight controls can be installed quickly in the field when two pilots are needed for special missions.

Conceived for the US Army of the 1980s, the OH-58D Aeroscout was a poor cousin to battlefield helicopters like the AH-1 Cobra and AH-64 Apache. Small, packed and far from ideal for heavy payloads, the OH-58D was not, itself, expected to become a 'shooter'. Bell, however, always saw potential for an armed version, especially for Third World air forces. Since neither Hellfire nor mast-mounted sight could be exported (in 1983), the company invested in a demonstrator Bell 406CS Combat Scout similar to the OH-58D but without the MMS, specialised electronics or integrated multiplex cockpit of

the US Army craft. The demonstrator Bell 406CS Combat Scout (registered N2500B) made its first flight at Arlington in June 1984, participated in a fly-off competition in Saudi Arabia in the summer of that year, and was shown at Farnborough in the autumn.

In 1987, Saudi Arabia's land forces ordered 15 Bell 406CS Combat Scouts in an $86 million contract. These have the rotor, transmission and engine of the OH-58D but have an Emerson roof-mounted sight. Of the 15 ships, five are configured to carry TOW anti-armour missiles. The first official flight by a Saudi Bell 406CS was made by Colonel Homood Al-Reshoodi, commander of Saudi Arabian Land Forces Army Aviation, at Arlington on 2 February 1990. The Saudi aircraft has no US military designation; references to it as the MH-58D are inaccurate.

Armed OH-58D (AH-58D)

The Bell 406CS was just one approach toward an armed reconnaissance helicopter based on the OH-58D scout. While OH-58D deliveries began, the United States entered into conflict with Iran over hostages being held in Lebanon and over Iran's harassment of shipping in the Persian Gulf. In 1987, the US Navy took on Operation Earnest Will, the air/sea escorting of nominally American (reflagged) oil tankers through the Persian Gulf. A lightweight, readily-

*One capability of all **406CS/OH-58Ds** is their use in the gunship role. Several gun pod options exist, including the **GIAT M621 20-mm cannon** shown here on the demonstrator, **N2500B.***

deployable helicopter – an armed helicopter – was needed to cope with small Iranian armed speedboats which were attacking the ships and laying mines in their path.

Under the larger mantle of Earnest Will, the US Army's augmentation of Navy operations in the Gulf was called Operation Prime Chance. As a stopgap measure to counter Iranian assault boats, the US Army's special operations Task Force 160 (TF-160) deployed AH-6 helicopters from Navy warships and from barges converted into helicopter bases. The AH-6s were subsequently needed elsewhere, so Bell and the US Army took on the task of arming 15 OH-58D Aeroscouts in what was then a classified, 'black' programme.

On 5 September 1987, Bell started conversion work on the OH-58D (Armed), the correct name of the manufacturer's second Model 406 variant, although pilots at first called it the AH-58D, a term found on an Army shoulder patch and in a manufacturer's brochure. The US Army distinguishes between an 'attack' helicopter (i.e. Apache) which rates the 'A' prefix and an 'armed reconnaissance' helicopter (the armed OH-58D) which does not – partly for reasons of battle doctrine, but mostly to ease applications to Congress for programme funding. So the AH-58D appellation was never official, and it was the OH-58D (Armed) which was to replace the AH-6 as Earnest Will's shooter.

Bell put key people to work on a 24-hour basis and the first Prime Chance OH-58D (Armed) was delivered in December 1987, 98 days after the go-ahead. The OH-58D (Armed) was equipped to carry four AGM-114 Hellfire and four Stinger missiles in two twin-tube launchers, two 2.75-in Hydra-70 folding-fin aircraft rocket (FFAR) pods with seven rockets each, and two 0.30-calibre (7.62-mm) Miniguns or 0.50-calibre (12.7-mm) M2/M2AC machine-guns with 500 rounds. (AGM-114A/B/C Hellfire missiles in US Army inventory are to be upgraded to AGM-114F standard, with length increased from 5 ft 4 in/1.65 m to 5 ft 11 in/1.80 m). Another feature is a pair of 15-ft (4.5-m) caving ladders for rescue work, released by a pull cable in the cock-

*The **406CS** is based on the **OH-58D** airframe, but its systems are to a lower standard to satisfy **US** export restrictions. Taiwan is hoping to procure a **Hellfire/MMS** version if approved.*

pit. Armed OH-58Ds are fitted with AN/ APR-39A and AN/APR-44 radar warning receivers and infra-red signature suppressors. Fifteen black boxes, four antennas and 11 new control heads and displays were added to the aircraft. Bell demonstrated in flight tests that the added weight, raising a typical gross figure of 4,500 lb (2041 kg) some 22 per cent to 5,500 lb (2495 kg), imposed no performance penalty.

By January 1988 the Army had received seven out of its planned 15 OH-58D (Armed) helicopters. All were delivered by April 1988, all drawn from among the first 135 OH-58Ds manufactured. The 15 aircraft were initially delivered to the 1st Battalion, 159th Aviation Brigade, XVIII Airborne Corps at Fort Bragg, North Carolina, which carried out development work and later fielded people for the Army's Task Force 118 (TF-118) in the Persian Gulf, named from the roman numeral assigned to the Corps. The task force initially used high-time instructor pilots and flew the armed OH-58D with two-pilot crews.

In considerable secrecy, soldiers at Bragg worked up in the Prime Chance armed OH-58D (the term for the military operation has come to be synonymous with the helicopters created for it). Most pilots had never before flown a helicopter from a ship. Early shipboard tests were carried out in September 1987 off the US East

Coast on the frigate USS *Truett* (FF-1095). Pilots found they could take off with tail winds of up to 20 kt (23 mph; 37 km/h) and side winds of up to 5 kt (5.7 mph; 9 km/h), and later, in the Gulf, did so regularly.

EFI (electronic frequency interference) testing, to assure the integrity of internal systems, was carried out secretly by 1/159th personnel detailed to NAS Patuxent River, Maryland between 31 August and 9 September 1987. Tests focused on the susceptibility of the mast-mounted sight to ship-generated electromagnetic emissions such as search and navigation radars.

OH-58D (Armed) flight crews did further EFI testing at the Naval Surface Weapons Center in Dahlgren, Virginia. These concentrated on performance not just of the helicopter but of its mission equipment package when exposed to emissions. Whatever EFI problems needed to be ruled out, no warning flag seems to have appeared to thwart shipboard operations in the Gulf. One re-

sult of these trials was that the Plexiglas rear cabin windows were replaced with aluminium sheet metal to provide an additional EMI (electronic magnetic interference) barrier. Copper electrical bonding straps were also added to the rear doors.

By November 1987 tests at Dahlgren were carried out with Hellfires installed. Actual firing of Hellfire and Stinger missiles took place in 1987 at Camp Pendleton (East), Virginia. No further obstacle stood in the way of putting the armed OH-58D in harm's way. The 1/159th deployed to the Gulf in July 1988, becoming TF-118 and replacing the AH-6s of TF-160 in the tanker escort effort.

Because the 15 Prime Chance armed OH-58Ds had been ordered under a quick reaction contract (a covert programme) cloaked in secrecy, the mistaken impression took hold in some quarters that these helicopters were flown by Navy aircrews. "I've got about 400 green-suiters down here [at Fort Bragg] who wonder how that impression got formed," says OH-58D squadron commander Lieutenant Colonel Jim Mitcham.

During Prime Chance, US Army helicopter crews operated from guided missile destroyers, guided missile frigates and Navy-operated barges equipped as support bases. The challenge which faced these soldiers in a real-life shooting situation exceeded anything they had covered in training: they flew from blacked-out decks and worked targets from altitudes of 50 ft (15 m) or below using NVGs and relying heavily on FLIR. Nightly, they saw action against Iranian assault boats attacking US and neutral shipping. At times the helicopters operated in ambient temperatures in excess of 113°F (39°C).

The armed OH-58Ds always launched in pairs and worked in conjunction with a US Navy Sikorsky SH-60B Seahawk LAMPS III (Light

Defences
Warning receivers fitted to the OH-58D include APR-44(V)3 RWR, AVR-2 laser detection set and APR-39(V)1 radar warning. The main defence is the ALQ-144 infra-red countermeasures system mounted behind the shrouded exhaust.

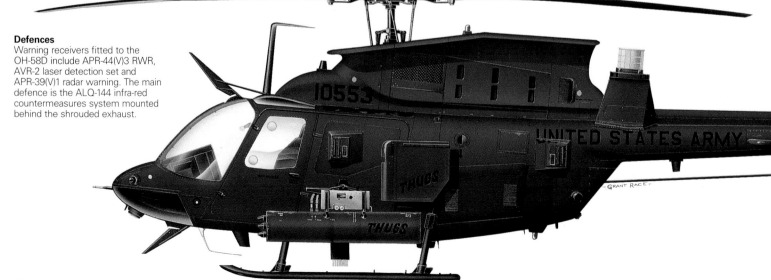

Ideal for many types of attack, the Hydra-70 2.75-mm FFAR (folding-fin aircraft rocket) is carried in a seven-round pod.

Bell OH-58D
Kiowa Warrior

Some of the best-equipped Kiowa Warriors are those issued to the 4th Squadron, 17th Cavalry, which is a designated seagoing unit known as the 'Thugs'. They are the replacements for the TF-118 Prime Chance aircraft which performed so well in the Gulf during both Desert Storm and the earlier Earnest Will tanker reflagging operations.

Powerplant
The OH-58D is powered by a single Allison 250-C30R (military designation T703-AD-700). The power rating is 650 shp (485 kW) but the transmission is limited to 550 shp (410 kW).

The MMS is built by McDonnell Douglas, and is mounted on a special bearing which does not transmit the helicopter's vibrations.

Mast-mounted sight
The sight contains a TV sensor and infra-red imaging system for sighting in both day and night conditions, and a laser designator/rangefinder. All are boresighted to each other, while the sight swivels through 360° azimuth, and ±30° in elevation.

Weapon options
Instead of the Hydra rockets and Hellfires shown here, the OH-58D can optionally replace either or both weapons with Stinger air-to-air missiles or machine-guns (30-calibre Miniguns or 50-calibre M2s).

Hellfire missile
Up to four AGM-114Cs can be carried, a maximum of two on each side. Each missile is 5 ft 8 in (1.73 m) long and has a launch weight of 106 lb (48 kg). Control is effected by surfaces on the aft wings.

Rotor
The four-bladed main rotor has composites blades and a carbon-fibre yoke. This turns at 395 rpm while the tail rotor turns at 2,381 rpm.

Caving ladder
The excrescence under the cabin of the OH-58D holds a caving ladder, which can be dropped down for the rapid rescue of personnel. They climb on to the ladder, and hang on while the Kiowa moves away.

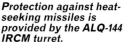

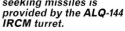

Protection against heat-seeking missiles is provided by the ALQ-144 IRCM turret.

Airborne Multi-Purpose System) which trailed behind and used its radar to search the target and provide vectors. Typically, one OH-58D would carry two Hellfires and a gun, the other two Stingers and two 2.75-in rocket pods. Used with NVGs, the ancient 0.50-calibre (12.7-mm) M2 machine-gun was rigged with the Israeli AIM-1DLR laser-aiming device which projects a spot of red light visible through NVGs, enabling the pilot to put an aiming dot on his target to see where rounds would fall. Tracer rounds – friendly and hostile – showed up on the helicopter's FLIR.

Nothing has been released about actual engagements between these hastily-fielded armed helicopters and their Iranian nautical adversaries, though one Pentagon expert says that the number of engagements was "in the hundreds, not in the dozens." In at least some of the low-level nocturnal actions, Hellfires were employed against Iranian vessels. More than 8,000 hours of combat patrol were logged in the tanker conflict. Earnest Will and Prime Chance were successful: the very last tanker out of Straits of Hormuz was escorted by armed OH-58Ds.

Production Armed OH-58D

Such was the prelude to the important decision to arm not just 15 Prime Chance shooters but all OH-58D helicopters. Based on a 6 December 1989 review of Army programmes, Army Secretary Michael Stone approved a plan to spend $640 million giving the entire OH-58D fleet the

armament proven in the Persian Gulf. The Production Armed OH-58D differs from Operation Prime Chance's OH-58D (Armed) in having minor changes to the skid aft cross tube, revised transmission gear assembly, and 250-C30X engine with an output diffuser (and no change in its T703-A-720 military designation).

A month after the Production Armed OH-58D was announced (that is, on 8 January 1990), Stone transferred OH-58Ds from the Field Artillery to the Air Cavalry. This meant removal of OH-58D scouts from Division Field Artillery units, retrofit to the armed configuration, and fielding to air cavalry regiments and corps armoured reconnaissance squadrons, replacing the AH-1 Cobra/OH-58C hunter-killer team with a single aircraft. The Cavalry is scattered among more traditional Army units and is a light vanguard of mobile, rapidly-moving forces. The rest of the Army has companies and battalions; the Cavalry has troops and squadrons.

Stone selected Kiowa Warrior as the popular name for all armed OH-58Ds. The US Army held a ceremony at Anadarko, Oklahoma, near Fort Sill, to celebrate the name. In attendance were native Americans of Kiowa stock – a small, fierce band of North American Plains Indians believed to have killed more white men than any other Plains Indian tribe, among them no small number of Cavalrymen.

For the anti-armour mission, the Kiowa Warrior uses the AGM-114 Hellfire. This has laser guidance, courtesy of the MMS.

Using the air transportability kit, two Kiowa Warriors can be carried in a C-130. Collapsible skids reduce the helicopter's height and the lower wire cutter is removed, while the MMS is cradled in a special stand.

The Kiowa Warrior was expected to serve in limited numbers and was deemed an interim solution until the RAH-66 Comanche (then called the LH, or Light Helicopter) could enter service. Since then, delays with the Comanche have given the Kiowa Warrior programme an unforeseen permanency. On Bell's line in Fort Worth, Texas, the dismantled carcasses of OH-58A helicopters once slated to be reborn as unarmed OH-58D scouts were converted instead to OH-58D Kiowa Warriors, beginning with OH-58D no. 207. Bell delivered the first production aircraft in May 1991.

From no. 207, all OH-58D Kiowa Warriors were built with an 'air transportability' kit, enabling them to be rapidly deployed in a crisis. This kit includes an internal platform for stowage of the MMS during shipment, collapsible skids, folding horizontal stabiliser and a two-position folding vertical fin, and a removable lower wire cutter. The object is to 'kneel' the helicopter for stowage (two in a C-130, four in a C-141, 12 in a C-5) and to keep reassembly time as short as possible to reduce the risk of discovery or attack by the enemy. The MMS is easily removable in a short time. In fact, the US Army routinely flies armed OH-58Ds for type training at Fort Rucker, Alabama without the MMS installed.

The rapid deployment kit results from tests carried out with a prototype kit during Prime

Bell OH-58D
Kiowa Warrior

1 'Stealth' profiled nosecone
2 Pitot head
3 Lower cable cutter
4 Radar warning receivers
5 Fresh air intakes
6 Battery
7 Forward avionics equipment bay
8 Air circulation fan and ducting
9 Downward vision window
10 Yaw control pedals
11 Cyclic pitch control column
12 Multi-function CRT cockpit displays

32 Main cabin door
33 Mission avionics equipment
34 Engine and transmission mounting cabin rear bulkhead
35 Anti-vibration gearbox mounting
36 Hydraulic reservoir
37 Control linkages
38 Rotor head hydraulic actuators
39 Main transmission gearbox
40 Filtered engine air intake

13 Instrument panel shroud
14 Tinted windscreen panels treated for laser protection
15 Upper cable cutter
16 Communications aerials
17 Cockpit eyebrow windows
18 Control rod housing
19 Pilot's seat
20 Safety harness
21 Seat armour
22 Crew door, port and starboard
23 Co-pilot/gunner's seat
24 Collective pitch control lever
25 Port landing skid
26 Forward skid strut
27 Avionics cooling air scoop
28 External stores (424-litres) mounting strut
29 Fuel tank housing
30 Self-sealing, crashworthy fuel cell, 93-Imp gal (424-litre) capacity
31 Equipment mounting shelf

41 Swash plate mechanism
42 Composite radar attenuating cowling panels
43 Rotor head control rods and blade pitch control links
44 Rotor mast and control rod fairing
45 Blade root attachment joints
46 Carbon composite yoke with elastomeric bearings
47 Four-bladed main rotor
48 McDonnell-Douglas/Northrop Mast Mounted Sight (MMS)

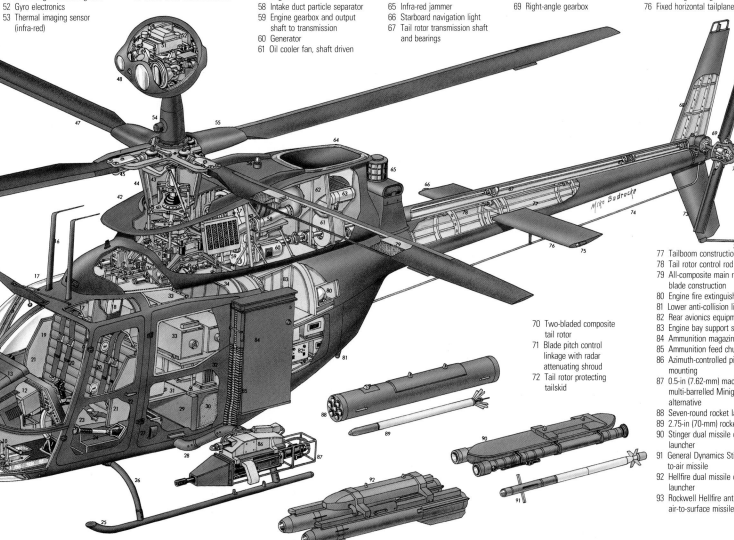

A simulator shot shows the thoroughly modern cockpit of the OH-58D. Large multi-function displays provide navigation, aircraft and targeting data, while the central screen gives a wider-picture nav plot.

Chance in 1989. During this protracted trial, a C-130 Hercules loaded with two armed OH-58Ds flew a two-hour mission and landed on a remote dirt strip. Army crews using standard tools were able to get both helicopters unloaded and airborne, ready for combat, in 10.5 minutes. The Army teams achieved this in darkness with no exterior illumination except hand-held minilights with red filters. According to Bell's Russ Rumney, "under realistic conditions we have actually gotten off the transport and into the air in five minutes, 46 seconds."

In 1991, Bell was manufacturing three OH-58Ds per month (in unarmed configuration) and had delivered 190 aircraft. Production of the OH-58D had been planned to end with the 243rd aircraft when a further batch of 36, raising the total to 279, was added in fiscal year 1991 for the Army National Guard. Congress funded the helicopters even though the Army did not ask for them, and authorised their delivery to regular Army units, rather than the Guard, if necessary. Necessity arose on 2 August 1990 when Iraq invaded Kuwait.

The Prime Chance helicopters had remained in the Gulf to carry out surface surveillance and searches. The Desert Shield build-up brought more Kiowas (as the unarmed OH-58D Aeroscout was now named) and Kiowa Warriors. For most participants, the war with Iraq was their first combat. For OH-58D crews, including those who operated from the guided missile frigates USS *Curts* (FFG-38) and USS *Nicholas* (FFG-47), the action capped years of sea duty inside the narrow confines of the Gulf. When build-up gave way to war with Operation Desert Storm on 17 January 1991, two Kiowa Warriors on an early combat mission identified four small Iraqi boats, launched two Hellfires, got a hit, and followed up with gun and rocket fire. On the

49 Optical boresight system
50 Television sensor
51 Laser rangefinder/designator
52 Gyro electronics
53 Thermal imaging sensor (infra-red)
54 Turret support and heat exchanger
55 Rotor head blade root cuffs
56 Anti-collision light
57 Allison 250-C30R turboshaft engine
58 Intake duct particle separator
59 Engine gearbox and output shaft to transmission
60 Generator
61 Oil cooler fan, shaft driven
62 Engine bay firewall
63 Oil cooler
64 Combined exhaust duct
65 Infra-red jammer
66 Starboard navigation light
67 Tail rotor transmission shaft and bearings
68 Upper fin segment; tailfin tilts in conjunction with tail rotor control
69 Right-angle gearbox
73 Lower fin segment
74 HF aerial rail
75 Port navigation light
76 Fixed horizontal tailplane

70 Two-bladed composite tail rotor
71 Blade pitch control linkage with radar attenuating shroud
72 Tail rotor protecting tailskid

77 Tailboom construction
78 Tail rotor control rod
79 All-composite main rotor blade construction
80 Engine fire extinguisher bottle
81 Lower anti-collision light
82 Rear avionics equipment bay
83 Engine bay support structure
84 Ammunition magazine
85 Ammunition feed chute
86 Azimuth-controlled pintle gun mounting
87 0.5-in (7.62-mm) machine-gun, multi-barrelled Minigun as alternative
88 Seven-round rocket launcher
89 2.75-in (70-mm) rocket
90 Stinger dual missile carrier/launcher
91 General Dynamics Stinger air-to-air missile
92 Hellfire dual missile carrier/launcher
93 Rockwell Hellfire anti-armour air-to-surface missile

night of 18/19 January, Kiowa Warriors flew top cover for a bloodless assault on armed oil platforms in which special operations troopers rounded up the first Iraqi POWs of the conflict.

On 26 January 1991, two OH-58D Kiowa Warriors left *Curts* to liberate an island in the Gulf belonging to Kuwait, 29 prisoners being taken. Other actions were kept veiled, and the world saw only snippets: three unarmed OH-58D Scouts played a critical role in a mine-clearing operation inside Kuwait; two of the original Prime Chance Kiowa Warriors flew from USS *Jarrett* (FFG-33) to attack and destroy an Iraqi Silkworm missile launcher; two Saudi land forces' Bell 406CS Combat Scouts engaged a column of Iraqi vehicles and destroyed an armoured personnel carrier and a dozen trucks.

Some of the sea-based Kiowa Warriors went ashore in February 1991 to support Special Forces operations in Kuwait. As the war rushed toward its conclusion, NVGs could not be used because of dense smoke from burning Kuwaiti oil wells, but the FLIR in the mast-mounted sight continued to work. Over 200 MMS units were employed in the Gulf War and maintained a greater than 90 per cent mission readiness rate.

When the war ended in February the Prime Chance aircraft were rotated back to Fort Bragg in October and have since been replaced with newer Kiowa Warriors in the 4th Squadron, 17th Cavalry. The 4/17th retains its maritime capability as a seagoing air cavalry unit for surveillance and interdiction. Its Kiowa Warriors are the only examples in the fleet currently equipped with GPS (global positioning system) navigation.

One problem with the Kiowa Warrior, because of the 'black boxes' required for radios

and mast-mounted sight, is its lack of space for extra personnel and limited usefulness for added missions, such as SAR or medical evacuation. To carry troops and cargo during rapid deployment and forced-entry operations with the 82nd Airborne Division, Bell developed MPLH kits which augment the aircraft with two externally-mounted seat modules each able to carry three personnel, or two litter modules each capable of carrying two litters, and a belly-mounted cargo hook (the same design as that on some civil Bell 206s) able to lift 2,000 lb (907 kg). When installed, any of these kits disturbs the clean lines of the Kiowa Warrior's fuselage by adding clumsy, external loads, but the increase in capability is significant. Just 81 MPLH kits have been delivered, to enable a portion of the OH-58D force to be converted for secondary missions.

Bell claims that the OH-58D Kiowa Warrior has the highest readiness rate in the Army's aviation fleet. The armed OH-58D has been tested in the field in Europe with a German army BO 105P helicopter with roof-mounted sight and a British Gazelle (under limited conditions) and has proved able to outperform both. In Joint Air Attack Team exercises, the Kiowa Warrior has designated targets for A-10 Warthogs equipped with Pave Penny sensors. The OH-58D's airborne target handover capability has proven effective working with F-16s.

Stealthy OH-58D

In 1987, Bell designed and prototyped modifications to the unarmed OH-58D scout to reduce its susceptibility to radar detection. This effort was sponsored by the Low Observables Technology and Application Office of the US Army Laboratory Command, Adelphi, Maryland. The

A test Kiowa Warrior launches an AGM-114. The Hellfire is available with either semi-active laser, imaging infra-red or RF/IR guidance. The warhead is a high-explosive blast fragmentation unit.

result is a reconfigured helicopter, referred to as the 'stealth Kiowa', although the correct name is Optimized Aircraft, or OA.

The much-modified OA features a needle nose and laser protection coating in its windshield, part of a broad package of shaping and absorptive lightweight materials to optimise radar attenuation for NOE missions. The 'stealth Kiowa' prototype (88-0312; c/n 43169) made its first flight at Arlington on 6 August 1990 with pilot Robert A. Williams and flight test engineer Chris J. Stroncek. The OA was tested against Soviet radar systems at Fort Irwin, California and proved more difficult to detect than the standard OH-58D.

Bell hails the Optimized Aircraft as "an excellent example of an effective low-cost kit approach to reduce the radar cross-section of a fielded helicopter system." Nothing was said publicly when 18 airframes were converted to Optimized Aircraft and delivered to the 1st Squadron, 17th Cavalry, 82nd Combat Aviation Brigade, at Fort Bragg, North Carolina, which also operates UH-60L Black Hawks and AH-1F Cobras. Unlike other Bragg-based units which report directly to their Corps, the 1/17th is a part of the 82nd Airborne Division, which is earmarked for rapid deployment in a crisis. While the 'stealth Kiowa' is not being developed further and the prototype is no longer flying, one squadron remains in service and Bell says it is still working on making some aspects of the kit more user friendly.

The needle-nose and treated windscreen distinguish the Optimized Aircraft, or 'stealthy' OH-58D. Eighteen of these special conversions fly with the 82nd Airborne Division's 1/17th Cavalry.

With laser-protective windscreen coating, the 'OH-58X' is a one-off company demonstrator with lengthened nose. This houses some avionics, allowing the rear seats to be used for passenger carriage.

OH-58D Variant

In a joint bid with Honeywell, which makes the avionics package, Bell has been flying an improved prototype officially known as the 'OH-58D Variant', and unofficially called the OH-58X. This aircraft was painted a brilliant gloss black with a colourful Kiowa chieftain's profile on its rear fuselage, although it has since been restored to standard US Army markings. Developed from one of the prototype OH-58D airframes which retains an OH-58A serial number (69-16322 c/n 43004), the OH-58D Variant made its first flight in the new configuration at Arlington on 19 March 1992 with Robert A. Williams as pilot and Michael Kiesov as flight test engineer. The helicopter has laser protection coating in its windshield, improved helmet-mounted display, radar altimeters, and CRTs.

In every step of Bell 406 development, including the MPLH configuration where seats and litters are mounted externally, there seems to be a constant struggle to create more space inside this very full aircraft. Unlike the 'stealth Kiowa' whose pointed nose serves only to foil radar, the lengthened needle nose of the OH-58D Variant has load-carrying capacity for radios and black boxes, freeing up sufficient space for two seats behind the pilots when flown in the armed configuration.

OH-58D (LUH)

With its mast-mounted sight removed, the OH-58D Variant becomes the Bell candidate for a next-generation light utility helicopter for the US Army. Though the Army once underwrote the UTARS (Utility Aircraft Requirements Study) which identified a need for 1,279 light utility helicopters to replace the ageing Bell UH-1H Huey, the service still has plenty of Hueys which, while uneconomical, retain thousands of hours of service life. Further, the Army's one-time UH-X requirement was wiped out by post-Desert Storm budget cuts, leaving the service with no enunciated need for a light utility helicopter. Partly because the Army National Guard remains free to define a separate need of its own – and despite any assurance of funding – both the Eurocopter/Vought Panther 800 (based

on the SA 365N Dauphin helicopter but with T800 engine) and the OH-58D Variant are being touted at conventions. Both claim to be NDIs (non-developmental items), meaning off-the-shelf products which can be readily available, and both claim far lower operating costs than any Huey.

The OH-58D (LUH), by dispensing with MMS and armament, can carry three people in its back seat; there are kits for stretchers on the side. Other features which Bell advertises for the OH-58D (LUH) variant are provision for night pilotage, FLIR, high frequency/SSB radio, helmet display system, digital map display and GPS. The OH-58D (LUH) was first exhibited publicly at a Fort Worth convention on 5 April 1993 and was scheduled to be shown at another in St Louis on 19 May 1993.

Following the example of Saudi Arabia, Taiwan wants to become the second overseas customer for the Bell 406. Arrangements are being sought to clear the Hellfire missile and mast-mounted sight to enable the Chinese Nationalists to acquire 26 Kiowa Warriors, probably fresh from the Fort Worth conversion line. The sale would face additional hurdles and could take years to finalise.

In addition to overseas sales, the OH-58D with its nocturnal eyes and high manoeuvrability has obvious potential for the US Border Patrol, Drug Enforcement Agency and Customs service, all of which have evaluated the type.

The US Army's paper requirement for OH-58D aircraft, once as high as 578 when the type was unarmed, and once as low as 243, now stands at 507. Given the 'stretch-out' of the higher-priority AH-64C/D Apache Longbow and RAH-66 Comanche programmes, it is thought likely that the last figure will never be reached and that the service may end procurement with the 351 OH-58D Kiowa Warriors for which funding is currently committed through fiscal year 1995.

A view of a Kiowa Warrior no enemy would want to see. Still thought of as a light scout, the OH-58D is in fact a powerful battlefield weapon, with a wide range of weapon options, excellent defences and a full sensor suite.

Sukhoi Su-27
'FLANKER'
& Su-30, Su-33, Su-35

Although to Western fighter pilots virtually every enemy aircraft is generically known as 'a MiG', the latest products of the well known Mikoyan Design Bureau are steadily being overshadowed by fighters produced by their great rival, Sukhoi, which previously specialised in heavyweight interceptors and lumbering fighter-bombers. One aircraft in particular is responsible for the Sukhoi OKB's dramatic change in fortunes: the Su-27, known to NATO as 'Flanker'. Air show appearances have demonstrated an almost unbelieveable level of agility and an ability to perform manoeuvres

that no Western fighter can emulate, while record-breaking flights speak volumes for the aircraft's incredibly high performance and ultra-long range. Routine Cold War encounters showe Western pilots an aircraft which regularly bristle with as many as 10 advanced air-to-air missiles, and whose bulbous radome clearly contained an advanced long-range pulse-Doppler radar, with genuine look-down/shoot-down capability. It seems little wonder that the Su-27 has been selected as the cornerstone around which the Russian air forces will enter the new millennium

Main picture: A PVO 'Flanker' lands, its tyres leaving a puff of smoke. The Su-27 is a huge aircraft for a single-seat fighter, larger even than America's broadly equivalent F-15.

Right: A pair of Su-27s in flight. Soviet fighter tactics began to change with the introduction of the MiG-29 and Su-27, with a corresponding reduction in the traditional reliance on tight GCI control and a move towards greater flexibility and more reactive tactics.

Sukhoi Su-27 'Flanker'

Above: The first of the 'Flankers'. The T-10 prototype pictured at the Flight Research Centre at Zhukovsky at about the time of its first flight, with camera calibration markings and without the distinctive anti-flutter weights added later in the flight test programme.

Right: Pilot of the T-10 on its first flight was General Vladimir Ilyushin (son of the famous designer), who continues to act as a consultant to, and ambassador for, the Sukhoi OKB, and is still one of the great characters of Russian aviation.

Below: The first prototype wore an attractive two-tone light grey/blue colour scheme. Pictures of the aircraft in flight are extremely rare, but give an impression of the very different wing planform, and other discontinued features.

Even today, the Su-27 is an enigma. Dazzling air show routines and a clutch of world records (snatched from the rival F-15) speak for an incredible level of performance and agility, while huge internal fuel capacity gives the aircraft an enormous range. The type has been selected as the multi-role cornerstone of the Russian air force into the next century, eclipsing all rivals. Lockheed YF-22 project personnel, writing in their own company magazine, referred to the aircraft thus: "The Russians are hot fighter jocks and the Su-27 and MiG-29 are sportier than anything we have in the inventory . . . but the F-22 will have better manoeuvrability than the Su-27, which is Top Gun at the moment." In Europe, supporters of the European Fighter Aircraft inevitably use the Su-27, or a fictitious 'Su-27 with X number of years development' as their baseline threat aircraft to explain why Europe's most advanced combat aircraft is essential.

The aircraft everyone is talking about had a difficult birth and a disastrous early history, and the weapons system and radar are still widely regarded as being primitive and of limited effectiveness. There is no shortage of admirers or detractors of the Su-27, and it remains difficult to discern the truth – is the aircraft an over-rated mediocrity or a multi-talented, enormously capable star?

When the Cold War ended, and the former Soviet Union split asunder, things changed overnight for the military, which immediately lost its unlimited funding and privileged status. The shock was no less severe in the aviation industry, since production of most military aircraft was halted or slashed, and countless new projects were cancelled. The Russian air force decided as an economy measure to move towards standardisation on a single tactical aircraft type. The aircraft they chose was the Su-27 'Flanker'.

This decision clearly demonstrated the success and popularity of the aircraft, and was a testament to its versatility and potential for further development but, perhaps more interestingly, it showed the extent to which the Sukhoi OKB (Design Bureau), under the charismatic leadership of Mikhail Petrovich Simonov, had gained a political ascendancy over its rivals. Thus, while the Su-27 has been selected as the 'backbone' aircraft with which the Russian air force will enter the new millennium, there are already impotent mutterings of anger and discontent from disgruntled rival 'firms' and from many senior air force officers who acknowledge the Su-27's capability as an interceptor, but who correctly and realistically point to its enormous price tag, its lack of suitability for the tactical air superiority fighter role, and to its shortcomings as a potential carrier-based multi-role fighter or land-based tactical bomber.

Look-down/shoot-down

When the aircraft was conceived, few would have dared predict the scale of its eventual success, and its early history was so disastrous that cancellation of the entire project seemed a real possibility on several separate occasions. The Su-27 was conceived during 1969, after the Sukhoi OKB won a design contract to design a long-range interceptor to replace the Tu-128 'Fiddler', Su-15 'Flagon' and Yak-28P 'Firebar' in IA-PVO service. Current OKB Designer General Simonov has since commented that "we won, but as so often happens, it was decided to adopt the losing aircraft as well!" This statement has been taken as being an indication that the Su-27 and MiG-31 were designed as competitors, and that the latter aircraft was also adopted as a low-risk 'insurance policy' and stop-gap. From an early stage, it was decided that the new Sukhoi aircraft would have a limited Frontal Aviation role as a long-range escort fighter for strike aircraft like the Su-24 'Fencer' and as a complement to Mikoyan's MiG-29, destroying high-value assets like tankers and AWACS platforms far beyond the front line, while the MiG-29 concentrated on fighters and fighter-bombers.

The growing importance of low-level penetration tactics dictated that the new fighter should be capable of look-down/shoot-down intercepts, while the increasing use of stand-off weapons such as cruise missiles made it necessary to intercept targets at very long range (preferably before their weapons could be launched) and to be capable of intercepting low-flying missiles. As if this requirement was not difficult enough, Sukhoi was instructed that the new fighter should be capable of destroying 'enemy fighter aircraft which protect the target zone', which was taken as a directive that the new fighter should be able to better the new American F-15 in air-to-air combat.

The design team for the new fighter was led by Yevgeny Ivanov, with Oleg Samolovich as his deputy and Designer General Pavel Osipovich Sukhoi giving the benefit of his considerable experience. Sukhoi died in 1975, and was replaced by Simonov, but no change was made to the design team. Samolovich has stated that after two years of preliminary work, the basic layout of the aircraft was drawn up over a single weekend (to avoid interruptions) by only three men, one of whom, Vladimir Antonov, worked on the project as part of his post-graduate university studies. Another (possibly apocryphal) story from the early days relates that in order to reduce weight, Ivanov designed the aircraft to 90 per cent of ultimate design load then strengthened only those areas shown to be deficient by static testing.

The first prototype, given the bureau designation T-10-1, made its maiden flight on 20 May 1977 at Zhukhovsky, in the hands of Vladimir Ilyushin, the bureau chief test pilot, whose CV covered 143 aircraft types, including the B-25 Mitchell, Northrop F-5E and Cessna A-37, as well as several Sikorsky helicopters. The aircraft was powered by AL-21F-3 engines, as used by the Su-17, with the afterburner nozzles completely enclosed within the rear fuselage, like those of the Su-24 'Fencer'. Spotted at Zhukhovsky (then erroneously referred to by Western intelligence agencies as Ramenskoye) by a US satellite, the aircraft was allocated the provisional reporting name 'RAM-J'. A handful of these images were eventually seen by the press, but the quality of the released images was so poor that little could be inferred about the new fighter. One well known and distinguished analyst was even convinced that he could see variable geometry wings. This prototype aircraft later provided the Western aviation press

with its first useful glimpse of the Su-27 in 1985, when stills from a TV documentary about the Sukhoi OKB were released, and the machine can now be seen in the air forces' museum at Monino, near Moscow.

Familiar configuration

The aircraft was of typical late 1960s/early 1970s configuration, with twin vertical tailfins, widely spaced underslung engines and a blended wing/forebody, with some features reminiscent of some aspects of the rival US F-15 and F-14. Since Western analysts at that time believed that Soviet

Below: The West's first view of the Su-27 was provided by a 10-second clip on Soviet TV during a documentary about Sukhoi. This showed the T-10-1 landing and taking off, perhaps on its first flight.

Left: The only other T-10 prototype photograph seen in the West shows an aircraft apparently coded 51, seen here.

The first T-10 ended its days in the impressive air forces museum collection at Monino, heading a row of Sukhoi OKB fighters and prototypes. The aircraft has had primitive anti-flutter weights added to the leading edges of the tailfins, wingtips and tailerons, and its camouflage has been faded and bleached by summer sun and winter snow.

Wing fences
Four small fences were added to the upper surface of the wing, well inboard, perhaps before the first flight. These reduced drag by cutting down spanwise flow of the boundary layer.

Radar
The T-10s were ready long before their intended radar, and were therefore completed with empty metal nosecones of simple conical shape. Ballast was fitted to maintain the centre of gravity.

Powerplants
The T-10-1 was powered by a pair of Lyul'ka AL-21F-3 turbojets, as used by the MiG-23, Su-17 and Su-24. An axial flow turbojet with a 14-stage compressor, the AL-21F-3 handles a mass flow of 104 kg (229 lb) per second and has a pressure ratio of 14.75. The engine produces 76.5 kN (17,200 lb st) in full military power (8,400 rpm) and 110.5 kN (24,800 lb st) in full burner.

Armament
The T-10-1 was fitted with four underwing hardpoints, but had no internal cannon, and may not have had hardpoints either between or below the engine nacelles.

Wing planform
The original T-10 prototypes had a gracefully curving wingtip, which was square-cropped and fitted with a missile launch rail-cum-flutter weight on production aircraft.

Sukhoi T-10-1

The first prototype T-10, forerunner of the Su-27, is shown late in its life. The aircraft made a long and valuable contribution to the flight test programme before being retired to the air forces museum at Monino, just outside Moscow. The aircraft was camouflaged overall in two tones of grey-blue, the disruptive pattern continuing on to the lower surfaces.

Afterburner
The fully variable afterburner nozzles are fully enclosed in the rear fuselage, as on the Su-24, and can be used over the whole power range from flight idle to maximum power, giving smooth modulated increases in power output.

Anti-flutter weights
The T-10-1 was fitted with prominent and rather crude leading-edge spikes on the vertical tailfins, the horizontal tail surfaces and the wingtips, some time after the first flight. These were intended to alleviate some of the original aircraft's flutter problems. In the end, a total aerodynamic redesign proved necessary. The T-10-1 retains its spike-like anti-flutter weights to this day.

Cockpit
The T-10s had a simple wraparound windscreen and a one-piece bubble canopy, both of which had to be reshaped and strengthened on the production Su-27. The priority of giving the pilot a good, unobstructed all-round view was apparent even at this early stage.

engineers were both backward and incapable of any original thought, this led inevitably to accusations that Sukhoi had copied one or other of the US aircraft. The wing was very clean, with a drooping leading edge but no leading-edge slats and no anti-flutter weights, and with conventional outboard ailerons and inboard flaps. The root was swept at about 80°, and the main part of the leading edge at 44° out to the gracefully curving tip. Four small fences were added on the inboard panels, perhaps before the first flight. The twin fins were uncanted and were mounted on top of the engine nacelles, just outboard of the centreline. Box section beams on the sides of the nacelles carried the slab tailerons. The main undercarriage units were mounted in the wingroots, retracting forward and swivelling through 90° to lie horizontally in the wing. Large forward undercarriage doors, hinged on their leading edges, acted as airbrakes, à la Folland Gnat. The tall nose gear was located well forward, below the windscreen, retracting aft.

The design team, drawing on extensive work carried out by the Central Aerodynamics Institute, TsAGI, chose to use what the Russians call an 'integrated airframe' in which forebody and wing are blended together to form, in effect, a single, unified lifting body. This blending (also used on the American F-16) gives a smaller wetted area (and thus lower drag) and greater internal volume for fuel and avionics. The configuration allowed a smooth change in cross-sectional area, even at the canopy and air intakes, significantly reducing wave drag. The Su-27's very high internal fuel capacity is partly a result of this, but mainly as a result of the fighter's sheer size.

Low-slung nacelles

The engines were housed in low-slung, widely separated nacelles, leaving a significant tunnel between them, suitable for low-drag, low radar-signature stores carriage. The engines were separated to avoid the chance of damage to one resulting in damage to the other – a significant risk unless engines are widely spaced or separated by an armoured titanium 'keel'. Separate, widely spaced intakes allow simpler, 'straight-through' intake ducts, which are easier to design and more efficient, and which are more effective when the aircraft is sideslipping. Their underslung location is superior at high angles of attack. The intakes are separated from the

underside of the fuselage/wing lifting body by a narrow gap, making the top of the intake effectively a splitter plate which removes sluggish boundary layer air. Boundary layer is also removed via tiny perforations in one of the three intake ramp sections. These are fully variable to alter intake area and angle, and thereby to control shock wave formation. They give the Su-27 its Mach 2 performance capability.

When Mikoyan's MiG-29 prototype was revealed, it

Norwegian air force F-16s began encountering Su-27s in early 1987, these aircraft usually being armed with six AA-10 'Alamos' but with wingtip and outboard underwing pylons empty.

Left: Early production Su-27s had a simple tailboom, with strakes on either side rather than the box-like fairings which on later aircraft house chaff/flare dispensers.

Below: Early Su-27s retained small anti-flutter weights on the leading edge of each tailfin.

Sukhoi Su-27 'Flanker'

Above: The traditional 'sunburst' air forces flag is lowered at a Frontal Aviation 'Flanker' base at the end of the day. In the background an armed Su-27 waits in front of its shelter.

Right: A g-suited pilot studies his briefing notes before climbing the ladder into the cockpit of his Su-27. Most Su-27 pilots wear the new lightweight Soviet flying helmet, which is distinguished by the row of holes across the top.

could be seen to have a similar overall configuration, with twin fins, widely spaced engines and a blended wing/forward fuselage incorporating prominent leading-edge root extensions. This gave rise to inevitable accusation and counter-accusation that one bureau had copied the other's design. In fact no copying went on, the similarities in overall configuration being the inevitable result of common solutions being found for common problems and of common access to the research work of TsAGI and other research institutes. Interestingly, the changes to the Sukhoi prototype to bring it to the eventual production configuration made the aircraft more similar to the MiG-29 in appearance, with more widely spaced tailfins on booms beside the engine nacelles.

Even more galling to the two Russian design bureaux than accusations that they had copied one another was the chorus of accusations that they had copied elements of the various contemporary Western fighters. The twin fins were inevitably cited to have been 'ripped off' from the F-14, F-15 or YF-17, the widely-spaced engines from the F-14, the blended fuselage from the F-14 or F-16, and other features from one or other of the US fighters. For a nation which had put the first

vehicle, animal and then man into space, and the nation whose aircraft industry had produced countless record-breaking aircraft, such misinformed comment was an unwelcome and unwarranted insult. "Just because you can see your neighbour toiling in his field doesn't mean you don't have to toil just as hard in your own," was a saying used frequently by irritated Russian designers.

Prototype crashes

The first and second prototypes were built by the OKB itself, in its Moscow 'workshop', albeit using wings and tails from the Komsomolsk-na-Amur production plant. The second prototype reportedly incorporated some improvements, including a flattened leading edge with moveable slats, canted tailfins and, according to some sources, was the first T-10 with the full standard fly-by-wire control system (originally developed for the T-4/Su-100, which was claimed by Sukhoi to have been the world's first operational FBW aircraft). It also had an extra tonne (2,204 lb) of internal fuel by comparison with the first aircraft's 9-tonne (19,841-lb) capacity. The T-10-2 was lost after a control system malfunction, which led to severe resonance. Yevgeny Soloviev was killed when he ejected outside seat parameters. The next two prototypes, T-10-3 and T-10-4, were also built by the bureau, but these were powered by the definitive production standard AL-31F (albeit with underslung accessories and gearboxes). T-10-3 made its maiden flight on 23 August 1979, and was followed by T-10-4 on 31 October. Five further prototypes were built by the production plant at Komsomolsk (T-10-5, T-10-6, T-10-9, T-10-10 and T-10-11), but these were powered by the AL-21F.

As the accidents were rocking the programme, information about the new US F-15 began to flood in, and it became clear that the T-10, which was failing to meet its own performance requirements, would be no match for the American fighter. This was caused by higher-than-expected drag figures, a performance shortfall from the engines, excessive specific fuel consumption figures and the excess weight of the newly developed avionics systems, which, since they were mainly fitted in the nose, also tended to in-

crease the longitudinal stability of the aircraft. The aircraft also suffered from flutter problems, and these necessitated the provision of anti-flutter weights on the leading edges of the tailfins, tailplanes and wings, and the removal of one pair of overwing fences. It was clear that to meet its original requirement the new fighter would need to be subjected to a major redesign, and Sukhoi received permission to undertake this on condition that output of the Su-25 attack aircraft would not be affected.

Accordingly, the next two prototypes under construction at the OKB's Moscow facility, T-10-7 and T-10-8, were completed to a completely new standard, which was claimed by the OKB to be an 'entirely new aircraft' retaining only the 'T-10 designation, ejection seat and mainwheels'. The redesign was personally supervised by Mikhail Simonov, who reportedly came up with the new designation T-10S (T-10 Simonov) for the revised design. The two prototypes thus became T-10S-1 and T-10S-2. Even after work began on the two redesigned aircraft, Komsomolsk continued working on T-10 prototypes to the original configuration, for use as equipment and avionics testbeds. Some sources suggest that some 20 original-configuration T-10s were produced, but little evidence can be found to support this contention, and it seems that only nine flew.

The new aircraft was not an entirely 'clean sheet of paper' design, but it did represent a very major redesign. The key to the redesign was an entirely new wing. The LERXes were improved to give more lift (thereby helping to destabilise the heavier, equipment-packed nose) and the wing lost its curved tips, replacing these with massive flutter weights which doubled as wingtip missile launch rails. The ailerons (which had suffered from reversal problems because of the flexibility of the wing) and the original flaps were deleted and replaced by inboard flaperons. Less obviously, but no less importantly, the fuselage was extensively redesigned. Changes to the nose and forward fuselage were the most obvious, with a more capacious radome and reduced forward fuselage cross-section, but with increased cross-sectional area and less height immediately aft of the cabin. A GSh-30-1 cannon was fitted in the starboard wingroot, the same weapon as is used

by the rival MiG-29. Designed by the OKB led by V. P. Gryazev and A. G. Shipunov, the cannon is used in conjunction with the laser rangefinder and is reportedly extremely accurate. The barrel has a 2,000-round life, equivalent to only 80 seconds of fire at the usual 1,500 rpm. (The gun can fire at up to 1,800 rpm). The fuselage adjacent to the gun is skinned in titanium to protect against blast and flash.

The fins were increased in size and were moved outboard

Above: The Su-27's extraordinarily large size belies its agility, which compares favourably with any lightweight fighter.

Above: The Su-27's slightly ungainly appearance has earned it the nickname Zhuravlik ('crane') in Soviet service. The lack of an official name is now bemoaned by some young pilots, who regard with envy Western names like Eagle and Falcon.

Right and above right: Twin braking parachutes are used to give maximum chute area, without scraping the parachute on the runway. Brake chutes are often not used, pilots preferring to use aerodynamic braking and the powerful cooled wheel brakes.

on to the booms which supported the tailplanes. The combined airbrake/main gear doors had caused severe tailplane flutter and were thus replaced by an F-15-style 2.6 m² (51 sq ft) spine-mounted airbrake which opened to a maximum angle of about 54°, while the undercarriage itself was refined, with canted-forward main oleos and a completely repositioned forward-retracting nose gear, located much further aft to improve the ground turning circle and to reduce the risk of debris entering the intakes. When lowered, the main oleos are braced at about half their height by an auxiliary arm which projects from the oleo and locks into a socket on the side of the intake duct. This is reportedly to brace the undercarriage for rough field operation. Development of the T-10S was expedited by the continued use of the surviving original T-10s as engine, armament, instrumentation and equipment testbeds, and for pilot training.

The original T-10s had a short, broad, flat beaver tail between their engine nozzles, capped by a dielectric fairing. On the T-10S this was replaced by a much longer cylindrical tail boom which reduced drag and served as a location for the aircraft's twin braking parachutes and 13 APP-50 chaff/flare launchers, each containing three 50-mm chaff cartridges or IR decoy flares. The original tailcone lacked the lateral box-like fairings and the associated RWR antennas fitted to the tailcones of later Su-27s, and contained a much smaller number of chaff/flare dispensers (27).

The first T-10S-1 made its maiden flight in the hands of Vladimir Ilyushin (shortly before his retirement) on 20 April 1981. This was, at last, an aircraft of which Sukhoi could be proud and which fulfilled some of the enormous potential of the original design. Ilyushin himself loved the aircraft, and said: "Before flying the Su-27, I piloted 142 different aircraft types, and always I knew that I was, if you like, more intelligent than the aircraft. Now with the Su-27 it was the other way round. It was more intelligent than me, more capable than the human pilot. Moreover, when I piloted this aircraft for the first time, I knew that this was the aircraft for which I had waited for all of my life. The smile still hasn't vanished from my face on account of the delight I felt in the air, and everyone who flies the Su-27 will feel the same. It's worth being a pilot of this fighter."

Further delays

This first T-10S looked much more like the production Su-27 we know today, although it still had uncropped vertical fins with horizontal tops, and lacked the second canopy frame level with the back of the ejection seat. Extensive trials with a number of aircraft eventually resulted in the adoption of small ventral fins mounted below the booms which carried the tailplanes and vertical fins, these improving both directional stability and spin characteristics. The original 'flat-topped' tailfins were used by a significant number of early production Su-27s, perhaps sufficient to equip one complete regiment.

These aircraft had an extraordinarily high attrition rate, one being lost in a fatal accident which claimed the life of Alexander Komarov. Another had to be written off after losing virtually an entire wing, although the pilot, Nikolai Sadovnikov, actually managed to land the aircraft. Both accidents were caused by an uncommanded pitch-up which ripped off the newly installed leading-edge flaps, causing tail-fin damage and loss of the outboard wing panels. One cure was to reduce the area of the leading-edge flaps, and another was to reduce their extension angle. Other problems were less easy to solve.

It is known that the Su-27 suffered major problems with its avionics, although details remain unclear. It is widely believed that at one time about 50 aircraft (often quoted as 'hundreds') were in open storage at Komsomolsk awaiting serviceable radars so that they could be delivered. These problems delayed service deliveries (for trials and evaluation) until 1985, although the first production Su-27 had been rolled out in November 1982.

One of the T-10S prototypes was destined to play a further part in the Su-27 story, providing shocking confirmation that in the field of performance, at least, comfortable assumptions of Western superiority would need to be reconsidered. Under the designation P-42 the aircraft was prepared for a series of world record attempts, challenging the records set by the specially stripped F-15 'Streak Eagle'. The Su-27 was stripped of all armament, radar and operational equipment, and was further lightened by removal of leading-edge flap actuators (which were locked shut), tailfin tips, tailcone, and even the radome, which was replaced by a lighter metal fairing. The aircraft even lost its paint, being stripped back to bare metal and then polished. The wingtips lost their launch rails, and the ventral fins (which may never have been fitted to such an early T-10S) were omitted. Take-off weight was reduced to 14100 kg (31,085 lb), according to figures later provided to the FAI. The engines were similarly modified and redesignated, this time as R-32s. Static thrust was increased to 13598 kg (29,977 lb), an increase of over 1000 kg (2,204 lb) which brought the P-42's thrust to weight ratio to nearly 2:1. The standard brakes could not hold this monster when it was run up for full power checks, so a novel solution was found: the P-42 was anchored to a stationary tracked armoured vehicle using twin cables and an electronic lock.

Flying records

R. G. Martirosov supervised the modifications, which were completed during 1986. Between October 1986 and the end of 1988 the aircraft was used to set a total of 27 records, flown by Victor Pugachev, Nikolai Sadovnikov, Oleg Tsoi and Yevgeni Frolov. These included time-to-height records to 3000, 6000, 9000, 12000, and 15000 m (9,843, 19,585, 29,528, 39,370 and 49,213 ft), a height record of 19335 m (63,435 ft), and time to height records with various payloads. The aircraft set records for Class N (STOL aircraft with a take-off run below 500 m/1,540 ft). The P-42 is still present at Zhukhovsky, and could be restored to flying status if further record attempts become necessary, but a more likely fate is retirement to a museum.

Another early Su-27 (actually T-10S-20) was prepared for

Below: The prototype Su-27UB made its maiden flight on 7 May 1985, as the T-10U-1. Three prototypes were constructed at Komsomolsk, before production began at Irkutsk.

An Su-27UB taxis back past a row of early Su-27 'Flanker-Bs'. The brake chute door is open, indicating that the aircraft has just landed. Almost unique among current Soviet/Russian two-seaters, the Su-27UB does not require a periscope for the backseater.

Sukhoi Su-27 'Flanker'

a similar record-breaking programme, which was abandoned for unknown reasons. The aircraft was extensively modified with cropped fin-tips, curved wingtips similar to those of the T-10-1, and with the nose radome replaced by a crudely shaped cone. This, and the extended tailcone, reportedly housed extra fuel. No ventral fins were fitted. The aircraft was intended to beat the world distance record in various classes.

Production powerplant

The definitive production Su-27s (and perhaps the T-10S-1) were powered by the production-standard Lyul'ka (MMZ/Saturn) AL-31F which necessitated a slightly redesigned intake to cope with the greater mass flow, although the differences were not visibly apparent. The T-10S-1 may have introduced the meshed intake FOD protection screens which pop up from the intake floor on start-up and retract after take-off, and may also have introduced the louvred auxiliary intakes below the inlet ducts which provide air during high Alpha flight. The gridded FOD protection screens result in a thrust loss variously described as 400 lb st or 2.25 kN (per engine?) and are actuated by a microswitch on the main gear. The 2-mm square mesh is strong enough to withstand birdstrikes at fairly high speeds.

The FOD protection screens were primarily designed to minimise the chance of foreign object ingestion when taxiing, taking off or landing from rough or semi-prepared strips – an integral part of Soviet combat doctrine even for the PVO. Whereas many Western tactical aircraft need a hard, well-swept runway from which to operate, Su-27s can make pairs take-offs even from stony strips. Such operations are also facilitated by the extremely sturdy undercarriage, which can withstand vertical impacts of up to 6 m/second and which consists of a hydraulically steerable cantilevered single KN-27 nosewheel. This measures 680×260 mm (27×10 in) and incorporates its own separate brake. The single KT-156D mainwheels are larger (1000×350 mm/39×14 in) and their hubs are said to incorporate electric fans for brake cooling.

The AL-31F – a major success

The new engine had its accessories mounted on top, and the new outboard position of the tailfins allowed easier access to these. The AL-31 was designed by A. M. Lyul'ka himself, though it has been improved and refined by the team led by Victor Mikhailovich Chepkin, the present MMZ Saturn OKB Designer General. The engine is a turbofan with a bypass ratio (according to Sukhoi) of 0.59, denoting the ratio of the airflow going through the fan which does not go through the combustion process.

The engine has 23 variable guide vanes in the inlet, and a four-stage low-pressure compressor, with snubbers on the first three stages and a split two-stage stator behind the fourth stage. Its two-dimensional blades are broad chord but of reduced camber and twist. The high-pressure compressor has nine stages, with at least two rows of variable guide vanes. Its blades are of progressively reducing chord and camber. The combustor is annular, and is followed by cooled single-stage high pressure and two-stage low-pressure turbines. The afterburner has multiple radial spray bars and two flameholders and is ignited by sending a hot streak of fuel through the turbine. The variable area afterburner nozzles incorporate inner and outer jet pipes, with cooling bypass air flowing between them to reduce the aircraft's IR signature. Overall pressure ratio is between 23 and 24, meaning that the air entering the intake is reduced to between 1/23 and 1/24 of its original volume. Mass flow is 112 kg (247 lb) per second.

The engine is rated at 12500 kg st (27,550 lb) in afterburner power (when it consumes 1.92 kg of fuel per kg of thrust per hour) and at 7600 kg st (16,755 lb) in military power (when specific fuel consumption drops to 0.75 kg of fuel per kg of thrust). Specific fuel consumption at cruise power is 0.67 kg/kg hour.

The AL-31F has proved to be a major success story, proving as reliable, robust and maintainable as it is powerful. It has a remarkably high TBO (by Soviet standards) of 1,000 hours and a life of 3,000 hours, although every 100 hours the engine is subjected to checks by borescope, oil analysis and vibration monitoring equipment. The 1,000-hour overhaul includes the fitting of a new high-pressure turbine, combustion chamber and some fan- and afterburner-section components with a total value equivalent to 10 per cent of a new engine cost. These and further parts are incorporated at 2,000 hours, with an equivalent value of 15 per cent of new engine cost. Although it is virtually standard in modern Western practice, the engines are noteworthy in being interchangeable left and right and easily accessed for maintenance and replacement.

The engine's most impressive feature is its tolerance to severely disturbed airflow, and its ability to go on running smoothly in such conditions, as demonstrated during tailslide and Cobra manoeuvres at air show altitudes. This extreme stability is due to excellent intake design and the use of sophisticated computer-controlled variable guide vanes and air data sensors which prevent compressor stalls from occurring. Chepkin and his team are rightly proud of their engine, even in its basic unimproved form, and invite comparison

with the Pratt & Whitney F100-PW-100 or F100-PW-220. They claim higher thrust, better economy in reheat or military power and a longer service life, with a comparable post-turbine temperature (higher than the -100, slightly lower than the -220). The Soviet engine is slightly heavier with 1 cm (0.4 in) less maximum diameter and 5 cm (1.9 in) greater length, with lower pressure and bypass ratios.

An example of the AL-31F has run for 12,000 hours on the test stand, and efforts are being made to further increase thrust, life and reliability. Improved single crystal turbine blades and improvements to the high-pressure turbine heat exchanger should allow higher operating temperatures (and thus higher thrust), although it is interesting to note that the cooling systems are so efficient that the turbine gas temperature limitation is already 100°C (212°F) hotter than the melting point of the blades.

Lightweight airframe

The Su-27's competitive performance is not solely due to Lyul'ka's superb engine, however. The airframe is surprisingly light, considering its strength and sheer size. Although composites are virtually unused, the airframe does incorporate advanced lightweight aluminium-lithium alloys, whose ability to be welded rather than riveted or bolted saves weight and increases internal volume.

The Su-27's fuselage is constructed in three basic subsections. The nose is of all-metal semi-monocoque construction, with the stressed skin reinforced by stringers, longerons and bulkhead frames. From front to rear are the radome, the forward fuselage, the cabin and under-cabin, the aft cabin, the avionics bays, the nosewheel well and the LERX. The nosewheel itself is anchored to the rear bulkhead of the forward avionics bay, while the rear bulkhead of the second avionics bay mounts the nosewheel retraction jack and dorsal airbrake.

The mid-fuselage and wing 'centroplane' are basically one unit, with anchor points for the engine nacelles and flanges for the outer wing panels. Much of the structure consists of an enormous integral fuel tank but also has the fuselage spine, mainwheel wells and three-spar wing centre-section.

The wing itself is vast but simple, with full-span leading-edge flaps and inboard trailing-edge flaperons which occupy about two-thirds of each trailing edge. The latter move in unison as flaps to provide extra lift and drag, or differentially as ailerons. Travel is from +35° to −20°. Both surfaces have a single manual setting for take-off and landing, but when under automatic control as manoeuvre flaps have an unlimited number of settings. They are of sandwich construction with a honeycomb core and carbon-fibre skins. The wing, which has about 42° of leading edge sweep and 2.5° anhedral, is built around three spars, with two auxiliary spars supporting the slats and flaperons. The wing ribs are perpendicular to the spars, with extra ribs parallel to the aircraft centreline to further reinforce the wing at the hardpoints. Inboard the wing has massive integral tanks.

The rear fuselage is a less simple and less cohesive structure, built around the central boom which extends back (as the rear fuel tank) to become the tailcone with its brake chute stowage, chaff/flare dispensers and ECM equipment. This is flanked by the semi-monocoque stressed-skin engine nacelles, which are in turn flanked by the two tailbooms, which act as platforms for the tail fins, ventral fins and tailplane, and which contain equipment bays. The slab tailplanes (with deflection limits of +16° to −21°, or ± 10° differentially) have multiple spars and nine ribs, each parallel to the tip. The trailing edges are of honeycomb construction. These operate in unison (controlled by the FBW system) as elevators for pitch control, and differentially as tailerons for roll control. The vertical tailfins themselves are each built around two spars forming a torsion box, with leading and trailing edges of honeycomb sandwich construction. A heat exchanger inlet is located at the base of each tailfin, the port unit being larger than the starboard.

To obtain the desired level of agility (and to reduce drag and weight) it was decided to design the Su-27 to be longitudinally statically unstable, which meant that a computer-controlled flight control system would be necessary to control the aircraft in pitch. This would be the only way of avoiding the loss of control and structural break-up which would inevitably occur if a human pilot attempted to fly the aircraft. The impossibility of flying a modern unstable fighter manually has been compared to trying to steer a bicycle backwards, by its handlebars, while sitting on the bonnet of a speeding car. The aircraft (or bicycle) would immediately begin to deviate from its course, and the deviation would rapidly become too great to rectify. Only a computer can react quickly enough, with sufficiently accurate control surface deflections, to keep the machine flying.

Four years before the T-10 was even launched, Sukhoi had flown the T-4 (Su-100), whose long, narrow fuselage flexed so much that the aircraft could only be controlled by using a fly-by-wire control system. This experience proved invaluable when the time came to design a similar system for the Su-27. This system, designated SDU-27, combines conventional hydro-mechanical controls for the rudders, flaperons and differential taileron movement with a quadruplex fly-by-wire control of symmetrical taileron movement for

Bottom right: Wearing a unit insignia behind its cockpit, this Su-27 is fitted with wingtip ECM pods, a rarely photographed option on all Su-27s and one which is usually seen on aircraft being used in the air-to-ground role.

Below: An Su-27UB lands. The Su-27's enormous spine-mounted dorsal airbrake is shown to advantage. The forward location of the main undercarriage makes tailscrapes a real hazard during a high Alpha landing.

control in pitch. The FBW system also provides stability augmentation in roll and yaw. The system uses four computers, each 'fed' by a separate air data source.

The SDU-27 also performs as a g (+8.5 to −2.5) and α (28°) limiter. These are, however, 'soft' limits, beyond which departure from controlled flight becomes progressively more likely. The pilot can switch off the limiter (or override the limits by using extra stick force to 'pull through' the stick stops) to make brief excursions into the extremes of the envelope. This is how manoeuvres like the Cobra are performed.

Leading-edge root extensions

Designing the Su-27 for instability in pitch allowed the inclusion of the long, flaring wing leading-edge root extensions (LERXes in Western parlance) known in Russia as 'sabres'. These generate lift forward of the centre of gravity (and the normal centre of lift), providing an increased nose-up pitching moment, with this effect becoming more marked at high angles of attack. The extent of this effect is governed by LERX shape, sweep angle, length, span and

*Left: Pilots compare notes after a formation sortie, a **GAZ** jeep waiting to convey them to the mess for post-flight refreshment. External ladders are used to gain access to the **Su-27's** cockpit, rather than using built-in steps, kick-in steps and hand-holds.*

*Left: A late production **Su-27**, with no fin leading-edge flutter weights and with box-like fairings on each side of the tailboom. These house chaff/flare dispensers.*

Below: A gaudy sharkmouth identifies this aircraft as belonging to a tactical training unit based at Lipetsk. One of this unit's machines has a huge shark painted along the fuselage, fin and nose.

radar has a claimed detection range of 240 km (149 miles) and a tracking range of 185 km (115 miles).

When the Su-27 first appeared, it was widely claimed that its radar was no more than an unlicensed copy of the Hughes AN/APG-63 of the F-15 Eagle, details of which had been obtained through effective espionage, most notably by a Polish agent. In fact, it now seems that the USSR gained access to the AN/APG-63 and AN/APG-65 when it was too late to be of direct use (although some of their technology may have been incorporated in later Russian radars fitted to the Su-27M/35 and MiG-29M/K). This information was of incalculable value in fine-tuning the Su-27's defensive systems and jamming equipment.

Multiple target capabilities

Experts cite the inability to engage more than one target at a time, and the relatively low number of targets that can even be simultaneously tracked (10), as a major disadvantage. In fact, simultaneous BVR target engagement is limited to those Western aircraft with long-range missiles which do not rely on the launch aircraft illuminating its targets throughout the missile's flight time, e.g. the inertial/active homing AIM-54 Phoenix (carried only by the F-14) and, under some circumstances, in some modes, the AIM-120 AMRAAM.

The lack of multiple target tracking capability is more serious, and is imposed by the aircraft's lack of processing capability (in turn due to Soviet backwardness in computer, and particularly software, technology). More serious still is the radar's inability to keep scanning/tracking while locked on to a target. The Su-27 gets around this by being datalinked to ground stations or AWACS aircraft which keep track of the 'big picture' and assign target priorities. This is not to say that this removes any disadvantage, since reliance on ground stations and AWACS aircraft imposes a level of tactical inflexibility that would be unacceptable in Western air forces. This has also obviously been recognised in the former USSR, where the latest generation of fighters has much better autonomous capability.

The radar is, in any case, backed up by the OEPS-27 electro-optical complex, which combines laser rangefinder (effective tail-on range 8 km/5 miles) and Infra-Red Search and Track System (effective range 50 km/31 miles). These use the same optics, which consist of a periscopic system of mirrors and an articulated glass sensor ball which moves in elevation (10° for scanning, 15° for tracking) and azimuth (60° and 120°) to allow the two sensors to be 'pointed'. The sensor

Below and bottom: The Su-27UB at Paris in 1989 was flown and displayed by Yevgeni Frolov, a self-effacing former aerobatic pilot with no front-line fighter experience who has nevertheless become a vital part of the Sukhoi OKB's demonstration team, and who seems to be chief test pilot Victor Pugachev's heir apparent.

Left and above: When the Su-27 made its Western debut at Le Bourget in 1989, it was flown to devastating effect by Sukhoi's highly experienced chief test pilot, Victor Pugachev, whose dynamic deceleration (the 'Pugachev Cobra') was the highlight of the show. Pugachev was the first Russian pilot to make an arrested landing aboard an aircraft-carrier.

aerofoil section, but is generally most marked with ogival strakes like those of the Su-27.

Any interceptor is only as good as its fire control system and weapons, and although the Su-27 is better equipped than previous PVO fighters, its radar and avionics have been widely dismissed as being inferior to their Western equivalents. The radar is a coherent pulse-Doppler air intercept radar, which may be related to the N-019 used by the MiG-29, with a larger diameter twist cassegrain antenna. It is believed to have the same 'Slot Back' NATO reporting name, indicating (if true) identical operating characteristics and signature (frequencies, PRFs, etc.). Its designation is unknown, although the service designation is RLPK-27. The

Despite its huge size, the Su-27 is a remarkably agile aircraft, especially at low weights. A delightful aerobatic mount, by all accounts, the Su-27 is surprisingly easy to fly, although many Western pilots would find its cockpit rather old-fashioned.

Above: The Sukhoi OKB's assault on the marketplace continued at the 1990 Farnborough SBAC show, where the Su-27 and Su-27UB gave dazzling displays. Here the single-seater leaps into the air, burners blazing.

Right: The sheer size of the Su-27's dorsal airbrake is evident in this view of the bureau's single-seat demonstrator aircraft.

can be slaved to the pilot's NSTs-27 helmet-mounted target designator, allowing the pilot to cue the laser or IRST on to a target simply by moving his head. The IRST allows the Su-27 pilot to detect and engage a target without using radar, thereby without making emissions which could be detected by the target's RHAW gear.

Medium-range missiles

The primary air-to-air weapon of the Su-27 is the Vympel R-27, a medium/long-range missile available in several variants and collectively bearing the NATO reporting name AA-10 'Alamo'. The R-27 entered production in 1982 specifically for use on the new MiG-29 and Su-27 then drawing close to service entry, in place of (and perhaps even derived from) the R-23 'Apex' used by the MiG-23. The basic semi-active radar homing version is the R-27R ('Alamo-A'), often carried in conjunction with an R-27T ('Alamo-B') IR-homing missile so that pairs of SARH and IR-homing missiles can be 'ripple-fired' for improved kill probability. Long-range

versions of both missiles can also be carried by the Su-27, these having a new boost sustain motor and being externally recognisable by their increased body length and a slightly 'fattened' rear fuselage. These are designated R-27RE and R-27TE respectively. Two further variants are under development: the R-27EM with an improved SARH seeker for better performance against low-flying and sea-skimming missiles, and the R-27AE with active radar terminal homing.

A maximum of six 'Alamos' can be augmented by up to four short-range missiles. Theoretically the weapon load could include examples of the R-60 (NATO AA-8 'Aphid') but usually consists of four Vympel R-73 (NATO AA-11 'Archer') IR-homing dogfight missiles. The R-73 was developed as a replacement for the R-60 and the earlier R-13M (AA-2 'Atoll') and is the first of a new generation of close-range AAMs. The R-73 has been described as being 'a decade ahead of current Sidewinder' variants, and as 'the most sophisticated IR-guided AAM in service'. The missile certainly has a new level of agility and is capable of off-axis launch from all aspects. The missile has a very wide-angle sensor which can be slaved to the pilot's helmet-mounted sight, allowing the missile to be 'locked up' at targets up to 60° from the aircraft axis.

Tremendous manoeuvrability (up to 12 g) is conferred by the missile's combination of forward-mounted moving canard control fins, 'rudderons' on the fixed tailfins, and deflector vanes in the rocket nozzle. AoA sensors are mounted ahead of the forward control fins. The missile has a 7.4-kg (16-lb) expanding rod warhead. Two versions of the R-73 have been produced, with service designations RDM-1 and RDM-2. The latter missile is some 5 kg (11 lb) heavier and has a 10-km (6.2-mile) increase in range (to 40 km/25 miles).

While its off-axis capability and very high manoeuvrability on launch can be extremely useful, it is not always an advantage, since a hard turn on launch uses up energy and

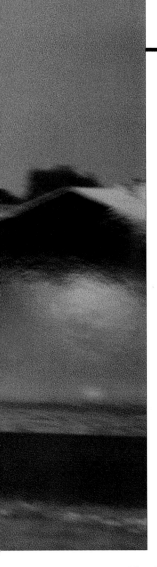

control power very quickly, dramatically reducing the missile's range. Thus it is always preferable to manoeuvre to place the opponent directly in the 12 o'clock position for an IR-homing missile (Fox Two) shot.

With only minor software changes the Su-27 should be compatible with the new Vympel AAM-AE (probable service designation R-77, and perhaps allocated the NATO designation AA-12, though no reporting name is yet known), unofficially dubbed 'AMRAAMski' in the West. This new weapon reportedly entered limited production during 1992, and is primarily intended for the new advanced versions of the Su-27 and MiG-29, including the Su-35, the Su-27K, the MiG-29M and the MiG-29K. The missile has a new mono-pulse-Doppler active radar-homing seeker developed by the Agat NII, giving true fire-and-forget capability. An improved variant may also have a supplementary IR-homing seeker.

New-generation AAM

The AAM-AE airframe is of similar dimensions to that of the R-27R 'Alamo', though it has very different aerodynamic and control surfaces. There are four very broad-chord cruciform 'wings' (which are actually more like strakes) well back, and moveable control surfaces even further aft, set just forward of the rocket nozzle. These consist of shallow rectangular 'boxes' set at right angles to the missile airframe, with their ends open to allow the airflow through. Set inside these 'boxes' is a latticework of aerodynamic vanes which offer better control at high speeds, high angles of attack and when airflow is disrupted. They also allow small hinge moments, with smaller lower-powered non-hydraulic actuators, saving weight and space. The missile is an excellent close-range weapon, with a manoeuvring performance of up to 12 g, but also has a maximum range of 90 km (56 miles), greater than the short-burn R-27 variants.

The Su-27 carries its missiles on the wingtips (R-73 only),

The Su-27's landing gear retracts forward, the main undercarriage units swivelling through 90° to lie flat in the wingroots.

Vortices stream from the LERXes as the Su-27 makes a hard turn in the moisture-laden English air.

Puffs of smoke from the tyres mark the successful conclusion of another display by Victor Pugachev. The Sukhoi OKB demonstrators hardly ever use brake parachutes.

Above: An Su-27UB leads in two of the 'Russian Knights' single-seaters during the team's first overseas visit – to RAF Scampton, home of the 'Red Arrows'. The team is formed from one squadron of the Kubinka-based 'Proskurovskii' Guards Regiment, which functions primarily as a display and demonstration unit.

The badge of the 'Proskurovskii' Guards Fighter Regiment.

The new Sukhoi OKB logo is also worn by the team's aircraft.

In order to use his sensors and weapons to best effect, the fighter pilot must maximise his situational awareness. Achieving this is dependent on a whole range of different factors. To a certain extent, the Su-27 pilot starts out at something of a disadvantage, relying too heavily on outside agencies to process, analyse and present basic target data. Many Western analysts dismiss the old-fashioned analogue cockpit as being a less-than-ideal working environment, and less ergonomically efficient than modern CRT-equipped Western cockpits. Similarly, some Western analysts have criticised the 'switchology' of the Su-27's cockpit, pointing, for example, to the tricky operation and inconvenient location of the short/long-range missile selector on the throttle and the HUD radar cursor on the control column.

The 'Flanker' cockpit

There is a counter-argument to the effect that the familiarity of the Su-27 cockpit (due to strong similarities with the MiG-29, MiG-23, Su-17 and other current/recent Russian/Soviet types) makes interpretation of information presented more a matter of instinct than observation. Interestingly, some Soviet and Russian pilots who have flown both the Su-27 and the MiG-29 operationally also criticise the ergonomic design of the Su-27 cockpit, but are full of praise for the outwardly similar and equally primitive MiG cockpit. In any event, the Su-27 pilot has a very versatile unified head-up display which can present the radar picture and data from the EO complex, as well as the normal piloting, navigation and weapons aiming information presented in Western HUDs.

Cockpit workload is also reduced by provision of the helmet-mounted target designation system. Since this frees the pilot from having to 'boresight' his target, he can maintain a better lookout over the rest of the outside world than if he had to get his enemy directly ahead of him. The system works by using a pair of head position sensors on the panel, on each side of the HUD.

A fighter is about more than just an airframe/powerplant/sensors/weapons combination, however, and the Su-27's 'back-up' systems have been much praised for their simplicity, robustness, maintainability and sensible design. The aircraft has two autonomous closed hydraulic circuits, each operating at a pressure of 280 kg/cm², and each driven

Above: The 'Russian Knights' 'Flankers' carry underwing pylons as a matter of course, and could quickly be returned to operational service.

under the outer wings (R-73 or R-77), underwing (R-27R, R-27T, R-27RE or R-27TE), under the engine nacelle (R-27RE or R-27TE) and in tandem between the nacelles (R-27R and R-27T). The ability to routinely carry a total of 10 AAMs, as a standard warload, is virtually unparalleled, and gives unmatched combat persistence.

**Left: 'Russian Knights'
Su-27s carry the team
name in red in an old-
fashioned Cyrillic script
on the port forward
fuselage, but nothing to
starboard. Here one of
the single-seaters taxis
out at the beginning of
a display.**

**Below: One of the
team's Su-27UBs had
the front cockpit fitted
with rails for an
instrument flying
training hood. During
their visit to Scampton,
the 'Russian Knights'
flew a number of RAF
officers in their
Su-27UBs, but few
reports have emerged
about these flights.**

by a separate engine-driven pump. The tailerons, flaperons, leading-edge flaps, undercarriage extension and retraction, mainwheel brakes, airbrake and air intakes and FOD screens are hydraulically actuated. The brake system and control surface servo actuator pressures are significantly reduced.

The electrical system runs using two engine-driven AC generators (producing 115 V at 400 Hz) with emergency DC from two 27-V NiCd 20NKBN-25 batteries. A pneumatic system is used for many systems that, on Western aircraft, would normally be hydraulically actuated. This includes the nosewheel brake, emergency undercarriage extension (a reservoir is located inside the inner face of the nosewheel door), brake chute deployment, canopy opening, as well as cockpit and avionics bay pressurisation. The oxygen system takes air bled from the seventh stage of the compressor for air conditioning and cooling. This is first cooled using air and fuel radiators and turbo coolers.

Production changes

The basic Su-27 has undergone some refinements during production. The current production tailfin shape (with cropped tips and upper trailing edge) was adopted early on, and other changes followed at regular intervals. The most apparent external changes were incorporated on aircraft from the 20th production series, which gained box-like fairings along the sides of the tailcone accommodating RWR antennas and making space for no less than 32 upward-firing APP-50 chaff/flare dispensers, containing 96 chaff cartridges or flares (42 per side fairing, and 12 in the centre). Distinctive anti-flutter weights on the leading edges of the tailfins were also deleted from the 21st production series, and have since been removed from many earlier production Su-27s.

Another modification retrospectively applied to all service Su-27s was the removal of the reticulated polyurethane fire-suppressing foam used to line the fuel tanks. The subject of an embargo, the USSR went to great lengths to import the material for the Su-25 and Su-27, but it proved insufficiently robust and rather troublesome, and has been replaced by a combination of self-sealing tanks and inert gas fuel tank pressurisation. Its only legacy is the number of long access panels in the fuel tanks, originally provided for foam replacement. The fuel used is T-1, TS-1 or RT kerosene, and the average specific density of 0.785 gives a capacity of 12000 litres (2,640 Imp gal) or 9400 kg (20,723 lb).

Radomes and dielectric panels were originally dark green, but have recently been replaced by white equivalents. There may also have been a change in the capacity of the ammunition tank, or to the weight of ammunition carried. Initially, Sukhoi claimed that 200 rounds of ammunition were carried

**Left: The pilots of the
'Russian Knights' team,
together with General
Antoshkin, commander
of the Moscow Military
District.**

**Below: The 'Russian
Knights' Su-27s wear a
colourful paint job, with
white noses and red/
white/blue leading edge
stripes.**

Above: An Alaska-based F-15 provides an escort for the OKB Su-27UB demonstrator during the aircraft's first visit to the USA. The similarities between the two aircraft types, in configuration and size, are clearly evident. Another noteworthy feature is the F-15's reliance on external fuel, carried underwing and in conformal 'FAST packs'.

Above: The Su-27s arrive at Oklahoma City, escorting their support aircraft, the massive An-225 Mriya, tailed by a US Navy F-14 Tomcat.

Above right: The first Su-27 to visit the USA was this LII aircraft from Zhukhovsky. It was one of a pair which visited Paine Field in Washington State.

ground level to 25000 m (82,020 ft). A version of the K-36 with only minor modifications was even used in the Buran space shuttle. A blast protector raises automatically to protect the pilot at speeds in excess of 800 km/h (497 mph), while the 3.2-kN (719-lb st) rocket (which burns for 0.4 seconds) imposes a peak acceleration of only 20 g, minimising the risk of serious spinal injury. The seat employs a KSMU-36 twin-stage ejection mechanism, and incorporates a PSU-36 rescue pack, with a 28-segment 60 m^2 (645 sq ft) parachute. The seat contains an NAZ-8 survival pack with a KOMAR-2M SAR beacon, a PSN-1 inflatable dinghy, food and 'camping tools'.

Two-seat trainer

Although the Su-27's cockpit was such that conversion from other Soviet aircraft (such as the MiG-23 or Su-17) is remarkably easy, the aircraft's unique handling and performance characteristics made it desirable to have a two-seat trainer which would be able to operate over a similar envelope. MiG-29UBs were used by Su-27 regiments as an interim measure while the dedicated two-seat Su-27UB trainer was being developed. The T-10U-1 prototype made its maiden flight on 7 May 1985, in the hands of Nikolai Sadovnikov. Production commenced at the Irkutsk Aviation Industrial Association in 1986, but its existence and the Su-27UB designation of the production two-seater were not

for the gun, but recently the figure of 150 rounds has consistently been given. Stencilled servicing information actually painted on the aircraft gives a slightly different story, with a total of 149 rounds, including 15 housed in the feed to the gun itself.

Avionics systems have changed during the production life of the Su-27, although many details remain sketchy. At least three different IFF systems (SRO-2M, Parol and Marka) have been quoted, while both ARK-19 and ARK-20 ADF/radio compass have been fitted under the dielectric panel immediately behind the airbrake. Current production Su-27s are believed to have an avionics suite which includes A-38 radio altimeter, SDU-10-27 'Command Retransmission System' (datalink), SPO-15 radar warning, and R-800 and R-864 UHF and HF radios.

Changes to the cockpit of the basic Su-27 fighter have been very minor, and the cockpit remains a 1960s/1970s working environment, dominated by conventional analogue instruments. It is well laid out, but intrinsically old fashioned. The pilot continues to sit on a Zvezda K-36DM Series II zero-zero ejection seat. Designed by Bureau Chief Guy Severin, the K-36DM is capable of safe operation at all speeds from zero to 1400 km/h (870 mph) or Mach 2, and at altitudes from

Left: Since the first Su-27 visit to the USA, others have followed on a regular basis. During 1992, an exchange was undertaken between the unit at Lipetsk and the 1st Fighter Wing.

Below: The Su-27 was also displayed at Singapore Aerospace, during which a mixed formation of Su-27s and F/A-18 Hornets was undertaken.

Above: This Su-27 carries an excellence award on the nose, together with a series of small red stars. It was photographed on approach to Chojna, home to the 582nd Fighter Regiment and one of two Polish Su-27 bases. The two-tone radome is noteworthy.

Right: The significance of the 'Batman' logo on the ventral fin of this Chojna-based Su-27 is unknown. Such personal badges (and even official unit insignia) are extremely rare on front-line Russian aircraft, where anonymity often remains the order of the day.

revealed in the West until May 1989, shortly before the Su-27 (accompanied by an Su-27UB) made its air show debut at the Paris Air Salon at Le Bourget.

The Su-27UB, unlike the two-seat trainer version of the MiG-29, was always intended to be fully operationally capable, and was thus fitted with the same avionics suite and weapons system, including radar. The aircraft has a lengthened forward fuselage with tandem cockpits under a single canopy. These are very stepped and consequently no periscope (common in Soviet two-seat trainer variants) is fitted. Sukhoi claims a better view from the rear cockpit of the Su-27UB than is enjoyed by the F-15B/D backseater. While the front seat pilot can see forward over the nose and downwards by -13°30′, the backseater can see forward and down by −8°. The F-15 backseater cannot see downwards at all, obstructions limiting his view forward to +3° above the horizon. The increased keel area forward necessitates an increase in fin height and area, and the area of the dorsal airbrake is also increased. A 740-kg (1,631-lb) increase in normal take-off weight, plus slightly increased drag, reduce maximum speed by about 70 km/h (43 mph) at low level and by 160 km/h (100 mph) at higher altitudes. Low-level range is similarly reduced, by about 100 km (62 miles), and high-level range by 680 km (422 miles). Turn radius, rate of climb and take-off/landing distances are less drastically affected.

Before 1988, little was known about the Su-27. Allied intelligence agencies had seen hundreds of satellite photos and, from January 1987, the type began to be encountered by Norwegian and Swedish interceptors during operations from one or more bases in the Kola Peninsula. Even when an

Right: Chojna-based Su-27s wore very dark blue codes, outlined in white. Most were drawn from earlier production blocks than the aircraft based at Kluczewo.

over-enthusiastic 'Flanker' pilot actually clipped the starboard outer propeller of a Norwegian P-3 with his port fin-tip on 13 September (netting the Norwegians some excellent close-up shots of red 36 in the process) few hard facts emerged. Realisation that the record-breaking P-42 was a 'Flanker' sub-type dawned slowly, and did little more than provide an indication of the aircraft's performance and engine thrust. The Su-27 remained a shadowy aircraft even after the MiG-29 stole the show at the 1988 Farnborough SBAC show, and many analysts expected it to remain in the background, since advanced PVO interceptors have seldom been offered for export (even to the USSR's most loyal allies).

The famous 'Cobra'

It came as something of a surprise, then, when an Su-27 and an Su-27UB flew into Le Bourget as part of the massive Soviet presence at the 1989 Paris Air Salon. The MiG-29's Farnborough performance had already sent a shock wave through the Western aviation industry, and the Su-27 was to cause a similar sensation, shaking more people out of their comfortable complacency about the nature of the Soviet threat. This was almost achieved in a single unforgettable (and still almost unique) manoeuvre, a dynamic deceleration nicknamed 'Pugachev's Cobra'. This was so-named because the aircraft seemed to mimic the motion of a striking snake.

To perform the Cobra, Pugachev rapidly pitched the nose back to an angle of between 110° and 120°, recovering by pitching the nose back to the horizontal. With an entry speed of about 230 kt (425 km/h; 264 mph), and with the power set to 85 per cent rpm, the aircraft decelerated at a rate in excess of 60 kt (110 km/h; 69 mph) per second, slowing to about 80 kt (148 km/h; 92 mph) during the manoeuvre. The aircraft climbed very slightly during the manoeuvre, but height gain is said to be negligible and predictable. There was no tendency to roll off during the manoeuvre and the pilot retained control throughout, being able to stop the pitch-up cleanly and to accurately recover to horizontal flight. The AoA limiter, usually set to 26°, can be turned off, or simply over-ridden by applying an extra 15 kg (33 lb) of stick force. The more forward centre of gravity of the Su-27UB has the effect of limiting the maximum pitch angle achieved during a Cobra to 90°, but the aircraft is capable of performing the manoeuvre.

Manoeuvres like the tailslide and Cobra have a dramatic PR effect, and also have a limited tactical significance. The

Above: The stylised aircraft and pentagon badge seen on this aircraft represents an award to the groundcrew, acknowledging the excellent condition of their charge.

Left: Su-27s from both Chojna and Kluczewo stood alert, with fully armed aircraft waiting to be scrambled at a moment's notice.

Left: Later Su-27s, like this Kluczewo-based Su-27UB, have white painted radomes and dielectric panels. Each Su-27 regiment will typically have three or four two-seaters on charge.

Electrics

The electrical system is driven by two integral AC generators, each producing 115 V at 400 Hz. They are backed up by a pair of nickel cadmium batteries. DC is supplied at 27 volts.

Two-seat trainers

Many Soviet fighters spawn two-seat trainer variants, most of which lack radar and other operational equipment, and most of which do not appreciably raise the second cockpit. The result is aircraft which are lacking in operational utility and which give the instructor pilot an appalling view forward, normally requiring the addition of a retractable periscope. The Su-27's full operational capability and very stepped cockpits thus marked a major improvement, with the only penalties being tiny reductions in absolute speed, range and radius, with even smaller effects on rate of climb and take-off/landing performance.

LERX

The highly swept wing leading-edge root extensions provide more lift (especially at high Alpha) and further destabilise the aircraft in pitch, increasing agility.

Cannon

A single GSh-30-1 30-mm cannon is carried by all basic Su-27 variants, with 149 rounds of ammunition. The two-seater normally has a much larger titanium blast shield surrounding the muzzle, in the starboard wingroot leading edge, although much of it has been overpainted on this aircraft.

Control surfaces

The control system actuates conventional control surfaces, with twin rudders, single-piece slab differential tailerons and single-piece trailing-edge flaperons and leading-edge slats. The latter have only one manual position for take-off and landing, but are infinitely variable when acting as computer-controlled manoeuvre flaps. All control surfaces have hydraulic servos.

Sukhoi Su-27UB 'Flanker-C'

This Su-27UB 'Flanker-C' of the 234th 'Proskurovskii' Guards Fighter Regiment at Kubinka wears the striking colour scheme of the 'Russian Knights' aerobatic demonstration team. This adds a white forward fuselage and red leading edges to the basic camouflage, with the tailfins decorated with the VVS flag and the undersides variegated from dark blue (aft) to white.

Wing/fuselage blending

The Su-27 was designed around what Sukhoi refers to as an 'integrated airframe' with the wing and forebody blended together to form a single 'lifting body'. This reduces wetted area (and thus drag) while increasing internal volume for fuel and avionics. The F-16 follows a similar approach but makes greater use of composite materials. The Su-27 is of largely aluminium alloy construction, though it uses a great deal of titanium, and advanced aluminium-lithium alloys. The wing has three main spars, with auxiliary spars fore and aft serving as mountings for the slats and flaperons.

Tailfins

The Su-27UB's tailfins are of increased height, with an extra section added at the base of the rudder. Ram air inlets are located at the bottom of each leading edge, the port inlet being lower and larger.

IRST

A glazed 'ball' mounted centrally in front of the windscreen accommodates the collimated optics for the electro-optical complex, consisting of a laser rangefinder and an infra-red search and track system. These have ranges of 8 km and 50-70 km (5 miles and 31-43 miles) respectively.

Ventral fins

Ventral fins were added to the Su-27 after the first flight of the T-10S. These significantly improved spinning characteristics.

FOD protection

To prevent foreign object ingestion during operation from rough strips, the Su-27 nosewheel is covered by a heavyweight debris deflector/mudguard, and the intakes are fitted with meshed intake screens which are closed until the nosewheel has lifted on take-off.

Fire control system

Like the MiG-29, the Su-27 uses three inter-linked sensors for target acquisition and engagement. These are the radar, the NSTs-27 (NSc-27) helmet-mounted target designator and an OEPS-27 electro-optical complex which combines a collimated infra-red search and track sensor and a laser rangefinder. These 'see' through an articulated sensor 'ball' centrally mounted ahead of the windscreen. The IRST has a range of 50-70 km (31-43 miles) and under some conditions allows the Su-27 to detect, identify and engage a target passively, without using radar (thereby avoiding making any emissions which might be detected by the target).

Autopilot

The Su-27 has an SAU-27 autopilot, which is linked to the PNK-27 piloting and navigation complex, the S-27 weapons control system and the SDU-27 flight control system. The system allows the aircraft to be recovered to straight and level flight from any attitude at the touch of a button, and can also allow a ground control station or AWACS-type platform to directly control the aircraft.

Short-range missile armament

For close-range engagements, the Su-27 can carry up to four Vympel R-73 (NATO AA-11 'Archer') IR-homing dogfight missiles on wingtip and outboard underwing pylons. Developed as a replacement for the R-13M (AA-2 'Atoll'), the R-73 is the first of a new generation of close-range AAMs, with a new level of agility and capable of off-axis launch from all aspects. Some analysts have described the missile as being 'a decade ahead of current Sidewinder missiles' and the 'most sophisticated IR-guided AAM in service'. The missile owes its manoeuvrability to a combination of conventional forward control fins, elevators on the fixed rear fins and deflector vanes in the rocket nozzle. Four AoA sensors are mounted ahead of the forward fins. There are two variants, the RDM-1 (with 30-km/19-mile range) and the RDM-2 (5 kg/11 lb higher weight and 10 km/6.2 miles greater range). Both variants have a 7.4-kg (16-lb) expanding rod warhead and can manoeuvre at up to 12 g. They can be fired at targets at 45° or 60° off the nose.

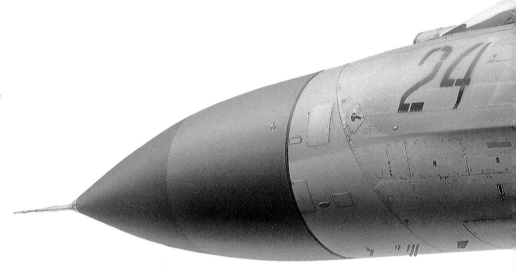

Combat persistence

With a typical combat load of six AA-10 'Alamo' medium/long-range missiles, four short-range AA-11 'Archers' and an internal cannon, the Su-27 can engage many targets before having to return to base and refuel. The internal cannon is the same GSh-30-1 as is carried by the MiG-29 'Fulcrum'.

Radar

The Su-27 is equipped with a coherent pulse-Doppler radar (service designation RLPK-27), with an inverse cassegrain antenna. This accounts for the bulged rear section and distinctive double curvature. Detection range is given as 240 km (149 miles), and tracking range as 185 km (115 miles). Some sources suggest that the radar set may be similar to the NO-19 (service designation RP-29) used by the MiG-29, with a larger-diameter antenna, and that it shares the same 'Slot Back' NATO reporting name. Although the radar is powerful, with long range and excellent look-down capability, the lack of processing capacity restricts it to tracking one target at a time. This is of little consequence in traditional Soviet tactics, where interceptors are datalinked to ground stations which provide target prioritisation, but is restrictive in autonomous operations, although all aircraft using SARH missiles like the AIM-7 Sparrow are similarly restricted. The radar display is on a small screen on the upper right-hand part of the panel, but a synthetic radar picture can also be generated in the HUD. Although the USSR obtained much data from Hughes by espionage, the radar is not now thought to be an APG-63/-65 copy in any respect.

Sukhoi Su-27 'Flanker-B'
582nd Fighter Regiment
4th Air Army (Soviet Northern Group of Forces)
Frontal Aviation
Chojna, Poland 1992

Blue 24 was one of the Su-27s allocated to the 582nd Guards Fighter Regiment at Chojna, one of two Poland-based Su-27 units withdrawn to Russia during 1992 as part of the general withdrawal from Europe. Dark green radomes and dielectric panels were applied to early Su-27s, later aircraft having dielectric fairings and radomes in white. This aircraft carries seven red stars under the cockpit, possibly denoting exercise 'kills' or live missile firings. The 'dart and pentagon' device below these is an excellence award, applied to individual aircraft in recognition of their condition as a reward to the crew chief. The excellence award is not, as has often been said, in any way equivalent to American outstanding unit citations. Although designed primarily as an interceptor for the IA-PVO, the Su-27 has also been delivered in significant numbers to Frontal Aviation units. The involvement of the PVO in the abortive coup against President Gorbachev undermined the organisation and led to further transfers of units to the control of the air forces (VVS), which stayed loyal. Frontal Aviation uses the Su-27 primarily as part of a high/low mixed fighter force concept in which the heavyweight, long-range 'Flankers' are targeted against high value enemy aircraft (tankers, AWACS platforms) further behind the front line, but also as a long-range escort for strike and attack aircraft.

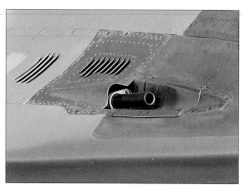

*Above: The basic **IRST** sensor ball used on the standard **Su-27** and **Su-27UB**. This has collimated optics for an infra-red search and track system, and a laser rangefinder.*

Below: The inter-nacelle tunnel accommodates tandem pylons for AA-10 'Alamo' missiles.

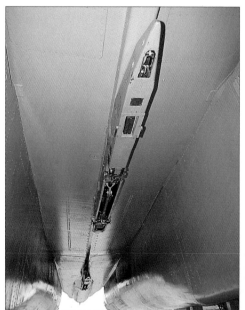

*Above: The muzzle of the **GSh-30-1** cannon is surrounded by a titanium blast/heat shield, and is generously provided with vents. The same gun is used by the MiG-29.*

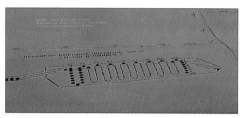

*Above: A stencil marking on the port **LERX** shows the position and configuration of the 149-round ammunition tank.*

*Above: The **Su-27** is fitted with enormous gridded intake debris guards, with a fine mesh between the squares of the grid which can be seen here.*

*The **Su-27** is powered by a pair of **Lyul'ka AL-31F** turbofans (below). These have distinctive concentric afterburner nozzles (above) with cooling air passing between the two sets of 'petals'. The afterburner spray bars and flameholders are also shown (left).*

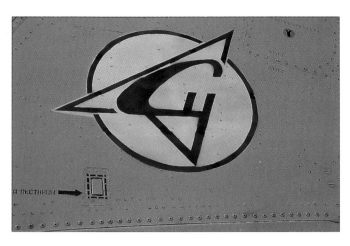

Right: The pitot static probe of the Su-27 incorporates wing-like vortex generators where it joins the radome. The radome itself covers an inverse cassegrain antenna for the radar. This retains the same NATO 'Slot Back' reporting name as the MiG-29's radar.

Left: The new Sukhoi OKB logo consists of the Cyrillic letters Su forming an integral part of a dart shape, within a circle. It is carried on bureau demonstrators, and by aircraft of the 'Russian Knights' team. A winged archer was the bureau's previous logo. Factory badges are not normally applied to Su-27s, and few have unit badges either.

Right: The current production standard tailcone accommodates radar warning and **ECM** antennas in the tips of the square-section fairings along its sides, with a brake chute door in the extreme point. Further forward, flush-fitting chaff/flare dispensers can be fitted.

Left: Prominent **ECM** antenna fairings (for forward hemisphere coverage) are located on the lower outboard corners of the engine air intakes, except on the Su-27K, Su-35 and Su-27IB.

Above: The nose of the Su-27 hinges upwards for access to the avionics bays. This arrangement is quite separate from the radome. The Su-27 is generously provided with access panels, many of them on the underside – a useful feature when the aircraft is being serviced in unfavourable climatic conditions, since the aircraft affords shelter for its groundcrew.

Right: The taileron actuator is housed in a streamlined fairing in the rear of the tailboom. The differential tailerons are the primary means of controlling the aircraft in roll, and are used in unison for pitch control.

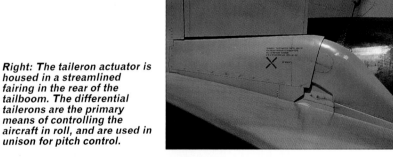

Left: The basic land-based Su-27 has a single nosewheel, with three landing/taxi lights mounted on the forward face of the oleo. The inner surface of the nosewheel door is painted in anti-corrosion **Dinitrol** paint, which comes in red.

Left: The inner face of an Su-27 single mainwheel. These are fitted with fan-cooled hydraulic disc brakes and are optimised for short field operation.

Long-range missile armament

The Su-27's primary armament is the Vympel R-27, known to NATO as the AA-10 'Alamo'. This is actually a family of missiles with long- and short-range IR-homing and semi-active radar homing variants, which entered production in 1982 for use on the MiG-29 and Su-27, in place of the R-23 (AA-7 'Apex') and earlier missiles used on previous fighters. The Su-27 carries R-27s on its inboard underwing pylons, on pylons below the engine intake ducts and in tandem between the engine nacelles. The basic semi-active radar homing R-27R ('Alamo-A') is usually carried between the nacelles (as seen here) or underwing, as is the IR-homing R-27T ('Alamo-B'). IR-homing R-27s are seen under the wing of this aircraft. Long-range versions of both SARH- and IR-homing variants have been produced, under the designations R-27RE and R-27TE ('Alamo-C' and '-D') with a boost sustain motor. They can be recognised by their increased body length and a slightly 'fattened' rear fuselage, and on the Su-27 are usually carried under the intakes. Two further variants have yet to enter service: the R-27EM with an improved SARH seeker for use against low-flying and sea-skimming missiles, and the R-27AE with active radar terminal homing, a true AMRAAMski.

Air-to-ground

Although the Sukhoi OKB head, Mikhail Simonov, quoted the same 'not a pound for air-to-ground' dictum used by the F-15's designers, the Su-27 does have a limited and seldom-practised air-to-ground capability. Sorbitsiya ECM pods are usually fitted to the wingtips, and a range of blast, cluster or incendiary bombs or unguided rockets can be carried on the AA-10 hardpoints.

Colour scheme
All operational service Su-27s seen in the West have worn an effective (if unusual) three-tone air superiority blue-grey camouflage scheme. Some reports suggest that a handful of aircraft were delivered in a fighter-bomber scheme of green and brown. Dielectric areas are usually in green or white.

National markings
Despite the break-up of the former Soviet Union, Russian air force aircraft retain the USSR's traditional red star as a national marking, with use of the pre-revolutionary tricolour so far confined to factory demonstrators and civil aircraft. Su-27s operated by other republics have received new national markings.

Sukhoi OKB insignia
Many Su-27s still carry this insignia on their tailfins, and the same badge has also been seen on Su-17s, Su-24s and Su-25s. Variously described as a 'winged helmet' or more correctly as a 'winged archer', the badge is the old Sukhoi OKB logo, since largely replaced by a simple triangle containing the Cyrillic equivalents of the letters 'Su' (Cy).

Tubular fairings on each side of the ejection seat headrest contain telescopic tubes and stabilising drogues.

Right: The rear cockpit of the Su-27UB is similar to the front cockpit, although it has a different head-up display and a system which allows the instructor to simulate emergencies in the front cockpit.

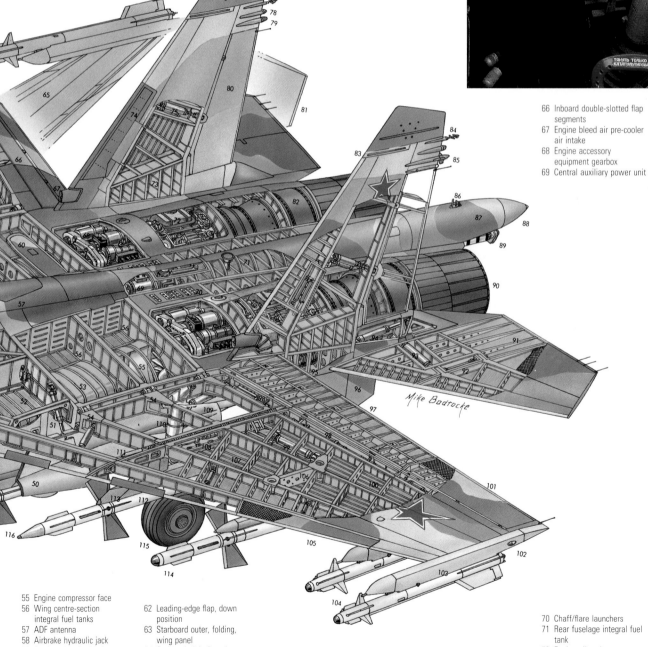

Mike Badrocke

66 Inboard double-slotted flap segments
67 Engine bleed air pre-cooler air intake
68 Engine accessory equipment gearbox
69 Central auxiliary power unit

70 Chaff/flare launchers
71 Rear fuselage integral fuel tank
72 Engine oil tank
73 Fin structure
74 Leading-edge HF aerial
75 Rudder hydraulic actuator

76 Fin-tip UHF/VHF aerial
77 ILS aerial
78 Tail navigation light
79 Radar warning antenna
80 Starboard rudder
81 Starboard tailplane folded position
82 AL-31F afterburning turbofan engine
83 Port tailfin
84 ILS aerial
85 ECM antenna
86 Upper SRO-2 'Odd Rods' IFF aerial
87 Tailcone fairing
88 Rear EW antenna fairing
89 Deck arrester hook
90 Variable-area afterburner nozzle
91 Port tailplane
92 Tailplane fold joint rotary actuator
93 Tailplane pivot bearing
94 Hydraulic actuator
95 Hydraulic accumulator
96 Ventral fin
97 Port inboard double-slotted flap segments
98 Flap hydraulic actuators
99 Wing-fold hydraulic jack
100 Outer wing panel structure
101 Outboard plain flap segment
102 Port navigation light
103 Wingtip missile launch rail
104 R-73 'Archer' air-to-air missiles
105 Leading-edge flap
106 Pylon attachment hardpoints
107 Port wing integral fuel tank
108 Wing-fold locking mechanism jack
109 Main undercarriage hydraulic retraction jack
110 Mainwheel leg strut
111 Wing-fold hinge joint
112 Leading-edge flush EW aerial panels
113 Missile pylon
114 R-27 'Alamo-B' IR air-to-air missile
115 Port mainwheel
116 R-27 'Alamo-C' radar air-to-air missile

55 Engine compressor face
56 Wing centre-section integral fuel tanks
57 ADF antenna
58 Airbrake hydraulic jack
59 Starboard mainwheel, stowed position
60 Fuel tank access panels
61 Wing-fold hydraulic jack
62 Leading-edge flap, down position
63 Starboard outer, folding, wing panel
64 Outboard plain flap, down position
65 Starboard wing, folded position

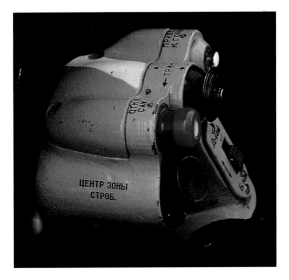

Right: The Su-27's stick-top is almost identical to that of the MiG-29 and incorporates a panic button (for recovery from unusual attitudes), trimmers, squawk, autopilot disengage and missile control buttons.

Left: The cockpit of the Su-27, with an Aresti notation of Yevgeni Frolov's aerobatic display routine clipped to the starboard side of the coaming. By comparison with the MiG-29, which has a very similar cockpit layout, the Su-27 cockpit is more spacious and the pilot sits higher.

Sukhoi Su-27K 'Sea Flanker'

1 Pitot head
2 Upward-hinging radome
3 Radar scanner
4 Scanner mounting
5 Radome hinge point
6 Infra-red search and tracking scanner
7 Refuelling probe housing
8 Radar equipment module; tilts down for access
9 Lower SRO-2 'Odd-Rods' IFF aerial
10 Incidence transmitter
11 Cockpit front pressure bulkhead
12 Retractable spotlight, port and starboard
13 Cockpit side console panel
14 Slide-mounted throttle levers
15 Flight-refuelling probe, extended
16 Instrument panel shroud
17 Pilot's head-up display
18 Upward-hinging cockpit canopy
19 K-36MD 'zero-zero' ejection seat
20 Canopy hydraulic jack
21 Dynamic pressure probe, port and starboard
22 Cockpit rear pressure bulkhead
23 Temperature probe

24 Nosewheel door
25 Twin nosewheels, forward retracting
26 ASM-MSS long-range ramjet and rocket-powered anti-shipping missile
27 Missile folding fins
28 Nosewheel hydraulic steering jacks
29 Deck approach 'traffic-lights'
30 Leading-edge flush EW aerial
31 Avionics equipment bay
32 Ammunition magazine, 149 rounds
33 HF aerial
34 Starboard fuselage chine-mounted GSH-30-1 30-mm cannon
35 Canard foreplane
36 Starboard wing missile armament
37 Dorsal airbrake
38 Gravity fuel filler cap
39 Centre fuselage fuel tank
40 Forward lateral fuel tanks

41 ASM-MSS missile carrier on fuselage centreline station
42 Variable-area intake ramp doors
43 Ramp hydraulic jack
44 Foreplane hydraulic actuator
45 Port canard foreplane
46 Engine air intake
47 Boundary layer bleed air louvres
48 Segmented ventral suction relief doors
49 Retractable intake FOD screen
50 Mainwheel door
51 Door hydraulic jack
52 Port mainwheel bay
53 Intake trunking
54 Wing panel attachment joints

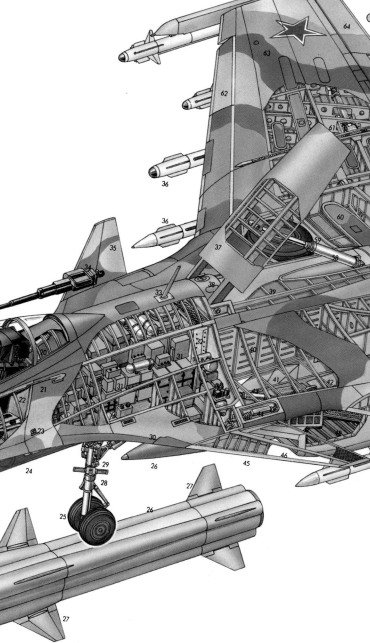

Defensive systems

The Su-27 is protected by an SPO-15 'Beryoza' passive radar warning receiver system, with antennas on the trailing edges of the tailfins. This gives 360° coverage and classifies, prioritises and displays threats using a built-in threat library, and indicates bearing, range and system-type. It is believed that an active jammer is also installed, though this equipment's designation is unknown. It has been quoted as SO-69 (a transponder designation) or Sirena 3 (which may be an alternative designation for SPO-15). The system is programmed to react automatically using appropriate countermeasures, whether flares or chaff cartridges. The aircraft also has comprehensive IFF equipment with interrogator (possibly SRE-15) and SO-69 transponder.

Engine nacelles

The engine nacelles are anchored beneath the mid fuselage and, together with twin side-mounted tailbooms and a central boom, form the rear fuselage. They are of semi-monocoque stressed-skin construction, reinforced by stringers and bulkhead frames. The whole rear end of each nacelle is of unpainted welded titanium alloy, the high quality welds showing clear signs that sophisticated computer-controlled welding equipment is used in their construction.

Tailcone

The long tailcone projecting aft from between the engine nacelles reduces drag and serves as an invaluable location for the twin braking parachutes and a variety of other equipment items. Perhaps most obviously there are 32 groups of chaff/flare dispensers above the tailcone, each containing three launchers.

Systems

Each engine has a top-mounted gearbox driving various accessories. A hydraulic pump, working at 280 kg/cm², is provided for each of the two autonomous closed hydraulic circuits that power the tailerons, flaperons, slats, undercarriage extension and retraction, mainwheel brakes, airbrake, engine intake actuators and anti-FOD intake grids. A pneumatic system provides emergency undercarriage extension, and cockpit and avionics bay pressurisation. The aircraft makes less use of pneumatics than the contemporary MiG-29, whose designers tried to avoid hydraulic systems wherever possible. An On Board Oxygen Generating System (OBOGS) provides oxygen for the pilot, while air bled from the compressor's seventh stage is cooled by air/air and fuel/air radiators and turbo coolers and used for air conditioning and pilot's g suit.

Development

The production Su-27 (which bears the OKB designation T-10S) represented a major redesign of the basic prototype/pre-production T-10, with many aerodynamic, structural and systems improvements. Externally the production 'Flanker-B' introduced a new adaptive wing, repositioned tailfins, a recontoured nose and a redesigned undercarriage, airbrake and LERXes. These improvements were prompted by major structural and aerodynamic problems suffered by the original prototypes, which were severe enough to threaten the future of the entire project.

Flight control system

The Su-27 has often been simplistically described as having a fly-by-wire (FBW) flight control system. This is only partially true. The aircraft is statically unstable only in pitch, since this is all that is necessary in order to achieve the benefits of high manoeuvrability, low drag, high lift and reduced weight. The Su-27's SDU-27 electronic and remote control system controls the aircraft in pitch, but provides only stability augmentation to the mechanical lateral and yaw control circuits. The control system consists of four computers, each 'fed' from a separate air data source, with quadruply redundant transducers and signal paths. The system was reportedly based on that fitted to the T-4 (Su-100), which Sukhoi claims as the world's first FBW-controlled aircraft, and which gave the Bureau four years of experience before work began on the T-10. The control system limits the aircraft to +8.5/−2.5 g and to 28 units of Alpha but these are 'soft' limits, which can be overridden by the pilot either by switching off the limiter switches or by using extra pressure (about 15 kg) to 'pull through' the stick stops.

Powerplants

The Su-27 is powered by a pair of widely spaced Lyul'ka AL-31F afterburning turbofans. These have a four-stage low-pressure compressor, a nine-stage high-pressure compressor and single-stage cooled high- and low-pressure turbines aft of the annular combustor. Sukhoi gives the thrust ratings as 12800 kg (28,219 lb) with reheat and 7700 kg (16,975 lb) in dry power, with the manufacturer's figures being 12500 kg st (27,557 lb) and 7600 kg st (16,755 lb). The separation of the engines was dictated by the need for a wide inter-nacelle tunnel for low-drag weapons carriage, and to simplify intake duct design, since handling considerations dictated that the intakes themselves should be widely spaced. The wide spacing also ensured that damage to one engine would be unlikely to cause damage to the remaining powerplant, without the need for a heavy armoured titanium keel, as is used in the Su-25 fighter-bomber. The engines themselves are broadly equivalent to the American F100-PW-100 and F100-PW-220, almost the same length and maximum diameter (within 5 and 1 cm/1.9 and 0.4 in respectively) but some 134-212 kg/295-467 lb) heavier. They operate at a similar post-turbine temperature. The Lyul'ka engines are more powerful in both dry and augmented modes, and have a lower specific fuel consumption. This runs counter to expectations, since the AL-31F has a lower bypass ratio (quoted by Sukhoi as 0.59) and a lower compressor ratio, though it does handle a greater mass flow. The engine's most remarkable characteristic is its tolerance to gross intake airflow disturbances (demonstrated by their ability to keep running during a tailslide or Cobra). This stability is contributed to by excellent intake design, and by the computer-controlled variable-inlet guide vanes, which prevent compressor stalls. The very high thrust-to-weight ratio provided by the twin AL-31Fs gives the relatively lightweight and low-drag Su-27 excellent performance characteristics, with an unequalled rate of climb, top speed and supersonic acceleration. It also contributes to the aircraft's excellent sustained turn performance. Victor Chepkin, the engine's designer, has also managed to overcome some of the problems which have traditionally plagued Soviet engines. Engine life stands at a respectable 3,000 hours, and TBO is set at 1,000 hours, although every 100 hours the engines are inspected using borescopes, oil sampling and vibration analysis.

Armament
The aircraft is seen carrying R-73s outboard, and R-77 (AAM-M) AAMs furthest outboard. Underwing it carries a Kh-29L (port) or Kh-29T (starboard) with a KAB series LGB inboard and a Kh-31 ASM under each intake.

Wingtip launch rails
Most 'Flanker' sub-variants have wingtip missile launch rails which also serve as anti-flutter weights. Only the R-73 (AA-11 'Archer') has been seen on this pylon, though presumably similar lightweight missiles (like the R-60 AA-8 'Aphid') could also be carried. The pylons can quickly be replaced by cylindrical ECM pods.

Inflight-refuelling probe
A retractable inflight-refuelling probe was first tested on an Su-27UB prototype (probably T-10U-2) and was then adopted on the Su-27K, Su-27KU/IB, Su-27P, Su-27PU and Su-27M/35. The probe is housed on the port side of the nose, this location necessitating relocation of the centreline IRST, when fitted.

Undercarriage
The Su-27KU has a redesigned and strengthened undercarriage (probably based on the Su-27K landing gear), with longer oleos and a relocated rearward-retracting nosewheel, covered by four separate nosewheel doors.

Su-24 replacement
The Su-27IB is a potential 'Fencer' replacement, if funding permits.

Canard foreplanes
Canard foreplanes were first flown on the T-10-24 during May 1985, and were later selected for use on several advanced 'Flanker' variants, including the Su-27KU. These foreplanes improve take-off performance by generating extra lift forward of the centre of gravity, instead of generating a down force behind it like conventional tailplanes.

Nose shape
The Su-27KU has an entirely new nose section, grafted on at the wing leading edge. The cockpit is provided with side-by-side seats and is moved forward to give a better view over the broad, flat nose which gives the type its 'Platypus' nickname. Chines flow back to join the LERX on each side.

Sukhoi Su-27KU (Su-27IB?)

The Su-27KU (often referred to as the Su-27IB, and possibly designated T-10-42 by the OKB) is believed to have originated as a demonstrator/aerodynamic prototype for a carrierborne trainer for Su-27K pilots. It was first seen in a TASS photo approaching the carrier *Kuznetsov* (formerly *Tbilisi*) although it has no arrester hook, no wing or tailplane folding and no carrier equipment. The designation Su-27KU is the only one used by the Sukhoi OKB, the suffix 'KU' denoting carrier trainer. When displayed for CIS leaders at the closed air show at Minsk Maschulische in February 1992 the aircraft had an information board describing it as the Su-27IB (Istrebeitel, or fighter-bomber), and carried an impressive array of air-to-ground ordnance, although it lacked attack radar or any electro-optical sensors.

Tailfins
The Su-27KU has the same increased height tailfins as those fitted to the Su-27UB, but surprisingly lacks ventral fins, despite its massive forward 'keel' area.

Configuration
The Su-27K/KU/IB configuration, with both tailplane and canards, is known to Sukhoi as an 'unstable triplane layout'. By destabilising the aircraft in pitch and providing control surfaces forward of the centre of gravity and centre of lift, canards improve manoeuvrability and counter the inevitable reduction of tailplane efficiency at high angles of attack.

Cockpit access
Access to the new side-by-side cockpit is via a ladder in the nosewheel bay, although the panels above the canopy look similar to the opening cockpit panels of the Su-24 'Fencer'.

Above: The Su-27s of the 159th Guards 'Novorossiisk' Fighter Regiment drawn up on the flight line at Kluczewo. The unit relocated to Biesowiese in July 1992.

Right: An Su-27 nears completion in the Komsomolsk factory, its markings showing it to be one of the 24 destined for the Chinese People's Liberation Army Air Force.

Below: A pair of Su-27s thunders into the air during the Soviet withdrawal from Poland.

tailslide is an excellent last-ditch method of spoiling an opponent's aiming solution, or of turning the tables in a vertical scissors, as well as demonstrating a remarkable degree of tolerance to airflow disturbances in the engine intakes. The Cobra demonstrates an unparalleled ability to point the nose (and gun, missile seekers, etc.) a long way off axis (away from the direction of flight) and is a phenomenal way of decelerating very quickly. Lost energy can rapidly be regained by using the enormous levels of installed thrust, due partly to the aircraft's low aerodynamic drag. Several Western fighter manufacturers have claimed that the manoeuvres are irrelevant, and that they could be performed by their respective aircraft, although none have so far demonstrated this. The regular inclusion of such manoeuvres in Su-27 air show routines shows a remarkable degree of confidence in the aircraft's handling at the most extreme edges of the envelope, since to perform them at low altitude means that they must be predictable and repeatable.

The Su-27's superb high Alpha capability, which it shares with the MiG-29, is due to several factors, including the FBW control system, sophisticated aileron/rudder interconnects which improve high AoA handling and help prevent departures, and superb aerodynamic design, which keeps air flowing into the engine intakes, keeps enough energised air flowing over the flight control surfaces and prevents the wing from stalling, in the conventionally accepted sense. Wing design is perhaps the key factor, the Su-27 using an adaptive wing with computer-controlled leading-edge flaps (inevitably known as slats) and trailing-edge flaperons. The effectiveness of these is enhanced by the unusual aerofoil section used. The deformed mid-section wing surface is also designed to keep an even distribution of pressure at high angles of attack, which allows airflow to remain undisturbed and

flowing back across the wing chord at higher Alpha values, and to give high lift (especially during manoeuvring) and low wave drag, particularly at transonic and supersonic speeds.

The Su-27's 1989 Paris appearance has been followed by a number of air show visits, which have won the aircraft many admirers, but few buyers. This is at least partly due to the OKB's inability to aggressively market the aircraft and to distribute information either to the press or potential purchasers. Ironically, the Mikoyan OKB, often regarded as old-school and unreconstructed, has been more open and more successful in this respect than the Sukhoi OKB which has always had a reputation for economic and political liberalism. The 1989 Air Salon at Le Bourget was followed by US air show tours during 1990, 1991 and 1992, by appearances at Farnborough (1990 and 1992), Dubai and Singapore, and by return visits to Paris in 1991 and 1993. Like Mikoyan (which very publicly lost a MiG-29 at Paris in 1989), Sukhoi has had an air show disaster. This occurred on 9 September 1990 during an air show at Salgareda in Italy, when pilot Rimas Stankyavichus failed to recover from a low-level loop.

Foreign pilots

A handful of Westerners have flown the Su-27, often from the front seat. Most of the Western pilots who have flown the aircraft have been senior officers whose front-line flying experience is irrelevant and out-of-date, or inexperienced journalists, and thus there are few independent witnesses who can give a truly objective and useful opinion of the aircraft's handling characteristics (especially in comparison with specific Western fighters) and its likely operational capability. This is in direct contrast to the MiG-29, which has been flown by pilots like John Farley (former BAe Dunsfold chief test pilot) and Bob Wade (6,000+ hour fighter pilot and CF-18 display ace). During such demonstration flights neither design bureau has allowed radar, HUD or other operational systems to be used, further limiting their usefulness. It is believed that the Su-27 underwent a marketing analysis by BAe after the 1992 Farnborough air show, and was flown by BAe and RAE/A&AEE test pilots, but these flights

Above: The second prototype Su-27UB acts as a tanker during trials of the first Su-27K.

Left: Still the only known picture of the T-10S-24, the first Su-27 'triplane', is a poor quality image published in the Soviet press.

Below: This aircraft acted as the Su-27K prototype, although it lacked wing folding.

Above: The Su-27K, whose production derivative is to be designated Su-33, is a canard-equipped navalised version of the basic Su-27 and not of the multi-role, glass-cockpit Su-35. It therefore lacks any real air-to-ground or multi-role capability.
Right: The second Su-27K seen during early trials aboard the Tbilisi, later renamed Kuznetsov. Chief test pilot Victor Pugachev flew the first shipborne Su-27K trials.

Right: Before embarking on the Tbilisi the Su-27Ks undertook extensive deck landing practice on the dummy deck at Saki in the Crimea.

remain shrouded in secrecy.

There are good reasons to suppose that the Su-27's formidable handling characteristics do not tell the whole story. During air show performances and demonstration flights, the Su-27s are inevitably very lightly loaded and flown at relatively low speed. At higher speeds and at higher weights, g limits, Alpha limits and agility are significantly reduced. Thus the Su-27 pilot's ability to override his various limiters to make brief excursions into the extremes of the envelope is severely limited, and at normal operational weights the Su-27 is no dogfighter. How much this matters is open to argument, since the primary role of any fighter pilot is to destroy his opponent at maximum range from himself and the point he is defending, preferably before he has even been seen. Here the Su-27's supersonic acceleration (which imparts greater energy to a missile at launch), excellent range and endurance and generous load of up to six BVR missiles is much more important than turn performance.

'Not a pound for air-to-ground'

Although designed specifically as an interceptor (unlike the MiG-29, which was always intended to be a more tactical fighter), the Su-27 has been adapted as a ground attack aircraft. Simonov once quoted exactly the same 'not a pound for air-to-ground' adage as was once applied to the F-15, and said that the Su-27 had been designed in just the same uncompromising way. In fact, like the F-15, the Su-27 has always had a secondary air-to-ground capability, although its radar and fire control system lacks software for more than the most basic ground attack mission. MBD-100, -250, and -500 or BD-250 or -500 pylons can carry a range of up to 16 250-kg (551-lb) or eight 500-kg (1,102-lb) blast, fragmentation, incendiary or cluster bombs, or six of the new KMGU cluster bombs. Alternatively, the aircraft can carry up to 80 S-8

Left: As well as folding wings and an arrester hook, the Su-27K introduced a whole new system of trailing-edge control surfaces, with drooping ailerons outboard and twin-section double-slotted trailing-edge flaps inboard.

80-mm rockets in four B-8M pods, 20 S-13 130-mm rockets in four B-13MT pods (or 16 rockets in four B-13-4 pods), or four S-25 250-mm rockets on individual O-25 launchers. Whereas the MiG-29 has a nuclear strike capability, carrying a single 30-kT RN-40 nuclear bomb on the left inner pylon, the Su-27 is not believed to have any nuclear role. When operated in the ground attack or intercept role the wingtip missile launch rails can be replaced by Sorbtsiya or Smalta ECM pods.

Su-27s have also been used for a variety of experimental tasks and as testbeds for various items of equipment and systems. These have included several inflight refuelling trials, in which Su-27s have acted as receivers and tankers. During 1987 an Su-27UB clocked up a 15-hour 42-minute, 13440-km (8,351-mile) sortie in the hands of Sadovnikov and I. Votint-sev. Similarly, the second Su-27UB prototype has been tested as a tanker, with a UPAZ pod on centreline. When the 'Flanker' is fitted with a retractable refuelling probe this is fitted on the port side of the nose, and necessitates relocation of the IRST/EO 'ball' from the centreline to the starboard side of the nose top decking. NIIKAM (The Institute of Aviation and Space Medicine) has used Su-27s to test fly various new-generation cockpits and cockpit displays and even a sidestick

Above: The cockpit of the carrierborne Su-27K differs in detail only from that of the basic land-based interceptor. There is certainly no provision for any dedicated air-to-ground capability using precision-guided weapons.

Left: One of the Su-27K prototypes about to 'trap' aboard the Kuznetsov. The new carrier has conventional arrester wires, but has no steam catapult. The Su-27K seems to have won the competition for a new naval fighter, despite being larger and less versatile than its competitor.

The Su-27K's nose oleo incorporates three green amber and red carrier landing lights.

The Su-27K displayed at the 1992 Moscow Aeroshow carried an **ASM-MSS** anti-ship missile below the belly, slung between the engine nacelles.

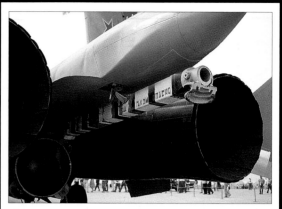

The crude, square-section arrester hook is painted white and black and is carried below the tailcone.

The main undercarriage of the Su-27K is modified and strengthened.

The wing of the Su-27K folds upwards, outboard of the inboard underwing pylon, for ease of stowage on a crowded hangar deck.

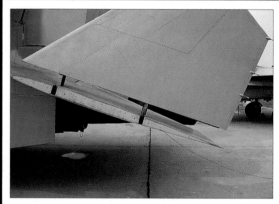

Even the tailplane of the Su-27K is designed to fold. Folded, the Su-27K is still a significantly larger aircraft than its rival, the MiG-29K.

The provision of a retractable inflight-refuelling probe in the port forward fuselage necessitates the relocation of the IRST away from the centreline.

control column. Thrust vectoring nozzles (initially circular, but then replaced by flattened nozzles like those fitted to the F-15 S/MTD) have been flown, and the type has served as a test pilot trainer and as a flying laboratory for Sukhoi's ambitious supersonic business jet project, which is heavily based on Su-27 technology and aerodynamics.

One of the most significant Su-27 testbeds was the T-10S-24, which was the result of a programme launched in 1982 to produce an Su-27 with moving canard foreplanes to improve agility and take-off/landing performance, and reduce trim drag. Sukhoi refers to this as an unstable three-plane (canard, wing and tailplane) configuration. After extensive wind tunnel tests, the heavily modified aircraft made its maiden flight in May 1985. The canard helped to offset the reduction in tailplane efficiency at high angles of attack, further destabilised the aircraft in pitch and improved take-off performance by exerting a lifting force on the nose, rather than a down force on the tail.

Export attempts

The basic aircraft has been offered for export to a number of customers, including India, Finland, Iran, Malaysia and even, in a fit of optimism, Australia. One report even suggested that the USA had been offered an option on 20 for aggressor/adversary training. In the early days, when prices were set by Aviaexport and bore no relationship to manufacturing or development costs, Sukhoi claimed that their aircraft's price was no more than 10 per cent higher than that of the MiG-29. Since the Gorbachev revolutions of *perestroika* and *glasnost*, many economic chickens have come home to roost, and the aircraft's price has risen dramatically, both in real terms and by comparison with the smaller and lighter MiG-29 (which is now half the price of a baseline Su-27).

Twenty-four Su-27s have actually been sold to the People's Republic of China. The contract, which stipulated that the aircraft could not be based within a certain distance of the Sino-Soviet border, was signed on 22 March 1991 and the first eight were delivered from August 1991. The aircraft are based on the island of Hainan, and Chinese pilots and ground crews trained at Serov Air Force Academy at Krasnodar. The break-up of the USSR brought a handful of new users, most notably the Ukraine. During mid-August 1992 an Su-27 regiment from Gudauta had to be relocated because of the dispute between Georgia and Abkhasia. An Su-27 was shot

Above: The Su-27IB made its public debut at Minsk, during a closed display for CIS leaders. Laden with advanced weaponry, including precision air-to-ground ordnance, the aircraft was described as a fighter-bomber.

Left: The Su-27IB's boarding ladder is located inside the nosewheel bay, immediately aft of the nose oleo.

Below: The Su-27IB has a broad two-seat side-by-side cockpit for its crew, which is understood to be equipped with advanced CRT displays. The prototype is believed to have been converted from a redundant Su-27UB.

down by Georgian forces during March 1993, over Abkhasia.

In Russia itself, the Su-27 was first delivered to PVO regiments for air defence of the Motherland, and then later to Frontal Aviation for tactical air superiority and escort duties. The participation of senior PVO commanders in the abortive coup against Gorbachev is believed to have led to further transfers to Frontal Aviation. The first non-PVO units to receive Su-27s were probably the 582nd Fighter Regiment at

Above: Sukhoi OKB test pilots Ivanov and Ivanov (strangely no relation!) pose in front of the Su-27IB. They are better known as the crew of the Su-24MR that has been demonstrated at some international air shows.

Right: An underside view of the Su-27IB clearly shows the aircraft's new broad, flat nose section. The deletion of the spine-mounted airbrake is obviously less apparent.

Below and right below: One Su-27 (Red 05) used by the LII at Zhukhovsky is used for NIIKAM cockpit experiments, and has a sidestick controller and a single Su-35-style CRT display.

bled to intercept NATO aircraft over the Baltic.

When the new Soviet political order began to take shape, Mikhail Petrovich Simonov was elected by popular vote to the new Congress of People's Deputies, and from there on to the Supreme Soviet, within which he became a key member of the powerful and influential Committee on Defence and State Security, and chairman of the sub-committee responsible for overseeing the 'defence/industrial complex'. From this lofty position, Simonov was able to further the interests of his own OKB, including organising an 'experimental grouping' of R&D, design and manufacturing concerns under the Sukhoi banner, an idea claimed by Mikoyan to be their own.

Mikhail Simonov has naturally continued to energetically and skilfully use his position and influence to further the interests of his bureau, and this has meant that the Su-27 has been less badly affected by defence cuts and drawdowns than have some other projects. Simonov is a mercurial figure, with enormous energy and considerable talent, whose ability to inspire and move others (even in the highly bureaucratic and often obstructionist Russian context) is matched by an enormous talent for design, and for getting the best out of other engineers and designers. He is not, however, a man to

Chojna and the 159th Guards Fighter Regiment at Kluczewo, both part of the 239th Fighter Division at Kluczewo in Poland. Each regiment comprised three front-line squadrons, each with about 12 aircraft (including two or three two-seaters) and 12 operational pilots and four staff pilots (squadron commander, deputy squadron commander, political and navigation officers). A fourth squadron had no aircraft assigned, and had junior pilots undergoing operational training. Until 1990 each regiment maintained a four-aircraft 24-hour QRA commitment, and Su-27s were frequently scram-

suffer fools gladly, and his alleged volatility is blamed by some for his unpopularity in some quarters. He is professionally respected and admired even by his detractors, and the Su-27's success is widely attributed to him, to an extent unknown in the West, where designers are anonymous and aircraft are very much the products of large teams.

Second-generation Su-27s

Simonov's political adeptness has shown itself in many ways, not least in ensuring funding for his pet projects. Because existing aircraft have tended to suffer more funding cuts than new projects, many new Su-27 derivatives have been quickly redesignated to allow them to appear to be entirely new aircraft, and these consequently attract appropriate levels of funding despite being, in fact, merely derivatives of the basic Su-27. Such variants are described briefly below.

The success of the MiG-31 in PVO service has been in part

Above: The 'Test Pilots' aerobatic team operates a handful of stripped-down Su-27Ps and Su-30s as dedicated aerobatic display aircraft, stripped of all operational systems, sponsored by the Jupiter Insurance Company. Here Anatoly Kvotchur taxis in at Boscombe Down's 1992 air show after a gruelling ferry flight.

Right: As the tailslide-performing Mikoyan OKB test pilot, Anatoly Kvotchur was the star of the 1988 Farnborough air show. He returned to Britain as leader of the 'Test Pilots' team in 1992.

due to its ability to operate in co-ordinated groups, covering huge swathes of territory, especially where there are gaps in ground radar cover. As well as freeing the aircraft from the need for tight GCI control this ability has increased tactical flexibility and minimised the impact of limited target tracking and engagement capability. It was therefore only to be expected that the PVO looked very hard at plans to bring similar capabilities to the Su-27, resulting in the development of the Su-27P and Su-27PU (also known as Su-30).

Su-27P

Little is known about the Su-27P, either in terms of its equipment fit or its present status. It is understood to be a dedicated interceptor closely based upon the existing production 'Flanker-B' but with a retractable inflight-refuelling probe and perhaps with the same improvements as the two-seat PU. The Su-27P may merely be optimised for 'group operations' under the control of an Su-27PU. The designation of the Su-27P is not known to have changed.

The Su-27PU is scarcely any better known than the Su-27P, although it has been inaccurately described as a 'command post'. In fact, the Su-27PU is a two-seat interceptor, optimised for long-duration missions, and/or for use in areas with difficult weather/navigation conditions, such as the featureless north, which is poorly served by radar

Right: The Su-27P prepares to take off from Boscombe Down alongside its support aircraft, a Tu-134 used by the LII at Zhukhovsky for transport and liaison duties.

and radio aids. An optional advanced datalink gives a new capacity for group operations, and it can operate as a kind of 'mini-AWACS' with other Su-27s, Su-27Ps or with MiG-29s (for example) as part of a mixed fighter force. The aircraft has been redesignated Su-30, and has been further developed into the Su-30M (Su-30MK for export) with secondary ground attack capability. On a 6 June 1992 proving flight Anatoly Kvochur (a former MiG test pilot now employed at Zhukhovsky) flew to the North Pole and back in 12 hours, with three inflight refuelling 'prods'. The first series production Su-27PUs are said to have been sold to the Jupiter Insurance Company, which uses them (and a handful of Su-27Ps) as the mounts of the 'Test Pilots' team.

Navalised newcomer

The conception of a new generation of carriers for the Soviet navy led to the development of a new 'Flanker' variant, the Su-27K. This was originally little more than a hooked Su-27 with folding wings, some additional corrosion protection, canard foreplanes, a refuelling probe and an optical carrier landing system, although a structural redesign was claimed. Twin nosewheels and a strengthened undercarriage were also provided, to meet the sink-rate requirements of landing on a pitching deck. It was originally intended purely as a fleet defence interceptor and had no multi-role capability. At least six prototypes have been converted, the first T-10K-1 (originally T-10S-37?) making its maiden flight on 17 August 1987. This aircraft lacked wing and tailplane folding, but was extensively used for development work using the dummy deck and ski jump at Saki in the Crimea, where at least one Su-27K prototype has been lost.

The T-10S-37 also retained the inboard flaperons of the basic, land-based Su-27 interceptor, which precluded its use in actual carrier trials. Subsequent Su-27K prototypes have completely new, full-span, three-section, trailing-edge flaps, the two double-slotted inboard sections operating symmetrically as flaps for take-off and landing, and the outboard sections operating differentially as (drooping) ailerons to provide roll control. Instead of the two inboard sections operating differentially as flaperons in normal flight, as on the basic Su-27, the Su-27K is controlled in roll by differential movement of the outboard and middle flap sections, augmented as before by differential tailplane movement. The

wing planform and section are believed to remain unchanged.

Another airframe change to the Su-27K is that the tailcone is of reduced length, to avoid the danger of a tailscrape during a high AoA landing. This reduces the space available for defensive systems, avionics and fuel, and may impose a slight transonic drag penalty. This has also necessitated a reduction in the number of upward-firing chaff/flare dispensers carried (12 three-shot dispensers) and their relocation further forward, inboard of the engine nacelles. The Su-27K is the only Su-27 variant so far to be compatible with the carriage of external fuel tanks, in this case a 1500-litre (330-Imp gal) centreline tank. There have been suggestions that at least some of the Su-27K prototypes have been re-engined, probably with the same increased thrust AL-31M that powers the Su-27M/Su-35.

Further tests followed on board the *Tbilisi* (now the *Kuznetsov*) and included Russia's first conventional carrier landing, which was made by Victor Pugachev on 1 November 1989. These tests showed that the Su-27K could take off from

Above: One of two Sukhoi Su-30s operated by the 'Test Pilots' team. These aircraft were the first production Su-30s and were built to a special order with no military systems. They thus bear little resemblance to the full-standard production Su-30.

Below: 'Test Pilots' Su-30s make a flyby. In operational service the Su-30 will be a dedicated long-range, long-endurance interceptor.

Right: The Soviets made extensive use of scale models (launched by rocket or air-dropped) for tests in the extreme corners of the envelope, before risking a full-size aircraft. This model, displayed on its launcher at Zhukhovsky during the 1992 Mosaeroshow, was used in the Su-35 programme.

Exciting air show routines not withstanding, the Su-27 has always been handicapped in service by its lack of agility at operational weights, and by its lack of multi-role capability. This has prevented it from completely eclipsing the smaller, and in some respects inferior, MiG-29 in VVS service, and especially in the export market. Development of an Su-27 with improved dogfighting characteristics and better air-to-ground capability was therefore accorded a high priority, with the aim of producing an Su-27 variant on which the Soviet (and later Russian) air forces could standardise (at the expense of the MiG-29), and which would appeal to foreign operators seeking a multi-role fighter.

Design of such a variant was entrusted to Nikolai Feyedorovich Nikitin, one of Mr Simonov's most talented and dynamic deputies. Under his direction the new variant, initially dubbed Su-27M, received the same canard foreplanes as the T-10S-24 and this 'unstable integrated three-plane' configuration was further destabilised through the clever use of fuel management (including the provision of

Above: The Su-35 (then still known as the Su-27M) was first shown at the closed air show at Minsk. The aircraft shown there lacked many of the Su-35's aerodynamic and airframe improvements, including the tall, square-topped tailfins.

the ski-ramp after a take-off run of 100 m (328 ft) (180 m/590 ft if fully laden), exiting the ramp at 14° Alpha and about 80 kt (148 km/h; 92 mph), in a semi-ballistic trajectory. The aircraft first runs up to full power against mechanical retractable restrainers set into the deck.

The breakup of the USSR led to the cancellation of one of the four new carriers, the scrapping of another on the slipway, and the freezing of the completion of another due to a dispute between Ukraine and Russia over ownership. With only one conventional carrier likely to enter service, the original plan of fielding an air wing with two aircraft types is becoming progressively less supportable, and the Su-27K may be developed into a multi-role aircraft more like its intended shipmate, and now rival – Mikoyan's MiG-29K. The new designation Su-33 is now being used. The existing Su-27K prototypes have already been seen carrying air-to-surface weapons with which they are at present totally incompatible. These have included the new ASM-MSS Moskito, an air-launched version of the Mach-3, 90-km range 3M-80 (NATO SS-N-22 'Sunburn') anti-ship missile. Sukhoi is talking of fitting vectoring nozzles to these aircraft if they win an order. Reports that the Su-33 is based on the Su27M/-35 have been categorically denied by Sukhoi, and it seems that the aircraft is basically a navalised, canard-equipped Su-27, with little multi-role capabilty, and with original control system.

Right: The Su-35 and Su-27 land at Farnborough. The aircraft which visited Farnborough was fitted with distinctive wingtip ECM pods, though it is understood that these can quickly be replaced by missile launch rails.

fuel tanks in the tailfins). The higher level of instability demanded changes to the flight control system, which was replaced by a completely new digital quadruplex fly-by-wire system with four longitudinal and three transverse channels. Extra thrust was provided by the new 13300-kg st (29,320-lb) AL-31SM engine, compensating for the aircraft's slightly increased weight. Vectoring engine exhaust nozzles have been tested on at least one Su-27UB, and are offered as an option on the new variant, by retrofit if necessary. These have a 15° ± vector angle and would improve both take-off and landing performance, and manoeuvrability, but their increased price may not be acceptable to the cash-strapped Russian air forces.

'Flanker' goes forward

The new variant has also been structurally redesigned, with increased use of both composite materials and aluminium-lithium alloys, reducing basic airframe weight and increasing the volume available for both fuel and avionics equipment. The tailfin fuel tanks are housed in a redesigned tailfin of greater height and with a square tip. The lower part of the fin is similar to that of the Su-27UB, but the rudder extends lower and is thus of greater area.

The Su-27M was given a completely new weapons system, with a new N-011 multi-mode radar and a new electro-optical complex, the latter with greater range, angular coverage and discrimination, and with collimated laser and TV designators. The radar may be related to the N-010 of the MiG-29M and is compatible with the use of various new air-to-air and air-to-ground weapons, and has new ground mapping and air-to-ground attack modes. The new radar has increased range, able to detect air-to-air targets out to 400 km (225 miles). Up to 15 targets can be simultaneously tracked (eight while in scanning mode) and six can be simultaneously engaged. The tailcone of the Su-27M has been redesigned and no longer accommodates a braking parachute. It is tipped, instead, by a dielectric radome, perhaps explaining rumours of a rearward-facing radar, 360° radar coverage and over-the-shoulder radar-guided missile capability.

The aircraft also has a redesigned cockpit, with three colour CRT multi-function display screens and a fourth navigation display. These are surrounded by conventional input buttons; there are no throttle and stick-mounted

Left: Moving canard foreplanes increase agility by longitudinally destabilising the aircraft, and by providing an aerodynamic control surface ahead of the centre of lift and centre of gravity. The same canards are fitted to the Su-27K and Su-27IB.

Left: There have been many oblique hints to the effect that the Su-35 has a 360° target detection capability. Interestingly, the tailcone of the aircraft has been reconfigured. It seems to be tipped by a dielectric fairing and lacks any provision for brake chute stowage, leading to suspicions that a rearward-looking radar may be fitted.

Left: The Su-35 has a retractable inflight-refuelling probe in the port forward fuselage, just below the windscreen. This is partially covered when retracted and is developed from the probe used on the Su-24. Small circular antennas are set into the skin, these serving an unknown purpose.

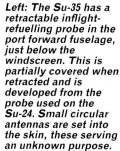

Left and left below: The Su-35 carries streamlined ECM pods on the wingtips, with white-painted dielectric fairings covering antennas fore and aft. A prominent hollow duct is fitted to the inner face, with an open front end. This may be a ram air inlet for avionics cooling.

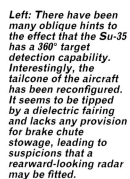

'sit' on the ground, there is little evidence of greater droop. The cockpit coaming is lowered, giving the pilot a better view forward despite his more inclined seat.

The first of six prototype Su-27Ms made its maiden flight on 28 June 1988, in the hands of Oleg Tsoi. The variant was first revealed at the closed air show at Minsk on 13 February 1992. By Farnborough's 1992 SBAC show, the type had been redesignated Su-35. The prototype at Minsk lacked square-topped tailfins and wingtip ECM pods, and wore the code '706', perhaps indicating that it was the sixth T-10S-70, whereas the prototype at Farnborough was built to a more advanced standard and wore the code '703', perhaps suggesting that it was the third T-10S-70. Some sources from Sukhoi stated that it was the fifth aircraft to fly and this may mean that '704' and '705' were completed to an interim standard, and flew before it.

Su-27 bomber

The multi-role capability of the Su-27M/Su-35 is impressive, but falls far short of that required for a potential Su-24 'Fencer' replacement, a role which many have suggested could be fulfilled by a dedicated Su-27 derivative. Such an aircraft would ideally be a side-by-side two-seater, with a new attack radar and dedicated night-attack equipment, including FLIR. Such a variant may already be under development by Sukhoi. An Su-27 with a side-by-side two-seat cockpit was photographed on approach to the *Tbilisi* during August 1991. The new cockpit was immediately apparent, as were the long flowing chines which flowed forward from the LERXes to the pitot probe, giving the aircraft a nose shape reminiscent of the SR-71 Blackbird. The aircraft was later revealed by the Sukhoi OKB to be designated Su-27KU, and was said to be a dedicated two-seat trainer for carrier-based Su-27K pilots, with side-by-side seats providing both crew with the same approach picture. This is obviously important when a precise approach angle needs to be maintained in order to successfully and safely engage an arrester wire.

Close examination of the Su-27KU revealed a strengthened undercarriage, like that fitted to the Su-27K, with the

Above: Having spent a small fortune getting the Su-35 to the 1992 Farnborough SBAC show, Sukhoi displayed the machine only statically; the aircraft flew only when it arrived and departed. Any extra agility could not be demonstrated.

Right: In the static display the Su-35 was laden with air-to-surface weapons, including laser- and TV-guided missiles.

Below: Like the Su-27, the Su-35 does not carry external fuel, even for a long ferry flight (e.g. from Farnborough to Moscow).

controllers, unlike the rival MiG-29M. Monochrome displays were chosen because Russian colour CRT technology lags behind that of the West, and their colour screens are difficult to read in conditions of extreme brightness or glare. This is a major drawback, since the lack of colour hinders the clear presentation of complex data.

Some Western analysts have suggested that the entire forward fuselage of the Su-27M droops more than that of the standard Su-27 but, while the aircraft does have a different

Weapons
This Su-35 is armed with a pair of R-73s outboard, four R-77s and a trio of the new long-range AAM-L, a very long-range anti-AWACS weapon, whose range can be further extended by the addition of a separate booster.

Radome
Since the new radar has a new flat-plate antenna, instead of the old inverse cassegrain unit, the radome has been reshaped, becoming less bulged aft.

Radar
The Su-35 has a new multi-mode radar, probably designated N-011, with significant air-to-ground capability. This may be related to the N-010 radar of the MiG-29M, itself a version of the Fazatron 'Zhuk' (Beetle). More importantly, the radar has much improved processing, allowing up to 15 targets to be simultaneously tracked, and six to be engaged at ranges out to 362 km (225 miles).

Cockpit
The Su-35 has a modern glass cockpit with three multi-function CRT displays. These mark a major improvement over the traditional 'steam-age' analogue cockpit of the basic Su-27 but have traditional input buttons surrounding them, rather than the throttle and stick-mounted controls of those fitted to the MiG-29M.

Powerplants
The Su-35 is powered by a pair of NPO Saturn (Lyul'ka) AL-31FM turbofans, each rated at 13300 kg (29,320 lb) with reheat. This is 800 kg (1,764 lb) more thrust than is produced by the standard aircraft's AL-31F, and compensates for the new type's increased weight. The AL-31FM may also have digital engine controls. The engine intakes do not seem to have been altered, so it may be assumed that the extra thrust is the result of higher operating temperatures (perhaps indicating a shorter life, or the use of advanced materials) and not greater mass flow.

Sukhoi Su-35 (Su-27M)

This aircraft is one of six Su-35 prototypes – probably the third, but said to have been the fifth to fly. Both Su-27M/Su-35s seen so far have carried 70 series codes, perhaps indicating the OKB designation T-10S-70. The Su-35 originated as the Su-27M and was designed as a follow-on to the basic Su-27 with better dogfighting characteristics (the primary goal according to its designer, Nikolai Feyodorevich Nikitin) and with better BVR combat and multi-role capability. Although the new type looks externally similar to the standard Su-27, it is in many respects an entirely new aircraft, with many new systems and some new structure.

ECM pods
Wingtip ECM pods replaced missile launch rails on at least two Su-35 prototypes, and are usually illustrated in Sukhoi publicity material relating to the aircraft. The forward radome is reportedly a receiver, while that at the rear is a transmitter, rather than both being transmitters for front and rear hemisphere coverage, according to Sukhoi documents.

Tailcone
The Su-35 has a reconfigured tailcone with a reshaped tip. This is a dielectric radome rather than the usual brake chute cover, perhaps tying in with oblique brochure references to rear hemisphere radar coverage, and 'over-the-shoulder' BVR missile capability.

Flight control systems
The Su-35 is controlled using a completely new digital fly-by-wire control system (the standard Su-27 using FBW only in pitch). The system is quadruplex, using four channels in pitch and three in roll/yaw.

Fins
The Su-35 has new tailfins (each containing an auxiliary fuel tank), based on the taller fin of the Su-27UB but with the rudder extended downwards to the fin base, as it would be on the single-seat Su-27, and uncropped square tips.

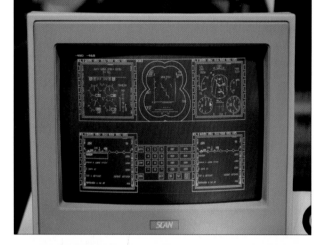

Above: The cockpit of the Su-35, unfortunately photographed through the canopy. The prominence of the four multi-function CRT displays is clear.

Right: The Su-35's cockpit displays and HUD shown on a computer screen. Interestingly, the CRTs appear to be multi-coloured, with reds, yellows and greens.

Right: A simulation of the Su-35 cockpit shown at Mosaeroshow '92. Input is via buttons around the CRT display screens, unlike the HOTAS controls which are used on the MiG-29M.

Top right (this page): The Su-35 is optimised as an interceptor, but has a significant air-to-ground capability. This aircraft carries AAMs outboard and ASMs inboard, and under the nacelles.

same twin nosewheels but with an even stronger-looking oleo and with no approach 'traffic lights'. The nosewheel unit has also been moved forward, and now retracts aft to lie in a bay covered by no less than four separate doors. The cockpits were located well forward, with a substantial hump behind, presumably housing fuel and/or avionics equipment. The dorsal airbrake seems to have been omitted, as have the ventral fins. Although at first glance the cockpit canopy appears similar to that fitted to the Su-24 'Fencer', the overhead panels do not seem to be openable, and cockpit access is via the nosewheel bay and a detachable ladder. The two-piece windscreen is very sharply swept.

The credibility of the 'carrier trainer' explanation was somewhat dented by the fact that it lacked wing folding, arrester hook and the redesigned flaps and ailerons of the Su-27K. It appeared to be further undermined when the same aircraft (reportedly one of two prototypes) was exhibited at Minsk in February 1992, festooned with air-to-ground ordnance and with an information board describing it as the Su-27IB (IB being the initials traditionally used to denote a fighter-bomber).

Trainer or fighter-bomber?

Despite this, the aircraft does not immediately seem entirely suited to the fighter-bomber role. The broad, flat metal nose would make the installation of an attack and/or terrain-following radar difficult, and the aircraft also seems to lack

any electro-optical sensors, designators or sighting aids. Furthermore, OKB head Mikhail Simonov has been quoted as stating that the aircraft is "better for instruction in carrier landing and air-to-surface weapons delivery" than as a dedicated operational strike aircraft, and the Su-27IB designation was denied until June 1993.

Thus the Su-27KU (or Su-27IB) remains an enigma. Is it the prototype of a carrier-based trainer (despite its lack of any navalised equipment) or the aerodynamic prototype of a new strike aircraft (despite its lack of attack radar, EO sensors, etc.)? Has the Su-27KU designation been used to cover the aircraft's true purpose? Whatever the answers, the Su-27 is clearly continuing to form the basis of new variants designed to fill new roles, and seems increasingly likely to form the backbone of the Russian air forces as they enter the new millennium.

Left: The Su-35 marks a major improvement over the original Su-27, and is in many respects a match for even the latest generation of Western superfighters. Moreover, it is ready for full-scale production right now.

Below: Political developments have made the Sukhoi OKB the major beneficiary of developments in Russia and the former CIS. Concentration on a smaller number of aircraft types has led to tough times for rival Mikoyan, but since the Su-27 has been chosen as one of the 'backbone aircraft' for the Russian air forces, Sukhoi's position is rather better.

Sukhoi Su-27 'Flanker' Operators

Russia

Sukhoi Su-27s were originally delivered to the integrated armed forces of the former Soviet Union, specifically to the air defence force (the IA-PVO) and to Frontal Aviation. The failed coup against Mikhail Gorbachev (in which the IA-PVO was implicated) led to some transfers of aircraft from the air defence forces, increasing the relative importance of Frontal Aviation as a 'Flanker' user. When the USSR disintegrated, its successor, the Commonwealth of Indpendent States, failed to keep central control of unified armed forces as newly independent states scrambled to set up their own armed forces. Most Su-27s were based in Russia, and therefore passed to Russian control, which retained the same structure for its own armed forces, with separate air forces and air defence force. All Su-27 production is centred within Russian territory, making the country the most important Su-27 operator. A handful of aircraft based at airfields outside Russia were absorbed by the air forces of various new independent republics, including the Ukraine, Byelorussia and Georgia.

*Right: **Somehow emblematic of the new Russia are the privately sponsored Su-27s and Su-30s of the Zhukhovsky-based 'Test Pilots' aerobatic display team. Revenue-earning overseas display tours are the raison d'être of these examples of Russia's foremost fighter.***

IA-PVO

The PVO is split into three commands: one controls radar stations, one controls air defence missiles, and the last, the IA-PVO, controls the massive force of manned interceptors. The Su-27 was originally designed to meet the specific requirements of the IA-PVO, with long range, extended endurance, good combat persistence and the ability to act independently or under the control of AWACS platforms or GCI stations. It entered service as a replacement for obsolescent Su-15 'Flagons', Tu-128 'Fiddlers' and Yak-28 'Firebars', as a counter to the new generation of Western low-level attack aircraft and cruise-missile-carrying bombers. The 'Flanker's' look-down/shoot-down capabilities gave the IA-PVO a welcome boost in capability, although production of the aircraft has been sufficiently small that large numbers of less effective interceptors (primarily MiG-23s, but also including Su-15s) have had to remain in service. PVO Su-27s wear no special markings which might differentiate them from VVS aircraft.

*Above: **An early Su-27 on tow at the end of the flying day. At many PVO bases Su-27s are accommodated in individual hardened shelters, but routinely operate from a conventional flight line. Wartime operating procedures would be very different.***

*Left: **An IA-PVO Su-27 in flight. The Su-27's rate of climb, speed, range and enormous warload make it the perfect PVO interceptor, as its creators intended. The aircraft's agility is a useful bonus. Defence of the Motherland remains an important job, even in post-Cold War Russia.***

Frontal Aviation

The Su-27 entered service with Frontal Aviation (part of the VVS or Air Forces) for long-range air superiority and as an escort fighter. It was seen as being particularly useful for the destruction of high-value targets behind the enemy front line, including tankers and AWACS aircraft. Units believed to be Frontal Aviation operators of the Su-27 include: 234th 'Proskurovskii' Guards IAP, including the 'Russian Knights' team at Kubinka (Moscow Military District); 159th 'Novorossiisk' Guards IAP at Kluczewo, Poland, then at Biesowice; 582nd IAP at Chojna, Poland, then flown to Smolensk to disband; 831st IAP at Mirgorod (Carpathian Military District); 54th IAP at Vainodo, and 689th IAP at Nivenskoye (both Leningrad MD); and the 61st IAP at Baranovidu and the 62nd IAP at Bielbek, which respectively became parts of the Byelorussian and Ukrainian air forces. Other Ukrainian-based Su-27 units were at Zhitomir and Sevastapol. An unknown regiment is based at Gaduata, and may be under Georgian control. Some of the units listed may have been (or may still be) under IA-PVO control.

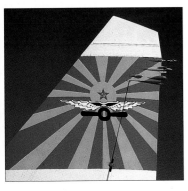

Above: The blue and gold sunburst flag of the VVS is proudly worn on the tailfins of the 'Russian Knights' Su-27s. The IA-PVO is not part of the Russian air forces, which have their own regiments of Su-27s.

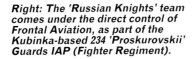

Above: For Frontal Aviation the Su-27 is a long-range complement to the MiG-29, specialising in the escort of strike aircraft and the destruction of high-value airborne targets further behind the enemy front line.

Right: The 'Russian Knights' team comes under the direct control of Frontal Aviation, as part of the Kubinka-based 234 'Proskurovskii' Guards IAP (Fighter Regiment).

AV-MF

The naval air arm is not believed to have any significant number of land-based Su-27s, though a handful may have been taken on charge for training duties, pending the service introduction of the carrierborne Su-27K/Su-33. The Su-27 has been selected as the aircraft which will equip the air wing of Russia's only conventional aircraft-carrier, the *Kuznetsov*. Originally there were to have been four such carriers, but one was cancelled, another (*Ulyanovsk*) was broken up on the slipway, and the third, *Varyag*, awaits its electronics, if the ownership dispute between Russia and the Ukraine can ever be solved. With four carriers planned, the USSR expected to field a dedicated long-range interceptor (the Su-27K) and a smaller multi-role fighter-bomber (the MiG-29K). With only one carrier it now seems likely that only one type will be procured, and Sukhoi's political ascendancy makes it almost certain that this will be the Su-27K, despite its lack of multi-role capability and very large size. This will increase cost, and reduce the number of aircraft that can be carried by comparison with an air wing composed entirely of MiG-29Ks. A batch of 20 Su-27Ks is reportedly nearing completion.

Above: Victor Pugachev blasts off from the Tbilisi to make Russia's second carrier take-off, having been preceded by Takhtar Aubakirov in the MiG-29K.

Left: The Su-27K is almost certain to be the only fixed-wing aircraft type deployed aboard the Kuznetsov when it finally becomes operational. It seems likely to be redesignated Su-33.

Experimental establishments

Despite its importance as a front-line fighter, relatively large numbers of Su-27s are in use as testbeds and trials aircraft, mostly at the massive experimental airfield at Zhukhovsky, known as the LII. Some of these aircraft fly missions on behalf of TsAGI (The Central Hydrodynamics Institute), while others are used for aviation medicine, cockpit trials and 'human factors' research by NIIKAM. Additional aircraft are used as engine testbeds, including at least one fitted with a massive two-dimensional thrust-vectoring engine nozzle. The Gromov Flight Research Centre is also home to a test pilots school, which uses Su-27s for training, and as the mount for its commercially sponsored aerobatic display team, led by Anatoly Kvotchur. The team's aircraft are actually Su-30s and Su-27Ps. Su-27s are also used as weapons trials work-horses, hauling aloft both air-to-air and air-to-surface weapons.

Right: The Su-30 (foreground) and Su-27P of the 'Test Pilots' team on approach at Woodford's 1992 air show. The aircraft are frequent visitors to Western air shows.

Sukhoi OKB

The Sukhoi Design Bureau itself uses a number of Su-27s for trials, tests and demonstration work, although the dividing line between Zhukhovsky- and Sukhoi-owned aircraft is a very fine one. It may be that the OKB aircraft are leased back or loaned back to the bureau, but actually belong to the Flight Research Institute. The well-known Paris/Farnborough/US/Singapore pair of aircraft seems to be on permanent OKB charge, but the bureau also appears to have unlimited access to the Su-27IB prototype, several Su-27Ks and a handful of Su-35s. The old P-42 record breaker is in external store at Zhukhovsky, and may be on OKB charge. The OKB does have its own pool of dedicated test pilots, led by Victor Pugachev.

Right: Sukhoi's aircraft are used for displays and customer demonstrations, and have become a well-known feature of the Western air show circuit.

Below: This Su-35 is used by the Sukhoi OKB as a demonstrator. The aircraft carries the old-style winged archer logo on its tailfins.

Right: The Sukhoi OKB's Su-27UB demonstrator lands at Oklahoma City. The bureau has its own Il-76s, but used the An-225 as a support aircraft during the Su-27's US tour.

Independent states

After the break-up of the former USSR, several Su-27 regiments were left on the soil of new republics. Some aircraft were flown back to Russia by their (predominantly Russian) pilots but others were used to form the basis of a number of new independent arms. The Su-27, as the most capable Soviet-built fighter in service, is obviously a highly sought-after symbol of national power and pride. In the Ukraine, Su-27s serve at Zhitomir, Bielbek and Sevastapol, the former aircraft being decorated with an eagle and sun badge. All Ukrainian aircraft are gradually receiving new national insignia, consisting of a golden stylised trident on a blue disc. This is applied to the tailfins of most Ukrainian aircraft. A blue and gold roundel is carried above and below the wings. The old Soviet red star marking is being removed with haste. At least one Su-27 was offered for sale by the Ukraine, in a mass sell-off of surplus aircraft inherited from former Soviet units based in the Republic. In Byelorussia Su-27s serve with the former 61st IAP at Baranovidu, and it is believed that Georgia may also have its own Su-27s. The national markings worn by these aircraft (if any)

remain a matter for conjecture. In all non-Russian states, operation of the Su-27 is dependent upon keeping the supply of spares open, and the supply of trained pilots (many of whom are native Russians) is another complicating factor. These difficulties may well lead to the sale of the Ukrainian Su-27s, and their replacement by types which are easier to support and maintain locally or which are in service in larger numbers.

Right: This badge was applied to the tailfins of Zhitomir-based Su-27s. It has reportedly been retained since the unit came under Ukrainian control.

Below: This Su-27 was photographed in full Ukrainian national markings at an airshow at one of the Antonov OKB's test airfields.

China

The first true export customer for the Su-27 was the People's Republic of China, whose People's Liberation Army Air Force has taken delivery of some 24 Su-27s (sometimes quoted as 22 aircraft). The number of Su-27UB two-seat trainers included in (or additional to) this total remains unknown. The delivery of the Su-27s to China marks the first large weapons purchase from the USSR/Russia since the big split during the 1960s, and gives China its first truly modern fighter aircraft, although the extent to which the Su-27s have been downgraded remains uncertain. Chinese Su-27s were delivered in a new medium grey colour scheme with the red 'star and bar' on the tailfins and on the wings. A two-digit code (ranging up to 24, at least) is applied to the nose, below the windscreen. The contract originally stipulated that the Su-27s could not be based near the Sino-Soviet border, and the aircraft were initially delivered to a base on Hainan Island, facing the Taiwanese threat. More recently there have been reports that China has broken the basing agreement and moved the 'Flankers' to a base near the Russian border.

The last of China's 24 Su-27s is seen outside the Komsomolsk factory. The colour scheme worn by these aircraft includes an unusual 'cut-out' in the lower part of the radome.

Marine Corps Assault

From the cockpit of Rick Mullen

As the United States' principal rapid deployment force, the Marine Corps have seen action in many parts of the globe, and regularly train in foreign countries. They were also heavily involved in the Desert Storm fighting. As a CH-53 pilot, Rick Mullen has flown in Norway, Tunisia, France, the Mediterranean and many other theatres, including war service in Iraq and Kuwait. This photo-essay provides a record of the Marine heavy lifters in action.

A pair of Sikorsky CH-53Es flies over Norwegian waters, landing gear down to prevent freezing problems. Norway is a major overseas commitment for the USMC, and the Corps regularly exercise in the country to test their ability to fight in Arctic conditions and to conduct operations with local forces.

Above: One of the techniques for insertion of Marines is the SPIE rig. Troops are attached to the rope by quick-release grips.

Below: On exercise at Twentynine Palms in California, a CH-53E moves in to pick up an LAV. Note the two cargo strops which carry the vehicle fore and aft.

Above: *A flight of CH-53Es lifts off from Bardufoss during a Norwegian exercise. The three-engined Stallion has been in USMC service since June 1981, greatly enhancing the Corps' heavylift capability. When deployed on board assault carriers as part of a composite squadron, there are typically four CH-53Es.*

Left: *View from the cockpit as a CH-53E refuels from a VMGR-234 KC-130T. After initial contact the receiver usually moves to the left to further separation between the two aircraft.*

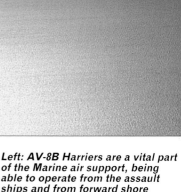

Left: *AV-8B Harriers are a vital part of the Marine air support, being able to operate from the assault ships and from forward shore bases. This example is seen at Bardufoss.*

Right: *Squeezing a CH-53E into a C-5 is no easy task, but it is a vital one to ensure the rapid transportation of Marine assets on a global basis.*

Above: Providing fire support for Marine amphibious and heliborne landings is the Bell Cobra, in this case an AH-1T. The current AH-1W introduced Hellfire missiles.

Below: Little brother – partnering the CH-53 on the air assault mission is the redoubtable CH-46 Sea Knight, principally used for personnel transport.

Above: Although based on the original CH-53 airframe, the E-model is readily identified by the third engine on the port side of the rotor mast fairing and the canted tail surfaces.

Below: On exercise in France, this CH-53E demonstrates the power of its landing lights in thick fog at Le Luc. The helicopter has superb avionics which allow operations in most weather conditions.

Marine Corps Assault

Above: A CH-53E raises a sandstorm somewhere in Saudi Arabia during Desert Storm. Alongside the CH-46, the Super Stallion played an important part in the land battles, including the skirmishes around Khafji prior to the main invasion of Kuwait. Helicopters were necessary to keep supplies and artillery up with the fast-moving ground forces.

Right: The sinister shadow of a CH-53E hovers over a Marine M198 artillery piece during the land war. Moving artillery and ammunition was a key job assigned to the CH-53 fleet. Each gun was suspended by four chains attached to two strops, this arrangement proving very stable for lifting.

Below: For the Khafji battle, the USMC established a forward operating location known as 'Lonesome Dove'. This became a major helicopter base for operations into Kuwait, mainly for Marine use but also for Special Forces machines. Here a US Army 'MH-47D', with floodlights, ramp and side gunners, FLIR and additional antennas lifts off for a covert mission above USMC RH-53Ds and CH-46s.

Above: The heat and sand of the Saudi/Kuwaiti desert was a tough and demanding environment for helicopter operations, but the CH-53E performed admirably throughout.

Right: More Special Forces aircraft at 'Lonesome Dove', representing the two principal types employed by the US Air Force. Just landed is an MH-53J Pave Low, followed by an MH-60G Pave Hawk.

Below: The threat of an amphibious assault on Kuwait was maintained by a large force afloat in the Persian Gulf. In fact this was merely a ruse, but the aircraft based at sea were widely used. AV-8B Harriers were stationed aboard USS Nassau.

Above: *Bell UH-1Ns are used by Navy and Marine Corps alike. Navy machines, like this one on USS Iwo Jima sailing in the Mediterranean, are primarily used for liaison and utility transport.*

Below: *Much of the materiel for the Norway Air Landed MEB (Marine Expeditionary Brigade) is pre-positioned in-country, but many of the helicopters arrive courtesy of the USAF's Air Mobility Command.*

Above: *CH-53Es fly along the Norwegian coast. The big helo is ideal for this terrain, where virtually everything has to be moved by air in a challenging and inhospitable environment. Marines have bolstered NATO's northern flank since an MoU was signed between the US and Norwegian governments in January 1981.*

Left: *Clutching TOW missile tubes on its stub pylons, an AH-1T overflies the crater of Mount Etna on Sicily. This model of Cobra is now out of service, even the Reserve units having re-equipped with the 'Whiskey'. In addition to Hellfire missiles, the AH-1W can now launch AIM-9 Sidewinder and AIM-122 Sidearm missiles while retaining its ability to fire TOW, unguided rockets or drop CBUs.*

Right: *Known as the 'Frog', the CH-46 has been the backbone of the USMC's airborne assault capability since the mid-1960s. A replacement is desperately sought, most Marine officers favouring the V-22 Osprey tilt-rotor transport.*

*Above: An evening refuelling from a **KC-130**. On each refuelling pod is a set of traffic lights to provide directions for the receiver pilot. Red signifies 'Tanker not ready', yellow signifies 'Tanker ready, contact' and green is for 'Fuel flowing'. If the light goes to red during contact, the receiver should break away immediately.*

*Left: **CH-53Ds** and **Es** on the flight line at **MCAS Tustin, California**. The older, two-engined D-models can be distinguished from the Es by having six-bladed main rotors instead of seven-bladed. Front-line **CH-53D** units at the base are **HMH-363** and **462**, while the **CH-53E** is flown by **HMH-361, 465** and **466**. Both variants are on strength with **HMT-302**, which acts as the training unit for the Stallion.*

Above: The CH-53E numbers para-dropping among its many capabilities. Seen here during an exercise at Camp Lejeune, a Marine Force Recon team jumps on a static line drop. The loadmaster recovers the lines and empty parachute bags as soon as the troops have departed.

Above: Another method of rapidly inserting troops is to deploy vehicles from the rear ramp. This is a Fast Attack Vehicle, fully equipped and ready to fight the moment the CH-53E has landed.

Below: Marines still use landing craft, but the helicopter is today equally important. Providing the real muscle is the CH-53E.

Mirage III/5/50
Variant Briefing: Part 2

Fives, Fifties, Foreigners and Facelifts

While the original Mirage III is of dwindling importance, the later Mirage 5 and 50 remain in use in significant numbers alongside the Israeli-built Kfir and a host of radically upgraded Mirage Deltas produced by Dassault and foreign manufacturers. The addition of canards, advanced avionics and compatibility might not turn a Mirage into a fourth-generation superfighter, but it does dramatically improve the aircraft's capability, making it a credible platform in many circumstances. It has also provided a cost-effective solution to the problems encountered by many cash-strapped air arms. Such improvements have ensured that the Mirage will remain a familiar shape even in the skies of the early 21st century.

Above: Foreigner and facelift in formation. A Colombian Kfir and an IAI-upgraded Mirage IIICOD of Comando Aéreo de Combate 1's Grupo 21. The Kfirs serve with Escuadron 213 and the single-seat Mirages with Escuadron 212, both based at BAM 5 'German Olano' at Palanquero.

Below: The Mirage 5 was originally known as the Mirage 5J, reflecting the identity of its intended customer – Israel (J for Jewish).

Mirage 5

In its second incarnation, the 'fifth' Mirage was briefly known by the Roman numeral 'V' before adopting the Arabic '5'. It stemmed from an Israeli requirement for an attack aircraft having as much as possible in common with the Mirage III already in service, but with radar and some other equipment removed for reduced cost and faster turnaround. Based on the IIIE airframe, the 'new-old' aircraft retained Mach 2+ performance and semi-prepared airfield operating capability, but dispensed with the SEPR rocket and added sixth and seventh hardpoints at the rear junction between wing and fuselage. Armament capability remained at 8,818 lb (4000 kg), however.

Most noticeable was removal of the nose radome, the sharper 'solid' cone increasing fuselage length by 20¾ in (53 cm). The pitot tube was now attached slightly below the tip of the nose so that an EMD (Electronique Marcel Dassault) Aïda ranging radar (not to be confused with Super Aïda originally intended for the Mirage IIIC) could be fitted if required. Repositioning some electrical equipment in the nose produced extra space in the equipment bay to the rear of the cockpit, this being used for a further 103 Imp gal (470 litres) of fuel, boosting capacity to 750 Imp gal (3410 litres) and combat radius from 745 to 800 miles (1200-1288 km).

First flown on 19 May 1967, the Mirage suffered a setback when the ordered 50 Israeli 5J aircraft were embargoed by the French government. They went instead to the AA as Mirage 5Fs in the attack role with almost the full range of 'extras' including radar warning receivers, VOR aerials, ESD Aïda ranging radar in a small nose radome, and a fin-root fillet. Eight more were delivered in 1983-85, No. 58

becoming the 465th and last Mirage III/5 supplied to the AA. External stores include RPK100 110-Imp gal (500-litre) fuel tanks with attachments for four 551-lb (250-kg) bombs, Belouga cluster bombs, 882-lb (400-kg) bombs, JL100 combined fuel/rocket pods (55 Imp gal/250 litres plus 18 SNEBs of 68-mm calibre), MATRA R.550 Magic AAMs and Philips-MATRA Phimat chaff/flare dispensers.

The elements that constitute a Mirage 5 have never been accurately defined by the manufacturer, although in the late 1980s Dassault did re-assess its sales totals to classify as Mirage IIIs those radar-equipped aircraft previously described as Mirage 5s. The Mirage 5DE, 5SDE, 5PA2 and 5PA3 have been included in the section on the Mirage IIIE. Two-seat trainers and reconnaissance versions are similarly indistinguishable from their progenitor, and are discussed under the Mirage IIID and IIIR headings. Optional items included Aïda ranging radar (Abu Dhabi, Egypt, Gabon, Libya, Pakistan, Venezuela), VOR aerials (Abu Dhabi, Colombia, Peru, Venezuela, Zaïre), radar-warning receiver (Abu Dhabi, Egypt, Gabon, Libya, Pakistan) and fin-root fillet (Colombia, Egypt, Gabon, Libya, Peru, Venezuela, Zaïre).

Export variants of the attack-optimised Mirage 5 lacking search radar were the 5AD for Abu Dhabi (12), the 5BA for Belgium (63, of which 62 were built by SABCA/Avions Fairey), the 5COA for Colombia (14), the 5E2 for Egypt (16), the 5G/5G2 for Gabon (three and two), the 5D for Libya (53), the 5PA for Pakistan (28), the 5P/5P3/5P4 for Peru (22, 10 and two), the 5V for Venezuela (six) and the 5M for Zaïre (eight). Belgian aircraft relied heavily on US avionics, while the Egyptian 5E2 used an Alpha Jet MS2 attack system including a SAGEM Uliss 81 INS and Una 81 nav/attack unit, Thomson-CSF VE110C HUD, T-CSF TMV630 laser rangefinder, TRT AHV9 radar altimeter and ESD Digibus digital multiplexed avionics databus. Some operators have upgraded their aircraft, as described in the section on Mirage upgrades.

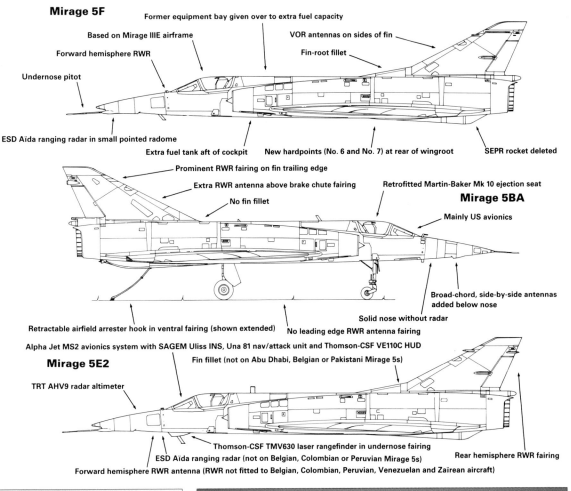

Mirage 5F

- Former equipment bay given over to extra fuel capacity
- Based on Mirage IIIE airframe
- VOR antennas on sides of fin
- Forward hemisphere RWR
- Fin-root fillet
- Undernose pitot
- ESD Aïda ranging radar in small pointed radome
- Extra fuel tank aft of cockpit
- New hardpoints (No. 6 and No. 7) at rear of wingroot
- SEPR rocket deleted

Mirage 5BA

- Prominent RWR fairing on fin trailing edge
- Extra RWR antenna above brake chute fairing
- Retrofitted Martin-Baker Mk 10 ejection seat
- No fin fillet
- Mainly US avionics
- Broad-chord, side-by-side antennas added below nose
- Solid nose without radar
- Retractable airfield arrester hook in ventral fairing (shown extended)
- No leading edge RWR antenna fairing

Mirage 5E2

- Alpha Jet MS2 avionics system with SAGEM Uliss INS, Una 81 nav/attack unit and Thomson-CSF VE110C HUD
- Fin fillet (not on Abu Dhabi, Belgian or Pakistani Mirage 5s)
- TRT AHV9 radar altimeter
- Thomson-CSF TMV630 laser rangefinder in undernose fairing
- Rear hemisphere RWR fairing
- ESD Aïda ranging radar (not on Belgian, Colombian or Peruvian Mirage 5s)
- Forward hemisphere RWR antenna (RWR not fitted to Belgian, Colombian, Peruvian, Venezuelan and Zaïrean aircraft)

Above: A fully laden Mirage 5 clearly shows the new sixth and seventh pylons at the rear wingroot.

Below: Egypt's Mirage 5E2s were equipped to a high standard with RWRs, new avionics and even an undernose laser ranger.

Above: Belgian Mirage 5BAs are among the few with no ranging radar, and this allows the pitot to be carried centrally on the nose cone.

Below: Only a handful of Pakistan's Mirages are non-radar equipped Mirage 5PAs, as seen here. This aircraft serves with the Combat Commanders School.

The Mirage 5Js destined for Israel were eventually absorbed by the Armée de l'Air and served primarily with EC 13 at Colmar/Mayenheim, where three escadrilles continue to fly the aircraft.

Milan

Improvements in low-speed handling and short-field performance were sought through the Milan (Kite) programme undertaken in collaboration with Switzerland. This did not result in production, but better flying characteristics were obtained eventually with the fitment of canards to Israeli Kfirs and during upgrade programmes. First experiments centred on retractable nose-mounted 'moustaches', although the first three trials aircraft had these fixed, or only adjustable on the ground in 10° increments. These were Mirage IIIA No. 09, Mirage IIIRD No. 363 and Israeli Mirage 5J No. 2, whose appendices earned it the nickname 'Astérix'. The last-mentioned (the first with ground-adjustable canards) flew at Melun on 27 September 1968. The true Milan No. 01 (Mirage IIIR No. 344, fitted with a Mirage 5-style radar nose) flew with retractable moustaches 1 m (39¼ in) long on 24 May 1969, being followed by the Swiss evaluation aircraft Milan S No. 01 (IIIE No. 589) on 29 May 1970. In addition to being the first Mirage III with an Atar 09K-50, S-1 had an advanced nav/attack system taken from the Mirage F1, and including EMD Decca RDN72S Doppler, a Thomson CSF 121RS HUD and a Thomson-CSF LT102 laser designator in the nose. Canards were each 0.8 m (21½ in) long, had an area of 0.35 m² (3.77 sq ft) and were swept forward at 15°. Their deployment (by electric motor) took several seconds. Despite demonstrating a 12 per cent reduction in landing speed, and a 1,970-ft (300-m) reduction in distance, it was not adopted by the Swiss as its shortcomings included restricted downward view caused by the extra 3-4 units of Alpha on approach and landing, as well as the air vortices generated ahead of the engine intakes.

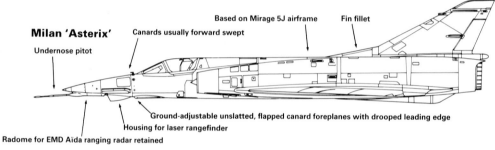

Milan S-01

Based on Mirage IIIE airframe

Curved leading edge to intake splitter plate

EMD Decca RDN72S Doppler without external bulge

Atar 09K-50 engine

Nose incorporates Thomson-CSF LT102 laser rangefinder and designator

New forward fuselage with electrically actuated retractable canard foreplanes swept forward by 15° when fully deployed

Milan 'Asterix'

Based on Mirage 5J airframe

Fin fillet

Canards usually forward swept

Undernose pitot

Ground-adjustable unslatted, flapped canard foreplanes with drooped leading edge

Housing for laser rangefinder

Radome for EMD Aïda ranging radar retained

Above: This early Dassault Mirage IIIA (09) served as a canard foreplane testbed for the Milan programme. The aircraft is seen here with a solid aluminium cover in place of its canopy. It was operated by the CEV.

Above: An unidentified Dassault test pilot poses alongside the little-known Mirage IIIRD that was fitted with fixed canard foreplanes early in the Milan programme. The canards were forward swept and extensively cambered.

Left: The dihedral on the Milan's foreplane often made it appear to be swept forward, but the sweep angle was much smaller than has often been supposed.

Right and far right: Two views of the Israeli Mirage 5J whose ground-adjustable retractable foreplanes (seen retracted and extended) earned it the nickname 'Astérix'.

Left and above: Despite the impression created by its radar nose, this aircraft, the Milan 01, was actually a converted Mirage IIIR, and marked one possible production standard with small-bore engine and Cyrano/Agave radar.

Right and below: The Milan S.01, as demonstrated to the Swiss, was a converted Mirage IIIE, with a recontoured nose housing a laser designator. The aircraft was also effectively the first Mirage 50, since it was the first of the deltas to be powered by an Atar 09K-50 engine.

Mirage 50

This out-of-sequence designation derives from fitment of an Atar 09K-50 powerplant in place of an 09C to both the basic Mirage III and non-radar 5. Similar in dimensions to its predecessor, the -50 develops 11,055 lb st (49.2 kN) 'dry' and 15,870 lb st (70.6 kN) with afterburning, its air mass flow being increased to 158 lb (72 kg) per second. All compressor stages are steel, but detail changes (such as provision for interior inspection by boroscope) are such that there is only 45 per cent parts commonality with the 09C. External signs of -50 installation are air intake splitter plates which, instead of being straight, curve forwards towards the point at which they meet the half-cone centrebody and a pair of cooling air intakes on the upper part of the rear fuselage. The Mirage 50 uses 90 per cent of the structural parts of the III or 5 and 95 per cent of the systems, while its additional thrust gives advantages such as a 15-20 per cent reduction in take-off . run; 1,896 lb (860 kg) extra gross weight; 87 miles (140 km) of additional range – or a combat radius of 807 miles (1300 km); sea-level climb rate increased 30 per cent to 607 ft (185 m) per second; 35 per cent reduction in time-to-height at Mach 2; a 0.5-1.0 gain in load factor during a tight turn; 6,562 ft (2000 m) increase in Mach 2 ceiling – i.e. 60,696 ft (18500 m); and typical patrol time increased by 40 per cent.

At first the Mirage 50 was seen as an uprated Mirage 5, with Aïda 2 ranging radar, TRT radio-altimeter, Crouzet air data computer and gyro weapons sight. Options

Mirage 50 demonstrator

Advanced new-generation avionics systems
Centrally mounted pitot with Cyrano or Agave, undernose with Aida ranging radar
Atar 09K-50 engine
No fin fillet
Airframe could be fitted with Cyrano IV multi-mode radar (shown) or Agave or Aïda 2 ranging radar
Auxiliary afterburner cooling intake

Indigenous ENAER Caiquen III RWR antennas
Provision for indigenous Eclipse chaff/flare dispenser
Mirage 50C
Atar 09K-50 engine
Curved leading edge to intake splitter plate
Twin air data probes ahead of windscreen
Mirage IIIE-style fuel tanks with weapons hardpoints
Chilean Mirage 50FC converted from Mirage 5F with similar ranging radar and undernose pitot
New-build Mirage 50C with Agave (?) radar in nose radome

were the 50A with Agave radar and 50C with Cyrano IV, and all could have EMD RND 72 Doppler coupled with a Crouzet 93 computer or a conventional INS. The non-radar option was backpedalled by Dassault in the 1980s, when the two versions promoted were redesignated Mirage 3/50 (Cyrano IV-M3) and 5/50 (Agave).

The Thomson-CSF Cyrano IV-M3 represents a considerable advance on the original Cyrano II. The -M3 combines the basic Series IV (as fitted to Mirage F1s) with technology developed for the RDM

and RDI radars (Mirage 2000) but is still compatible with the avionics of older-generation aircraft. Modular in design, it has air-to-air, -ground dand -sea modes, presenting information to the pilot in head-up and -down displays as well as providing navigation functions such as ground mapping, IFR letdown and iso-altitude splitting. INS and nav/attack computer are standard for this and the Mirage 5/50 – which can either be non-radar or mount the maritime-optimised Agave for use with Exocet anti-ship

missiles (see Mirage IIIE). Some Mirage 5/50 versions have the seven hardpoint option, but the norm is five, with individual load maxima of 2,601 lb (1180 kg) on the centreline, 3,704 lb (1680 kg) on the inboard wing position and 370 lb (168 kg) outboard, although the total must not exceed 8,818 lb (4000 kg). Improved reliability and accessibility features reduce maintenance man-hours per flying hour to 13.

Claimants to the title of Mirage 50 prototype are legion. The first Atar 09K

Above: Claimants to the title of Mirage 50 prototype are legion. This unprepossessing machine, wearing standard AA camouflage and national insignia, was the former Milan S-01, which was the first Mirage to fly with an Atar 09K-50.

Below: This former Mirage IIIR gained a radar nose when it became the Mirage 50 demonstrator. Its configuration foreshadowed that of the production Mirage 50C batch for Chile, the other FAC aircraft being ex-Armée de l'Air Mirage 5Fs with an Aïda ranging radar.

testbed was the Mirage IIIC-2, while the 09K-50 became airborne in the Milan S-01 (IIIE No. 589) on 29 May 1970. Next, four IIIR2Zs were exported to South Africa without fanfare, despite being the first 'production' aircraft. Then, on 15 April 1975, having relinquished its 'moustaches', the former Milan flew the official Mirage 50 'preliminary' prototype with an Aïda nose. It was supplanted on 15 May 1979 by the IIIR No. 301, now complete with search-radar nose (but lacking VOR aerials) and also purporting to be No. 01.

First Mirage 50s to be exported under that designation were eight Mirage 50FCs delivered to Chile during 1980 in the form of re-engined AA Mirage 5Fs, the initial new production concerning a further six

for the same customer, designated Mirage 50C and fitted with search radar in the nose, radar warning receivers (initially only rear-facing) and fin-base fillet. Radar is believed to be Agave, as the length of the radome is between the full-size unit for Cyrano and the small cone needed for Aïda. Twin air data probes are ahead of the windscreen (as per Mirage IIIR). Also delivered were three Mirage 50DC two-seat trainers, the first two apparently having Atar 09C-3 powerplants.

Venezuela is standardising its fleet on the 50EV and 50DV trainer, acquiring six and one respectively from new production, plus nine and two by conversion, as described in the section on Mirage upgrades.

Above: The choice of colour scheme on this demonstrator made it plain that Dassault expected the Mirage 50 to appeal most to African and Middle Eastern nations. In the event, the aircraft sold only in Latin America.

Below: A Chilean Mirage 50C gets airborne. Chilean Mirage 50Cs are believed to be equipped with the Agave radar, and serve with Grupo 4 at Santiago alongside up-engined ex-French Mirage 5Fs which were redesignated Mirage 50FC in service.

Mirage 50M

At the 1987 Paris air show, Dassault displayed statically a non-radar Mirage 50M, apparently the 3NG prototype. The designation was assigned to cover upgrades of the basic Mirage III/5 with canards but not the fly-by-wire system. Numerous combinations of improving features are offered under the broad Mirage 50M heading and are covered in the section on Mirage upgrades.

The Mirage IIING prototype served as the demonstrator for the Mirage 50M, which would have been a non fly-by-wire canard-equipped Mirage 50. The aircraft is fitted with a Mirage F1-style inflight-refuelling probe.

Mirage 3NG

The most far-reaching upgrade proposed for the Mirage III was a conversion to relaxed stability configuration and fitment of a fly-by-wire control system borrowed from the Mirage 2000. The Mirage 50 definitive prototype (IIIR No. 301) took to the air on 21 December 1982 wearing a blue and white colour scheme and fitted with foreplanes on the upper sides of the engine air intakes. Marked 'Mirage IIING' but referred to in company literature as the 3NG, this 'Nouvelle Génération' aircraft also featured a leading-edge wing extension (known as APEX) below the

The Mirage IIING prototype (which later became the Mirage 50M demonstrator) had previously served as one of the Mirage 50 prototypes, and had begun life as a Mirage IIIR.

canards, an inertial navigation system, CRT HUD, optional laser rangefinder, a Martin-Baker Mk 10 zero-zero ejection seat, detachable refuelling probe ahead of the cockpit and the Mirage 2000's Thomson-CSF/ESD radar warning system comprising a rearward-facing antenna near the top of the fin and two forward sensors close to the wingtips. Later, it was repainted in green and sand camouflage and fitted with

a Cyrano IV-type nose radome (more pointed than Cyrano II of the Mirage IIIE) although Agave was offered as an alternative. Compared with the Mirage 50, refuelling probe fitment involves addition of a small nose 'plug', increasing fuselage length by 3½ in (90 mm), while APEX slightly increased wing area to 376.7 sq ft (35 m²). Two further hardpoints were added beneath the air intakes to increase weapon attachments to nine, including four underwing.

Empty weight is upped to 16,387 lb (7432 kg) and a further tonne is allowed on maximum weight, raising that to 32,409 lb (14700 kg). Performance increases are in many respects similar to those obtained by the Mirage 50, the take-off run being further shortened – by 25 per cent in the case of an aircraft at maximum weight, compared with a Mirage IIIE – and instantaneous turn improved by 40 per cent. One shortcoming was in ceiling: down 4,921 ft (1500 m) to 54,134 ft (16500 m). This Dassault offer to turn a Mirage III almost into a Mirage 2000 has so far failed to find a backer.

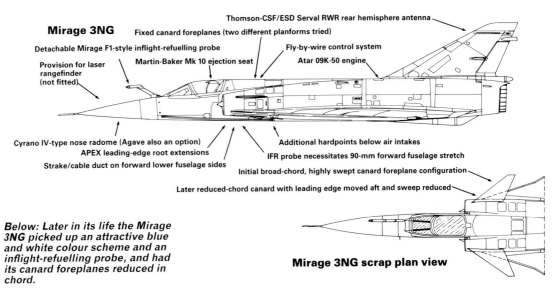

Mirage 3NG

Thomson-CSF/ESD Serval RWR rear hemisphere antenna

Fixed canard foreplanes (two different planforms tried)

Detachable Mirage F1-style inflight-refuelling probe

Fly-by-wire control system

Provision for laser rangefinder (not fitted)

Martin-Baker Mk 10 ejection seat

Atar 09K-50 engine

Cyrano IV-type nose radome (Agave also an option)

Additional hardpoints below air intakes

APEX leading-edge root extensions

IFR probe necessitates 90-mm forward fuselage stretch

Strake/cable duct on forward lower fuselage sides

Initial broad-chord, highly swept canard foreplane configuration

Later reduced-chord canard with leading edge moved aft and sweep reduced

Mirage 3NG scrap plan view

Below: Later in its life the Mirage 3NG picked up an attractive blue and white colour scheme and an inflight-refuelling probe, and had its canard foreplanes reduced in chord.

The blue and white *3NG* was demonstrated at *Farnborough* and at *Paris*, but export orders for this *FBW* Mirage, effectively a poor man's Mirage *2000*, did not materialise.

Mirage IIIEX

This version, announced at the 1989 Paris show, refers to a further upgrading option, closely related to the Mirage IIIE (of which several were by then being retired from AA service and thus becoming available for rework and export). Fitted with the more pointed, Cyrano IV-type nose, the IIIEX deletes the Doppler blister but is unique in having the two underfuselage cable ducts fitted to the two-seat, non-radar Mirage III/5D. Other features include a detachable refuelling probe and fixed canards. None has been sold.

The Mirage IIIEX represents the most advanced standard to which Dassault will upgrade an existing customer's Mirages, as described below.

Mirage III/5/50 upgrades

Both Dassault and IAI are offering upgrades to other Mirage operators, which are able to pick and choose from a broad range of extra features, all of which aim to give the basic Mirage III/5/50 increased and improved operational capability, effectively turning near-obsolete aircraft into credible modern warplanes. Some customers demand a high degree of participation by local industry, while others are content to let contractors' working parties modify the aircraft in country, or return their aircraft to the factory for upgrade. The list of possible changes include installation of an Atar 09K-50 turbojet (as used in the Mirage 50) to improve performance, and the addition of canard foreplanes and other aerodynamic refinements to improve handling and expand the flight envelope. Modern avionics are offered, including a new INS, cockpit CRT displays, a modern wide-angle HUD, and HOTAS controls. Operational equipment can also be

improved, and Dassault offers Cyrano IV or Agave radar, a Thomson-CSF laser rangefinder, a Mirage F1-style inflight-refuelling probe, single-point pressure refuelling, zero-zero Martin-Baker ejection seats, a liquid oxygen breathing system, nosewheel steering, conformal fuel tanks totalling 264 Imp gal (1200 litres), and provision for a 'buddy' refuelling pod. Provision is also made for a range of ECM, reconnaissance, laser spot tracking, laser designation and guidance, IR imagery and other pods.

This Venezuelan Mirage IIIDV has been fully upgraded by Dassault, with new avionics, new defensive systems, a structural rework and fixed canard foreplanes.

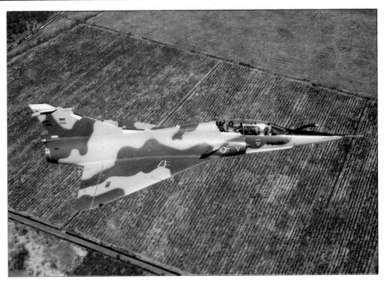

105

Dassault upgrades

Dassault has offered to its Mirage customers upgrade programmes which have been largely based on its Mirage IIIEX and Mirage 50M. These have been centred on the provision of small fixed canards and a detachable Mirage F1-style refuelling probe, with the addition of modern French avionics and ECM/ESM systems and compatability with new-generation French weapons. Depending on the options selected, a customer can turn its first-generation Mirage III into a Mirage 50, or an aircraft with many of the features of the latest Mirage 2000, at a fraction of the cost.

Comprehensive overhauls of Libyan Mirage 5s were undertaken in France during the early 1980s and presumably involved the addition of new systems and equipment. No details have been revealed, but it is understood that the work undertaken fell far short of later modification programmes.

Some 12 Peruvian Mirage 5P/P3s and three 5DP/DP3s have been modified in a Dassault-led programme, agreed in 1982 and undertaken locally. Now to 5P4 and 5DP4 standard, they have a Litton LN-33 INS, Thomson-CSF HUD, CSF laser rangefinder, new nav/comm avionics, a radar warning receiver (believed to be a Thomson-CSF SERVAL), a fixed inflight-refuelling probe and provision to launch MATRA R.550 Magic 2 IR-homing AAMs. Proposals to fit Cyrano IV and/or Agave radar have not been implemented. Airframe changes on single-seat aircraft include underfuselage cable ducts as fitted to Mirage IIID and Mirage 5 two-seat trainers.

During 1988 and 1989 Dassault modified five ex-French Mirage IIIEs and two IIIBEs to revised IIIEBR and IIIDBR standard with canards, pressure refuelling, improved DEFA cannon and provision for Magic 2 AAMs (plus VOR aerials and a fin-root fillet), and delivered the aircraft to Brazil. The surviving 10 EBRs and two DBRs of the aircraft originally delivered to Brazil began a similar rework in Brazil in 1989.

Six surviving single-seat Venezuelan Mirage III/5s and two tandem-seat trainers are being converted to Mirage 50EV and DV standard respectively, to augment

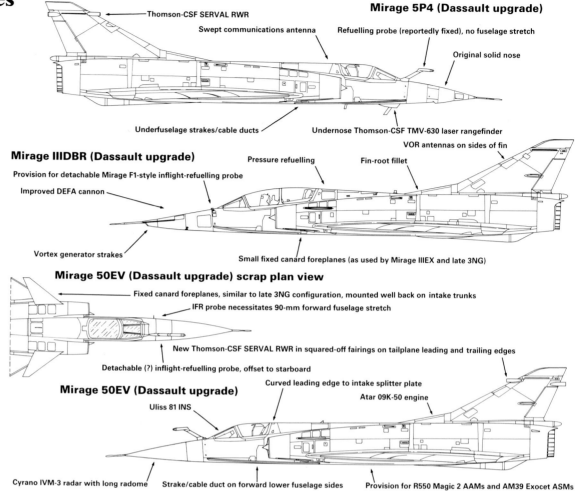

Mirage 5P4 (Dassault upgrade)
- Thomson-CSF SERVAL RWR
- Swept communications antenna
- Refuelling probe (reportedly fixed), no fuselage stretch
- Original solid nose
- Underfuselage strakes/cable ducts
- Undernose Thomson-CSF TMV-630 laser rangefinder

Mirage IIIDBR (Dassault upgrade)
- Provision for detachable Mirage F1-style inflight-refuelling probe
- Improved DEFA cannon
- Pressure refuelling
- Fin-root fillet
- VOR antennas on sides of fin
- Vortex generator strakes
- Small fixed canard foreplanes (as used by Mirage IIIEX and late 3NG)

Mirage 50EV (Dassault upgrade) scrap plan view
- Fixed canard foreplanes, similar to late 3NG configuration, mounted well back on intake trunks
- IFR probe necessitates 90-mm forward fuselage stretch
- New Thomson-CSF SERVAL RWR in squared-off fairings on tailplane leading and trailing edges
- Detachable (?) inflight-refuelling probe, offset to starboard

Mirage 50EV (Dassault upgrade)
- Curved leading edge to intake splitter plate
- Atar 09K-50 engine
- Uliss 81 INS
- Cyrano IVM-3 radar with long radome
- Strake/cable duct on forward lower fuselage sides
- Provision for R550 Magic 2 AAMs and AM39 Exocet ASMs

1990-91 deliveries from Dassault of newly built Mirage 50EVs and DVs. The FAV fleet will then be standardised on aircraft powered by Atar 09K-50 turbojets, with Cyrano IV-M3 radar. All are also being upgraded by Dassault at Merignac with canard foreplanes, ULISS 81 INS and inflight-refuelling probes, plus provision for Magic 2 IR AAMs and AM39 anti-ship missiles.

Below: Peru's Mirages have been brought up to Mirage 5P4 standards, with a comprehensive new avionics fit including Mirage 2000-generation RWRs, but still without radar.

Above: Brazilian Mirage IIIEBRs and DBRs have been upgraded by Dassault in France and in-country.

Right: This Mirage 50EV is seen in Venezuela, awaiting respray, following its upgrade.

Although little changed by even the most extensive upgrade, the overall appearance of a reworked Mirage (like this 50EV) is surprisingly modern.

This fully marked-up Mirage 50EV is back in service with Grupo Aéreo de Caza 11 at El Libertador after rework.

Israeli upgrades

With an eye to selling surplus Kfirs to countries to which the J79 powerplant cannot be exported because of US restrictions, IAI obtained five Atar 09K-50s in 1989. The first aircraft to be re-engined was due to start trials late in 1990, becoming effectively a Mirage 50 with Israeli avionics. IAI has also conducted a great deal of work in devising upgrade programmes for existing Mirage users to turn their aircraft into 'Kfirs', with or without J79 engines. This expertise resulted in Chile's ENAER Pantera and South Africa's Atlas Cheetah, which are described separately. Other upgrades have seldom been quite so extensive, and are outlined here.

Beginning in 1982, when their performance in the Falklands War with the United Kingdom had shown equipment and performance shortcomings, Argentina's IAI Daggers were upgraded with Israeli-supplied avionics upgrade kits under the 'Finger' Ia, IIa and IIIa programmes. Similar upgrades were applied to Argentina's surviving Mirage IIIEAs, and to the Mirage IIICJs delivered from Israel after the war, and to the ex-Peruvian Mirage 5Ps. They now possess a HUD, INS, radar warning and deception jamming equipment, a laser rangefinder and an optional refuelling probe. They have been armed with Rafael Shafrir Mk IV IR-homing AAMs to augment the DEFA 553 cannon and locally-produced FAS 260, 280, 300 and 500 bombs.

Before and after: Similar angles show two Colombian Mirage 5COAs before and after modification by IAI working parties. The aircraft on the right could almost be a Kfir, if it did not retain its Atar engine.

Mirage 5COA (IAI upgrade) scrap plan view

Kfir C2/C7 nose grafted on ahead of plug

Kfir-style nose vortex-generator strakes

Constant-section plug ahead of windscreen gives discontinuity

Kfir-style bolt-on inflight-refuelling probe with external pipe running back past starboard side of cockpit

'75 per cent' (area?) fixed Kfir-style canard foreplanes

Mirage 5COA (IAI upgrade)

ELTA ranging radar

Undernose pitot

Increased-height cooling airscoops added

Plans to re-engine with F404 or J79 abandoned

Camera window in ventral fairing

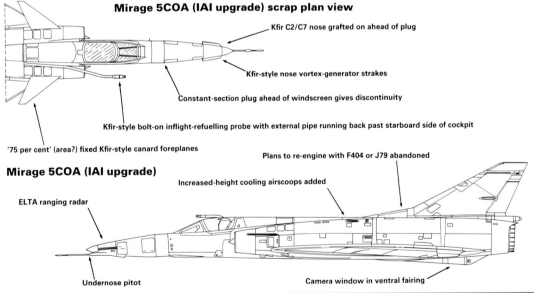

Left: This shot of a Colombian aircraft undergoing rework clearly shows some of the major changes made, including canards.

Colombia's two-seaters are equipped with reduced-area canard foreplanes, but do not have a Kfir-style nose.

Colombian Mirage 5COAs and 5CODs have been updated with Kfir-style canard foreplanes, though these are said to be of reduced size, 75 per cent canards on the single-seaters and 50 per cent canards on the trainers. On the single-seaters, Kfir-style vortex generator strakes are also added to the sides of the nose, which has been extended by the addition of a constant section plug ahead of the windscreen. Israeli avionics have also been integrated, almost certainly including an ELTA ranging radar. Single-seaters and trainers have all been fitted with Kfir-style inflight-refuelling probes. The original proposal to fit Kfir-C7 avionics and General Electric F404 reheated turbofans was over-ambitious, and conversion to full Kfir standards with J79 engines was too expensive.

Indigenous upgrades

Several Mirage customers have upgraded their own aircraft, with a lesser degree of assistance from Dassault or IAI. Such programmes have often been similar in scope to those offered by the French and Israeli programmes, but have kept foreign exchange expenditure to a minimum and have provided work for indigenous industry. In Switzerland, where the Mirage IIIS had been built under licence, an ambitious upgrade programme was finalised during the early 1980s. A Mirage IIIS with canards and nose strakes was flown on 23 August 1983, but several shapes of foreplane were tunnel-tested before the design was finalised. Having rejected an Israeli upgrade offer as too expensive, Switzerland adopted a canard only two-thirds the size of the Kfir's in order to minimise the airframe strengthening required. There is a dissimilarity in positioning of vortex generators, the Swiss having theirs at the intersection of radome and pitot probe to generate controlled and symmetrical vortices and allow higher angles of attack to be reached. Other changes planned include the incorporation of audible/visual angle-of-attack warning, Martin-Baker Mk 6 zero-zero ejection seats, IR jammers, Dalmo Victor radar warning receivers, new VHF radios, improved gunblast deflectors, wing refurbishing, a braking parachute and provision on the centreline pylon for an Israeli 160-Imp gal (730-litre) drop tank. The proposed Northrop AN/ALQ-171 jamming system was cancelled, and an alternative is being sought.

In Belgium, where a fleet of Mirage 5s had been built under licence, details were agreed in 1989 of a Mirage Safety Improvement Programme (MirSIP), far less comprehensive than originally proposed. Five 5BD trainers and 15 5BA attack aircraft are being updated by SABCA with canard foreplanes, a Ferranti HUD, Thomson-CSF TMV 630 laser rangefinder, SAGEM ULISS 92 INS, SAGEM UTR 90 nav/attack computer, single-point pressure refuelling, liquid oxygen breathing system, strobe anti-collision lights and a complete rewiring. Martin-Baker Mk 10 zero-zero ejection seats are also being fitted. The impending withdrawal of Belgium's Mirage fleet in December 1993 did not halt the update programme, which will be completed in November because cancellation charges would have been prohibitive. Instead, Belgium hopes to sell the upgraded aircraft.

Mirage IIIO(R) indigenous recce upgrade

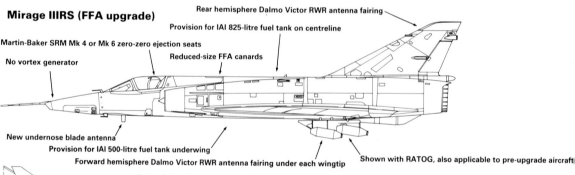

Radome replaced with streamlined fairing, painted black to resemble Cyrano IV radome

Radar removed

Camera bay housing single panoramic camera

Mirage IIIRS (FFA upgrade)

Rear hemisphere Dalmo Victor RWR antenna fairing

Provision for IAI 825-litre fuel tank on centreline

Martin-Baker SRM Mk 4 or Mk 6 zero-zero ejection seats

Reduced-size FFA canards

No vortex generator

New undernose blade antenna

Provision for IAI 500-litre fuel tank underwing

Forward hemisphere Dalmo Victor RWR antenna fairing under each wingtip

Shown with RATOG, also applicable to pre-upgrade aircraft

Swiss-designed vortex generators at intersection of pitot and forward part of radome

Refurbished wing

Mirage IIIS (FFA upgrade)

Short-span, relatively broad-chord fixed canard foreplanes

Canard area reduced to allow lighter structure

Reduced-size FFA canards

Mirage IIIBS (FFA upgrade)

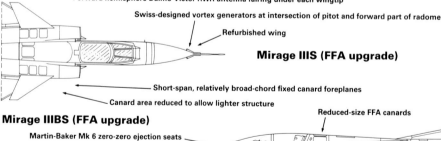

Martin-Baker Mk 6 zero-zero ejection seats

IIIDS has simple strake like that fitted to Mirage IIIDBR, IIIBS uses IIIS strake

A Spanish programme to update its surviving 18 Mirage IIIEEs and five Mirage IIIDEs has been cancelled and the aircraft have been prematurely retired. The aircraft were to have been modified by CASA and CESELSA with Emerson Electric AN/APQ-159 radar, a Honeywell AN/AYK-1 mission computer, HUD, radar warning receiver, tactical navigation equipment, multi-function displays, pressure refuelling, new radios, ILS, IFF-SIF, HOTAS controls, radar altimeter, TACAN and inflight-refuelling probes. Two-seat aircraft were also to have been fitted to carry 'buddy' refuelling pods. This programme replaced an earlier plan involving Israeli canards and avionics.

Other nations to have upgraded their Mirages include Egypt, where some EAF Mirage 5s are understood to have received improved avionics in an unannounced and now completed programme.

Pakistan has also upgraded some of its Mirages, having fitted a Litton LW-33 nav/attack system to non-radar Mirage 5PAs during the early 1980s. Pakistan bought 50 Australian Mirage IIIOs in 1990, some of which will be upgraded for local use and others resold after modification at Kamra. (Because of delays in selecting a successor, RAAF Mirages had been fitted with new wings only a few years before their retirement.)

Swiss Mirages are being indigenously upgraded, with reduced-size canard foreplanes and much new equipment. Vortex generators are added on the nose.

Top right: An upgraded Mirage IIIRS lands. The reconnaissance aircraft do not have the pitot-mounted vortex generators, but have the same avionics upgrade as the IIIS single-seat fighters.

Right: Switzerland chose to use relatively small canard foreplanes for its upgrade, to reduce loads on the airframe. The aircraft also have a widely flaring vortex generator mounted on the pitot tube.

IAI Nesher and Dagger

To replace the 50 Mirage 5Js and two 5DJs embargoed by the French government, Israel 'acquired' plans for the aircraft and its Atar 09C turbojet, to be built without the benefit of permission by Israel Aircraft Industries (IAI) and Bet-Shemesh Engines respectively. Fifty-one single-seat and 10 two-seat airframes were produced locally as the Nesher (Eagle) S and T, with serial numbers 'scrambled' in the 500-599 range. The prototype flew in September 1969 and included some avionics built by Elta Electronics and a Martin-Baker Mk 6 zero-zero ejection seat.

Deliveries began in 1972 and the aircraft saw service in the Yom Kippur War the following year, flying in the air defence role with IAI Shafrir IR AAMs. Despite being fitted with a large, sharply-pointed radome (as per Cyrano IV) there is no evidence to suggest that the Nesher was equipped with anything more than a ranging radar, its defensive tasks being undertaken only in fair weather. One-quarter of the 450 Arab aircraft claimed destroyed in the 1973 Yom Kippur War are attributed to Neshers. Armament and capabilities are identical to the Mirage 5. Between 1978 and 1982, 35 Ss and four Ts (apparently all the survivors) were supplied to Argentina, where they became known as Dagger As and Bs respectively. Though armed with Shafrir, they functioned as fighter-bombers during the 1982 Falklands War. They were later upgraded.

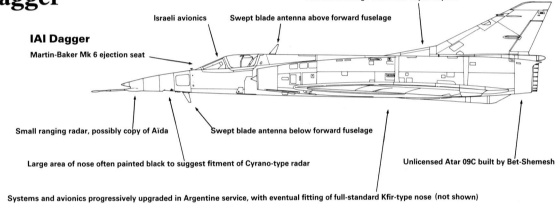

IAI Dagger

- Unlicensed Mirage 5 airframe copied by IAI
- Israeli avionics
- Swept blade antenna above forward fuselage
- Martin-Baker Mk 6 ejection seat
- Small ranging radar, possibly copy of Aïda
- Swept blade antenna below forward fuselage
- Large area of nose often painted black to suggest fitment of Cyrano-type radar
- Unlicensed Atar 09C built by Bet-Shemesh

Systems and avionics progressively upgraded in Argentine service, with eventual fitting of full-standard Kfir-type nose (not shown)

IAI Dagger
(Argentine Finger-I upgrade)

- Basic Dagger airframe refurbished
- No nose extension plug
- Swept blade antenna above forward fuselage
- Nose-mounted vortex-generator strakes
- Unidentified strake below nose
- Conical radome houses Elta EL-2001 ranging radar
- Completely new Kfir-style nose

Surviving Neshers were exported to Argentina as Daggers, where the type remains in service, having been used intensively during the Falklands War.

An IAI Nesher in Israeli service, where the aircraft was used primarily as a fighter-bomber. Noses were painted black to give the appearance of a radome.

Above: After the Falklands War, Argentina's Daggers were upgraded with new avionics which gave the nose a completely new, Kfir-like appearance.

Below: Compare the nose of this 'Finger 1' upgraded Dagger with that of the unmodified aircraft illustrated at the base of page 109. Vortex generators are fitted.

Above: A modernised Dagger taxis. The aircraft can carry Dassault or IAI underwing fuel tanks, of various sizes and capacities.

Below: Argentina's Daggers are being repainted in this unusual overall dark grey colour scheme, similar to the colour applied to South African Cheetahs.

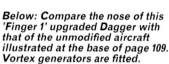

IAI Kfir 1 and F-21

Israel's long-term aim in acquiring Mirage 5 data was to produce a better aircraft than the original. Following the last Nesher, IAI immediately began building the Kfir (Lion Cub) for the IDF/AF, this variant differing substantially from the basic Mirage. While producing Neshers and putting its French-built Mirage IIICJs through a life-extension programme, Israel undertook trials with a Mirage IIIB trainer (988) fitted with a General Electric J79-GE-17 (later J1E) reheated turbojet – as in the McDonnell Douglas F-4 Phantoms it had just ordered from the USA. The J79 Mirage flew on 21 September 1970. The true Kfir prototype, a Nesher airframe (788) converted on the production line, flew on 4 June 1973, code-named Ra'am A, and was followed by the second prototype (712, another Nesher) on 7 August 1974.

Compared with the Atar 09C, GE's engine is 25¼ in (64 cm) shorter – at 17 ft 4½ in (5.30 m) – and of slightly reduced diameter: 3 ft 3 in (0.99 m) versus 3 ft 4¼ in (1.02 m). At 3,835 lb (1740 kg) it is 715 lb (324 kg) heavier, the pay-off being a dry thrust of 11,890 lb (52.89 kN) and a reheated rating of 17,900 lb (79.62 kN), which is 2,027 lb st (9.01 kN) up on even the 09K-50. As a consequence, the J79 has an 11 per cent greater mass flow – demanding larger air intakes – and a substantially higher turbine inlet temperature of 954°C (1,750°F), resulting in its external walls being almost twice as hot.

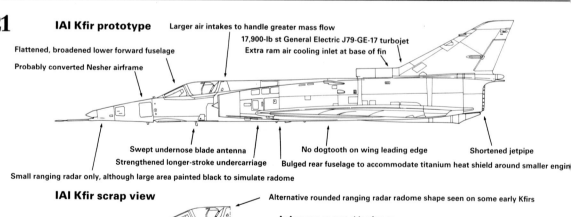

IAI Kfir prototype

Larger air intakes to handle greater mass flow

Flattened, broadened lower forward fuselage

17,900-lb st General Electric J79-GE-17 turbojet

Extra ram air cooling inlet at base of fin

Probably converted Nesher airframe

Swept undernose blade antenna

No dogtooth on wing leading edge

Shortened jetpipe

Strengthened longer-stroke undercarriage

Bulged rear fuselage to accommodate titanium heat shield around smaller engine

Small ranging radar only, although large area painted black to simulate radome

IAI Kfir scrap view

Alternative rounded ranging radar radome shape seen on some early Kfirs

AoA sensor on port side of nose

Some early Kfirs had nose painted black to simulate larger radome for spurious attack r

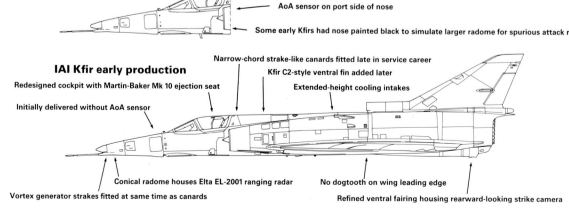

IAI Kfir early production

Narrow-chord strake-like canards fitted late in service career

Kfir C2-style ventral fin added later

Redesigned cockpit with Martin-Baker Mk 10 ejection seat

Extended-height cooling intakes

Initially delivered without AoA sensor

Conical radome houses Elta EL-2001 ranging radar

No dogtooth on wing leading edge

Vortex generator strakes fitted at same time as canards

Refined ventral fairing housing rearward-looking strike camera

The first production **IAI K**fir was preceded by a number of re-engined and converted Mirages and Neshers.

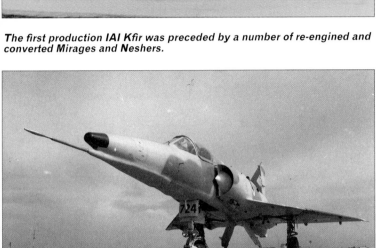

IAI Kfirs on the production line. The aircraft on the right of the picture have their noses painted to simulate radomes. It is interesting that the two types of nose colour scheme were applied at the same time.

Left: At least one early Kfir was fitted with a round-tipped radome for its Aïda ranging radome. This was not widely adopted, however.

Right: Some of the weapons available to the Israeli Kfir squadrons are ranged in front of an early aircraft. From the beginning, the Kfir was primarily a fighter-bomber.

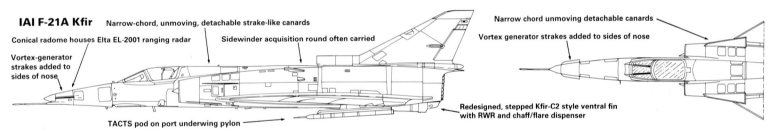

IAI F-21A Kfir — Narrow-chord, unmoving, detachable strake-like canards — Narrow chord unmoving detachable canards

Conical radome houses Elta EL-2001 ranging radar — Sidewinder acquisition round often carried — Vortex generator strakes added to sides of nose

Vortex-generator strakes added to sides of nose

Redesigned, stepped Kfir-C2 style ventral fin with RWR and chaff/flare dispenser

TACTS pod on port underwing pylon

Only a titanium shield could protect the airframe, as a result of which the Kfir has a bulged rear fuselage, despite its smaller engine. Demands for extra cooling air are met by an intake in the extended base of the fin and an extra four scoops on the fuselage sides, and the tailpipe is some 2 ft (0.61 m) shorter.

Other changes are a strengthened undercarriage with longer-stroke oleos, a flatter and wider forward underfuselage section and a redesigned cockpit incorporating a Martin-Baker Mk 10 ejection seat. Following introduction of the Kfir-C2, early aircraft were converted to Kfir-C1 standard with smaller-sized canards and nose strakes, plus an angle-of-attack sensor vane on the port side of the forward fuselage. Internal armament is two Israeli-built DEFA 30-mm cannon, and the nose contains an Elta EL-2001 ranging radar rather than the French Aïda. Early colour drawings of the Kfir showed an Aïda-type radome, but all appear to have had the double-cone shape of an EL-2001 cover. Reports of an interceptor version with search radar appear to have been generated by second prototype (712), which had the area behind its small radome painted a similar matt black. 'Clean' take-off weight of a Kfir 1 is 22,905 lb (10390 kg) and maximum is 32,408 lb (14700 kg).

Deliveries began in April 1975, but in 1985-88, 25 survivors were leased to the US Marine Corps (13) and Navy (12) as 'aggressor' trainers under the designation F-21A.

The **US Navy** leased **IAI K**firs (upgraded to **Kfir-C1** standards with intake-mounted canard strakes) for the adversary role under the designation **F-21A**. The aircraft served with **VF-43** until replaced by **F-16N**s.

Dassault Mirage III/5/50 Variants

Above: This F-21A carries a range instrumentation pod under the port wing, to allow real-time monitoring of engagements and in-depth post-flight analysis.

Below: With the return of the US Marine Corps aircraft to Israel at the end of their lease, the status of the original Kfir and Kfir-C1 is uncertain.

Above: Three differently coloured F-21As of the US DoD's second batch. They were leased to the US Marine Corps for adversary training until replaced by F-5E Tiger IIs, which some saw as a retrograde step.

IAI Kfir-C2

The 'C2' is the definitive, canard version of the Kfir, revealed in 1976. Compared with its immediate predecessor, the C2 features (apart from the obvious foreplanes, totalling 17.87 sq ft/1.66 m² and requiring local structural reinforcement) aerodynamic changes in the form of a small strake on each side of the nose and 'dog tooth' wing leading edges – the last-mentioned augmented on some aircraft by small fences at one-third span. These changes add 187 lb (85 kg) to the structural weight. The C2 has better sustained turning capability with improved lateral, longitudinal and directional control, a low gust response, improved handling at all angles of attack and reduced take-off and landing distances, but canards can be quickly removed, if required, at the expense of performance.

The Kfir-C2 introduced new, much larger canard foreplanes, which can be removed if required. They provide such an improvement in performance that they are a virtually permanent fixture.

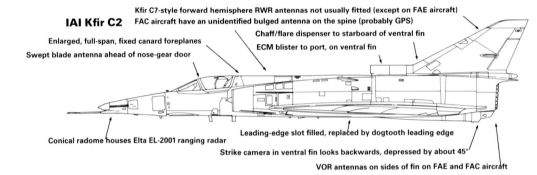

IAI Kfir C2

Kfir C7-style forward hemisphere RWR antennas not usually fitted (except on FAE aircraft)
FAC aircraft have an unidentified bulged antenna on the spine (probably GPS)
Chaff/flare dispenser to starboard of ventral fin
Enlarged, full-span, fixed canard foreplanes
ECM blister to port, on ventral fin
Swept blade antenna ahead of nose-gear door
Conical radome houses Elta EL-2001 ranging radar
Leading-edge slot filled, replaced by dogtooth leading edge
Strike camera in ventral fin looks backwards, depressed by about 45°
VOR antennas on sides of fin on FAE and FAC aircraft

Kfir-C2s differ from the Mirage IIIE in the following basic areas: length overall 51 ft 4¼ in (15.65 m); height 14 ft 11¼ in (4.55 m); empty weight of 16,060 lb (7285 kg); internal fuel of 713 Imp gal (3243 litres); 35,715 lb (16200 kg)

maximum take-off weight; maximum speed in excess of Mach 2.3, or 863 mph (1389 km/h) at sea level; initial climb rate of 45,930 ft/min (14000 m/min); and a 58,000 ft (17680 m) stabilised ceiling. Combat radius with drop-tanks is 482 miles (776 km) as an interceptor or 737 miles (1186 km) with 2,600 lb (1179 kg) of bombs.

Canards and strakes were first flown on the J79-engined Mirage IIIB Technolog (988) on 16 July 1974, the aircraft by then

having a solid nose and underfuselage cable ducts. The Ra'am A (788) was similarly modified and flew on 23 March 1975, but was lost in an accident on 25 May the same year. It was replaced by Kfir 1 714 a few months later. Kfir-C2 serial numbers covered the range 700-899 before extending into the 500 series. Late-production aircraft reportedly have EL/M-2001B ranging radar. Other equipment includes an MBT twin-computer flight

Nose contours

All Kfirs have a long, slender nose packed with avionics but lacking a modern multi-mode radar. A small conical radome covers the antenna for an Elta EL/M-2001B ranging radar. The pitot probe is underslung and a pair of strakes on the sides of the nose generates powerful vortices at high angles of attack, improving controllability.

Armament

Ecuador's Kfirs are primarily used in the intercept role, although they are part of a multi-role wing and train in the fighter-bomber role. The aircraft are normally armed with a pair of Rafael Shafrir IR-homing air-to-air missiles, and a variety of US or Israeli free-fall bombs. They retain the Kfir's standard internal armament of a pair of Rafael-built DEFA 553 30-mm cannon, each with 125 rounds of ammunition. The FAE aircraft do not appear to have the extra hardpoints below the intake ducts fitted to other Kfir-C7s.

Export Kfirs

Kfir exports have always been hampered by tight US regulations governing the re-export of sensitive US technology, primarily the J79 engine. There have often been suspicions that such regulations have been applied with particular rigour in order to encourage potential Kfir customers to purchase a US-built alternative. Ecuador's interest in the Kfir dated from 1979, when the US decided that the country could receive the J79, having previously been offered only the Atar-engined Nesher. Ecuador's aircraft are prominently marked as Kfir-C2s, but incorporate many of the advanced avionics systems of the later C7. The aircraft have fin-mounted VOR antennas. Colombian Kfirs do not have the later RWR, but are armed with the more advanced Python AAM.

Canard foreplanes

Fixed canard foreplanes reduce take-off run by about 1,500 ft and have a similarly dramatic effect on turn performance. IAI also claims an extension in airframe life, on the basis that they reduce stress on the foreplanes and fuselage.

Wing

The Kfir retains the basic Mirage delta wing, with few modifications. The leading edge 'sawcut' slots are filled in and the conical cambered leading edge is extended on the outboard section, with a dogtooth discontinuity. This improves high AoA handling by generating a strong vortex which energises air flow over the elevons.

Engine

The Kfir is powered by a single General Electric J79-J1E augmented turbojet rated at 17,860 lb st with reheat. The J1E is a modified version of the J79-GE-17 and is claimed to be the most powerful version of the J79 in production. The J79 engine was chosen for the Kfir when French support for Israeli Mirages was disrupted by arms embargos, while US support for US-built aircraft continued. The J79 was already in use to power Israeli F-4E Phantoms, and this made it doubly attractive as a powerplant for the Israeli's new unlicensed Mirage copy. The J79 requires bigger intakes for its higher mass flow, although a smaller engine requires a bulged rear fuselage to accommodate the titanium heat shield. Cooling requirements are also increased.

IAI Kfir-C2

Although officially classified as a Kfir-C2, this aircraft seems to have been upgraded to virtually full C7 standards. It wears the colourful markings of Escuadrón de Combate 2113, part of the Fuerza Aérea Ecuatoriana's Grupo 211 at Taura. Ecuador took delivery of 10 C2s and two TC2s (and a sophisticated simulator) during 1982, losing one to a birdstrike in 1985 and another in a fatal take-off accident in May 1989. Some sources suggest that the total of 10 aircraft included the two-seaters. The squadron helped Colombian pilots convert to their Kfirs when they were delivered in June 1989. The Grupo's other two squadrons fly the Jaguar and Mirage F1.

Dorsal airscoop

A ram air inlet at the base of the fin provides extra cooling air for the hot-running J79 engine and is the Kfir's most obvious recognition feature.

control system, angle of attack sensor vane on the port side of the forward fuselage (retrofitted to early aircraft), Elbit S-8600 multi-mode navigation and weapons delivery system (alternatively Elbit/IAI WDNS-141), Tamam central air data computer and Israel Electro-Optics HUD. Weapons carried by the Kfir include Shafrir 2 and Python 3 IR AAMs and a broad range of bombs, rockets, jamming pods and chaff/flare dispensers. After delays with getting US approval to export the J79 powerplant, IAI sold 12 Kfir-C2s to Ecuador in 1982, their equipment including radar warning receivers and VOR. Another 12 were sold to Colombia from surplus stocks in 1988-89.

Left: Colombia's Kfir-C2s are very well equipped, with advanced avionics and RWR equipment, and have often been erroneously reported as being Kfir-C7s.

Above: One of Ecuador's Kfir-C2s in flight. A large number of IDF/AF Kfirs are now in storage, and may be exported to other customers.

IAI Kfir-C7

The last Kfir was built in 1986, late production aircraft from at least 1983 being to C7 standard with two additional hardpoints (making nine) beneath the engine air intakes; an engine overspeed provision known as 'combat plus', boosting thrust to 18,750 lb (83.41 kN) for a limited period; and revised avionics including a HOTAS cockpit. External stores load is raised to a maximum of 13,415 lb (6085 kg) and maximum weight goes up to 36,376 lb (16500 kg). At a combat weight of 20,660 lb (9371 kg), thrust:weight ratio is 0.91, compared with 0.87 for the C2, while positive g limit is 7.5 – although the IDF/AF imposes a limit of 6.7 to extend aircraft lives.

Equipment improvements involve a WDNS-391 weapons delivery and navigation system, an Elbit 82 stores management system, armament control display panel, video subsystems and the ability to release 'smart' weapons. Aerial refuelling provision with either probe or receptacle is optional. Most C2s in IDF/AF service have been upgraded to C7, and the potential is present to replace ranging radar by an Elta EL/M-2021 I/J-band multimode radar as installed in some of Israel's General Dynamics F-16 Fighting Falcons. Not all C2s had radar warning receivers – at least initially – but late-production machines have an Elisra SPS-200 comprising two hemispherical sensors under the lower forward fuselage and two on the fin, immediately above the rudder. Jamming pods such as the Elta E/L-8202 can be fitted on the port inboard wing pylon. Exports have involved 11 C7s to Colombia from Israeli surplus in 1988-89.

Above: The Kfir-C7 features extra hardpoints below the intake trunks, as seen in this photo of a fully-armed Israeli aircraft. The advanced RWR equipment has also been retrofitted to some C2s.

Right: An IDF/AF Kfir-C7 seen in typical air-to-air configuration, with four AAMs and a centreline fuel tank.

IAI Kfir C7

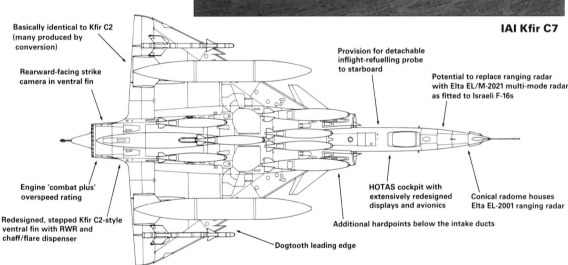

Basically identical to Kfir C2 (many produced by conversion)

Rearward-facing strike camera in ventral fin

Provision for detachable inflight-refuelling probe to starboard

Potential to replace ranging radar with Elta EL/M-2021 multi-mode radar as fitted to Israeli F-16s

Engine 'combat plus' overspeed rating

Redesigned, stepped Kfir C2-style ventral fin with RWR and chaff/flare dispenser

HOTAS cockpit with extensively redesigned displays and avionics

Conical radome houses Elta EL-2001 ranging radar

Additional hardpoints below the intake ducts

Dogtooth leading edge

IAI Kfir-T

In February 1981, IAI flew a two-seat Kfir-TC2, based on the C2. Its fuselage length is given by IAI as 53 ft 8 in (16.36 m), or 2 ft 4 in (0.71 m) longer than the original C2, although the manufacturer is also on record as saying that the second cockpit was installed without stretching the airframe. The answer appears to be the aircraft's longer nose, which is canted downwards for an improved view from the cockpit. IAI apparently has repositioned avionics and the air conditioning system from the centre fuselage to the elongated proboscis, as suggested by a cooling air scoop below the pitot probe anchor. The nose is sugar-loaf shaped, the sharper

There are two-seat trainer versions of both the Kfir-C2 and the Kfir-C7, respectively designated Kfir-TC2 and Kfir-TC7. The avionics displaced from the spine are accommodated in the lengthened nose.

taper being illustrated by a radome that lacks the dual-cone configuration of the C2's fitment and a strake which is well back from the tip. Ranging radar is fitted, as the TC2 is claimed to be fully combat capable – albeit with reduced internal fuel. With upgraded systems, the TC2 becomes TC7, two of each having been exported to Ecuador and Colombia.

The C7's range of weapons includes the two internal DEFA cannon with 140 rounds each; Shafrir 2 or Python 3 AAMs; Mk 82, 83, 84, M-117 and M-118 bombs; CBU-24, -49, TAL-1 and -2 cluster bombs; LAU-3A, -10A and -32A rocket pods; Shrike, Maverick and GBU-13 guided weapons; napalm, flares and various pods and tanks.

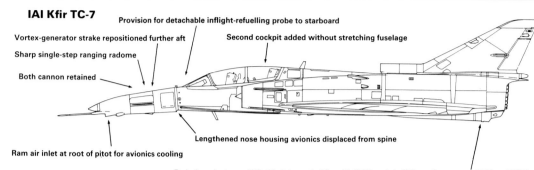

IAI Kfir TC-7

Provision for detachable inflight-refuelling probe to starboard

Vortex-generator strake repositioned further aft

Second cockpit added without stretching fuselage

Sharp single-step ranging radome

Both cannon retained

Lengthened nose housing avionics displaced from spine

Ram air inlet at root of pitot for avionics cooling

Redesigned, stepped Kfir C2-style ventral fin with RWR and chaff/flare dispenser on TC-2 and TC-7

IAI Nammer

In January 1988, IAI's Bedek Division revealed its Nammer (Tiger) project, for which a joint development partner was (and still is) being sought. Using the Kfir's wing, Nammer adds a further fuselage plug behind the cockpit, pushing the rear of the canopy ahead of the air intakes, but

wheelbase is retained unaltered, at 15 ft 11¾ in (4.87 m). Canards are fitted, and there is a refuelling probe relocated behind the cockpit, on the starboard side. Primary engine choice is the General Electric/Flygmotor F404/RM12 reheated turbofan, rated at 12,500 lb st (55.6 kN) dry and 18,140 lb st (80.7 kN) maximum, although use of a Pratt & Whitney PW1129 or SNECMA M53 would also be considered.

The rear fuselage reverts to a more Mirage-like shape, as does the fin, which is devoid of its base-mounted cooling air intake. External stores load increases only marginally, to 13,800 lb (6260 kg) in comparison with the Kfir-C7, but there is substantially more internal fuel: 828 Imp gal (3750 litres). Gross weight is 36,400 lb (16511 kg) – 40 per cent up on the Mirage IIIC – and speeds are comparable with the

Kfir. There is still a pair of 30-mm cannon (now with 140 rounds per gun), but the envisaged radar is an Elta EL/M-2032 pulse-Doppler with look-down capability. Typically, the Nammer would be able to mount a 60-minute CAP 859 miles (1382 km) from base, whereas the Kfir's range is only 548 miles (882 km).

ENAER Pantera 50C (Chile)

Empresa Nacional de Aeronautica de Chile (ENAER) is responsible for upgrading 13 Mirage 50FCs and 50Cs plus the two surviving 50DC trainers to Pantera (Panther) standard. The first, serial number 514, was converted early in 1986 as an aerodynamic testbed with Israeli-designed canards (broader in chord and less swept than on the Kfir-C2) and nose-strakes, but otherwise unaltered. Following completion of early trials, 514 underwent a second transformation with Israeli avionics and was rolled out on 14 October 1988 as the prototype Pantera with Elta EL/M-2001B pulse-Doppler range-finding radar. The nose has a constant-section plug inserted immediately ahead of the windscreen (reducing forward/downward vision) and an angle-of-attack sensor vane is on the port side, just ahead of the cockpit.

Associated modifications, also from the Kfir, comprise an inertial navigation system, computerised HUD and modified electrical, hydraulic and armament control systems. From local technology have come an ENAER Caiquen (Wild Goose) III radar warning receiver and Eclipse chaff/flare dispensers. A narrow blade aerial is fitted on the spine, but the aircraft has not

Curved leading edge to intake splitter plate

ENAER Caiquen III RWR antennas

Gun faired over on prototype at least

Atar 09K-50 engine

Kfir-style nose

Vortex-generator strakes

ENAER Pantera

Undernose pitot with underslung yaw vane

Elta EL/M-2001B pulse-Doppler rangefinding radar

Constant section 'plug'

Conversions from Mirage 50C and 50FC airframes

IAI-designed fixed canard foreplanes; broader chord and less sweep than those on Kfir

Top: The prototype Pantera, early in the development programme, had only canards and vortex generators to differentiate it from a standard Mirage 50C.

Right: The Pantera prototype now has a Kfir-style nose and many new avionics items.

adopted any Israeli wing modifications. A second Pantera was converted late in 1990.

ENAER worked closely with IAI to produce the Pantera, which in many ways represents an Atar-engined Kfir. Chilean-Israeli co-operation later led to a major upgrade of Chilean F-5Es.

Above: The leaping panther logo is applied to the nose of the Pantera prototype.

Above: A similar panther is carried on the tail of the aircraft.

Atlas Cheetah (South Africa)

In July 1986 Atlas unveiled a considerably modified Mirage, renamed Cheetah and clearly benefitting from Israeli technology. Conversion has been effected of the SAAF's later Mirage IIIs to similar standards, the IIICZs and IIIBZs being excluded. First to be upgraded were eight IIID2Z two-seat trainers, declared operational in August 1987 as the Cheetah DZ, and they have been followed by some 14 Cheetah EZs (Mirage IIIEZs), four RZs and three R2Zs, plus at least four DZs and five EZs produced from Mirages acquired from an undisclosed source. All ex-SAAF aircraft retain their original powerplants – Atar 09C-3s, apart from D2Zs with 09K-50s – and the RZs and R2Zs also keep camera noses. Modifications to the airframe (including previously non-radar trainers which have an additional combat-support role) include addition of Elta EL/M-2001B ranging radar in the nose, which is extended to accommodate additional avionics. The trainers have a Kfir-TC2-type nose (with an air scoop also mounting forward antennas for an unknown radar warning system), but Cheetah EZs feature a fuselage plug ahead of the windscreen, standard Israeli mini-radome and SPS-200 RWR antennas beneath the lower forward fuselage and on the fin trailing edge. An Israeli angle-of-attack sensor vane is on the port side of the forward fuselage.

Kfir-style canards and nose strakes are added as outward manifestations of an extensive structural strengthening programme involving replacement of about half the airframe and, effectively, 'zero-houring' it. Israeli-inspired wing leading-edge modifications are the 'dog-tooth' and, further inboard, replacement of the original slot by a small fence. At a later stage it is proposed to convert to the Advanced Combat Wing, featuring drooped leading edges with a kink outboard of the 'dog-tooth' plus additional capacity for 57 Imp

gal (260 litres) of fuel and wingtip missile rails. This modification has yet to be funded, however. Air scoops in the fuselage have been replaced by taller units of Israeli design and, as with the Pantera, there is a blade aerial on the spine of some

aircraft. Control surfaces have probably been rephased and provision is made for a refuelling probe mounted on the starboard air intake (as per the IAI Nammer). There are additional weapon hardpoints at the forward point of the wing/engine air intake

trunk joint. Internally are installed an Elbit HUD and inertial nav/attack system including weapons computer, plus a locally-designed pilot's helmet sighting system. Weapons include the usual two internal DEFA 30-mm cannon (single-seat aircraft

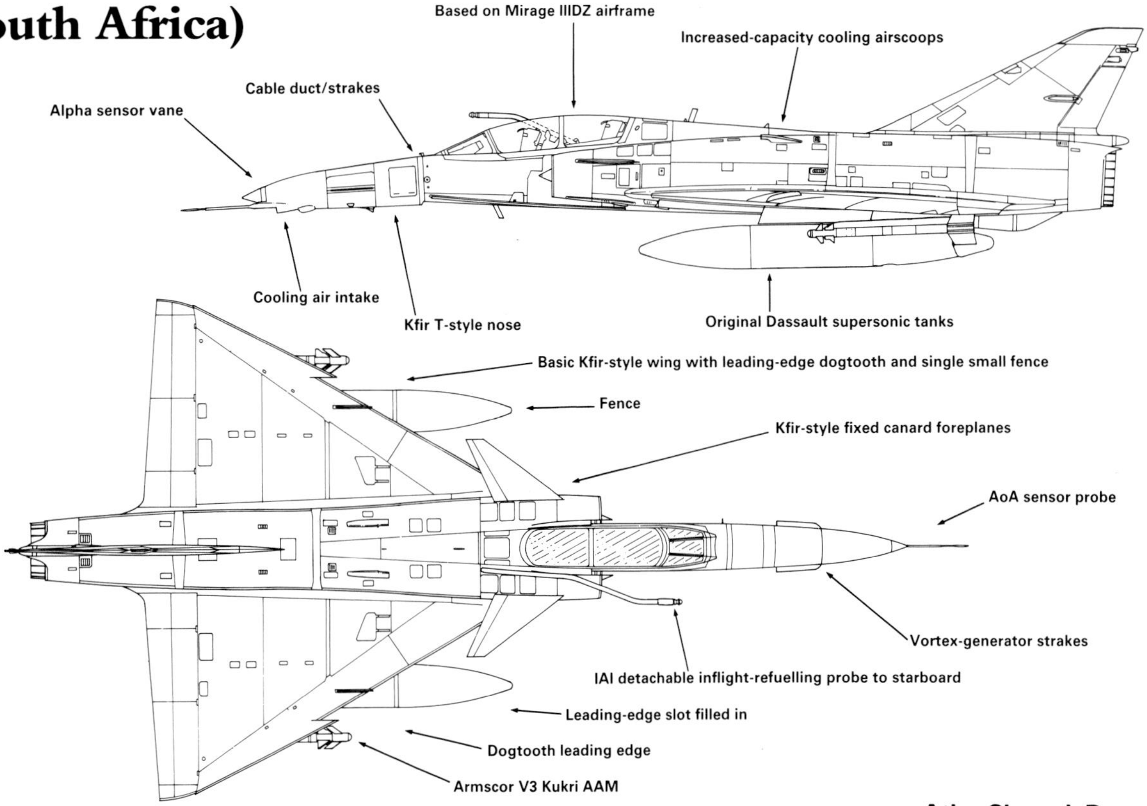

Diagram labels:
- Based on Mirage IIIDZ airframe
- Increased-capacity cooling airscoops
- Cable duct/strakes
- Alpha sensor vane
- Cooling air intake
- Kfir T-style nose
- Original Dassault supersonic tanks
- Basic Kfir-style wing with leading-edge dogtooth and single small fence
- Fence
- Kfir-style fixed canard foreplanes
- AoA sensor probe
- Vortex-generator strakes
- IAI detachable inflight-refuelling probe to starboard
- Leading-edge slot filled in
- Dogtooth leading edge
- Armscor V3 Kukri AAM

Atlas Cheetah D

Below: An SAAF Cheetah D in flight. The two-seat Mirage IIIs were upgraded before the single-seaters. The canards can clearly be seen.

Below: A Cheetah D lands. These aircraft were initially assigned to No. 89 CFS, but have since gone to No. 2 Squadron.

Above: The two-seat Cheetah retains full combat capability, and may have a dedicated ground attack/interdiction role, where a backseater is useful.

Right: The new wing, canard foreplanes and vortex generators give the Cheetah an invaluable increase in agility.

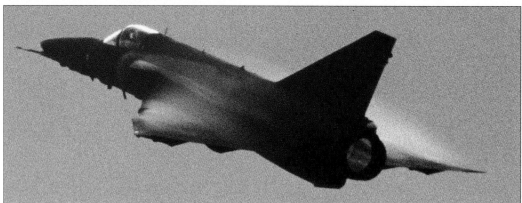

Above: Externally the Cheetah D bears a close resemblance to the Kfir-TC7, with similar equipment and avionics. All SAAF Cheetahs wear this overall dark grey colour scheme.

only), V3B Kukri and V3C Darter IR AAMs, AS30 ASMs, laser-guided bombs, cluster bombs and rockets. One typical weapons fit comprised eight 500-lb (227-kg) free-fall bombs, two V3B Kukris and two drop-tanks.

Atlas Cheetah E

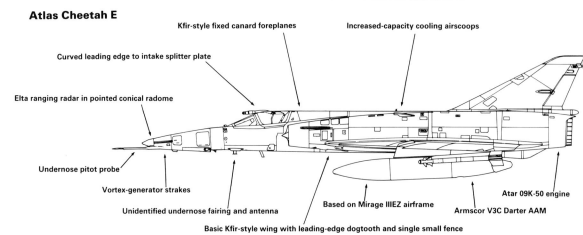

Kfir-style fixed canard foreplanes

Increased-capacity cooling airscoops

Curved leading edge to intake splitter plate

Elta ranging radar in pointed conical radome

Undernose pitot probe

Vortex-generator strakes

Unidentified undernose fairing and antenna

Based on Mirage IIIEZ airframe

Atar 09K-50 engine

Armscor V3C Darter AAM

Basic Kfir-style wing with leading-edge dogtooth and single small fence

Below: This Cheetah E wears the Pegasus badge of No. 5 Squadron on its tailfin, small and very toned down. All SAAF Cheetahs now serve with No. 2 Squadron.

Above: The Cheetah upgrade includes installation of a forward fuselage plug and a Kfir-style nose, with the same Elta ranging radar and vortex generators.

Right: A Cheetah fires off IRCM decoy flares as it climbs away after a low pass – an impressive display of pyrotechnics which considerably enhances survivability.

Atlas Cheetah R2 '855'

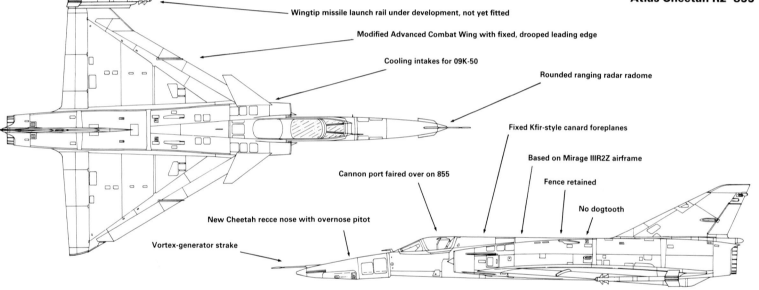

Wingtip missile launch rail under development, not yet fitted

Modified Advanced Combat Wing with fixed, drooped leading edge

Cooling intakes for 09K-50

Rounded ranging radar radome

Fixed Kfir-style canard foreplanes

Based on Mirage IIIR2Z airframe

Cannon port faired over on 855

Fence retained

No dogtooth

New Cheetah recce nose with overnose pitot

Vortex-generator strake

Above: Sometimes erroneously dubbed the Cheetah C, no. 855 is the first Mirage IIIR2Z Cheetah conversion, and the prototype for the new Advanced Combat Wing.

Right: The Advanced Combat Wing seen close up. The drooped leading edge can clearly be seen. Plans exist for a wingtip missile launch station.

Atlas Cava

The Mirage III design, modified for the Atlas Cheetah, was expected to be further developed by South Africa as the basis of its next combat aircraft, due to enter service in the late 1990s. Power would be provided by the Atar 09K-50, for which South Africa has a production licence, and both single- and twin-engined designs have been considered. The Cava is intended to be multi-role, armed with local V3 close-combat IR AAMs and air-to-ground ordnance, but its future has been put in doubt by recent defence cuts and the move to majority rule.

In the next volume of *World Air Power Journal*, we will describe all the units which have flown the Mirage III/5/50 in all its variants and derivatives.

Österreichische Luftstreitkräfte

Left: After many years without an interceptor, the ÖLsk eventually received 23 ex-Swedish *Drakens*. The *Überwachungsgeschwader* has two squadrons of *Drakens* at its Graz base, 1 *Staffel* (*blau/blue*) and 2 *Staffel* (*rot/red*). A pod system gives a reconnaissance capability.

Above: Returning from a training sortie, a J 35Ö drags its tail bumper along the Graz runway.

Right: Austria's *Drakens* have been more active since the start of the fighting in former Yugoslavia. Incursions into Austrian air space occurred during the Slovenian crisis.

Situated at the heart of Europe, Austria maintains only a small army, hampered by very low defence spending and political restraints stemming from the 1955 declaration of neutrality, a measure taken to avoid partition of the nation. The air force is subordinate to the army, and is administered by that service under the title 'Fliegerdivision'.

Austria's principal warplane is the Saab J 35Ö Draken, which flies with two squadrons of Fliegerregiment II's Überwachungsgeschwader. Small unit badges have appeared on the fins (right).

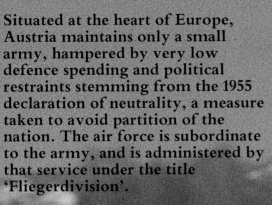

Above: Saab 105s are based at Hörsching with the Jagdbombergeschwader. The unit has two squadrons, 1 Staffel (gelb/yellow) and 2 Staffel (grün/green).

Below: This is the badge of 1 Staffel, carried on the fins of Saab 105s.

Above: 2 Staffel provides tactical reconnaissance for the army, some Saab 105s being fitted with an underwing Vinten reconnaissance pod containing five cameras. The squadron also undertakes conversion training on the type.

Left: Some 40 Saab 105Ös were purchased for the ÖLsk, of which about 30 remain active. Prior to delivery of the Drakens, the type was called upon to provide air defence, in addition to its close support functions with the Jagdbombergeschwader. The JBG is part of Fliegerregiment III, and is directly assigned to support for the ground forces. 1 Staffel is assigned to ground attack duties, for which its Saab 105s carry various light stores underwing. Shown here is a gun pod under each wing, flanked by unguided rockets.

Confusingly assigned to Hubschraubergeschwader (helicopter wing) I, the 12 Pilatus PC-6 Turbo-Porters are used for utility work. One speciality is aerial firefighting.

Above: The Porters serve with 4 Flachenstaffel, based at Tulln alongside other fixed-wing transports and helicopters. The Swiss-designed Porter is a perfect vehicle for this mountainous country, able to operate from impossibly short strips which are often snowbound.

Above right: Some 15 Cessna O-1 Bird Dogs fly on liaison and spotting duties. They fly with 4 Flachenstaffel at Tulln, and with the Saab 105 and Draken wings.

Right: Ten Pilatus PC-7s were delivered in 1983-84 to partially replace the Saab Safirs in the pilot training role, these now serving with the Übungsstaffel of the Pilotenschule at Zeltweg. Students are graded on the Safir prior to graduating to the JetRanger or PC-7.

Above: Although plans exist for a considerable increase in the fixed-wing transport force, for the time being the pair of *Short Skyvans* delivered in 1969 continues to provide the bulk of the 'heavy' transport capability. They operate from Tulln with 4 Flachenstaffel.

Above left: The JetRanger serves in sizeable numbers with Hubschraubergeschwader I at Tulln. 2 Staffel flies the Agusta-Bell AB 206A model for training and rescue purposes while 3 Staffel operates the Bell OH-58B on observation missions.

Left: Hubschraubergeschwader III at Hörsching still flies eight Agusta-Bell AB 204Bs with its second squadron. Twenty-six were originally delivered, of which the eight were refurbished for continued service.

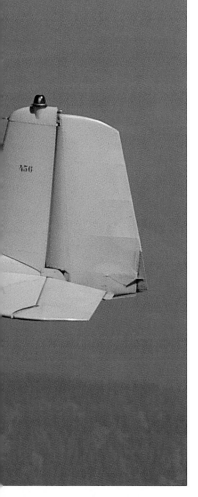

Left: Saab 91D Safir deliveries totalled 24, and about 15 remained in use with the Pilotenschule for initial training until 1992. These veterans had been delivered in 1964-65, and were retired as training commitments were met elsewhere.

Above: The principal helicopter type is the Agusta-Bell AB 212, which offers twin-engine safety in the mountainous regions. They serve with the first squadrons of Hubschraubergeschwader I at Tulln and III at Hörsching.

Below: Alouette IIIs fly with 1 and 2 Staffel/Hubschraubergeschwader II at Aigen (SA 319B), 2 Staffel/ Hubschraubergeschwader III at Hörsching (SE 3160 and SA 316B), and with various mountain rescue detachments.

*Illustrating the two variants derived from the SS-2 design, the prototype **US**-1 (foreground) is joined by the first **PS**-1.*

Shin Meiwa PS-1/US-1

Japan's Big Boat

Few nations persevered with the large flying-boat after the end of World War II and, until the recent resurgence of interest in the genre, Japan stood alone as a producer and operator of big 'boats. The type in question was Shin Meiwa's SS-2 design, a thoroughly modern and highly impressive performer.

*Left: The five-engined Albatross. The **UF-XS** was a much-modified **Grumman UF**-1 featuring four engines for power and a fifth to blow air over the flaps for extra lift.*

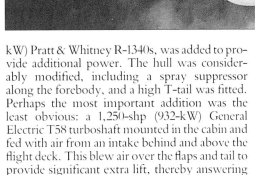

At the end of August 1967 the first prototype of the SS-2 was rolled out at the Kohnan plant (above). On 5 October the aircraft flew for the first time, entering an intense flight and sea trials period (above right and right). During these trials the type demonstrated its ability to operate safely from much higher sea states than possible with the previous generation of flying-boats, and also at much lower speeds. These in turn reduced the landing and take-off runs considerably. Among the notable features of the SS-2 was the exhaust for the auxiliary engine mounted in the rear centre-section.

Prior to World War II, the flying-boat was the principal vehicle for long-range maritime patrols and, in the ensuing conflict, it reigned supreme in this arduous arena. However, the use of very-long-range landplanes, notably the Focke-Wulf Fw 200 Condor and Consolidated Liberator, began to make its mark as the war progressed, and the big 'boats went into a slow but steady decline.

Of all the wartime flying-boats, none were better than those designed by the Japanese company Kawanishi which, in its H8K 'Emily' design, produced arguably the best flying-boat of the war. In the post-war world, Kawanishi became Shin Meiwa, and it never lost its interest or expertise in building large flying-boats. From as early as 1952, Shin Meiwa began a prolonged but active programme into designing a truly modern flying-boat for the JMSDF, applying many new technologies to build upon its own considerable wartime achievements. Key areas for further development were stability in high seas, short take-off/landing and the reduction of spray ingestion.

To test many of their innovations, Shin Meiwa used a Grumman UF-1 Albatross, which was designated the UF-XS. First flying on 25 December 1962, the UF-XS not only acted as a technology demonstrator but also as a scale model of the full-scale design. In addition to its two standard Wright R-1820 radials, each offering 1,425 hp (1063 kW), a further pair of radials, 600-hp (447-

kW) Pratt & Whitney R-1340s, was added to provide additional power. The hull was considerably modified, including a spray suppressor along the forebody, and a high T-tail was fitted. Perhaps the most important addition was the least obvious: a 1,250-shp (932-kW) General Electric T58 turboshaft mounted in the cabin and fed with air from an intake behind and above the flight deck. This blew air over the flaps and tail to provide significant extra lift, thereby answering the STOL requirement.

PX-S requirement

Data provided by the UF-XS proved of inestimable value to the design team led by Dr Shizuo Kikuhara, working on the full-scale machine, but it was not until January 1966 that the JMSDF finally awarded a development contract to the company to answer its PX-S re-

quirement. By that time, of course, the full-scale flying-boat design, known as the SS-2, was very advanced.

In terms of construction, the SS-2 was entirely conventional. A semi-monocoque fuselage mounted a straight, two-spar wing on a raised attachment. The hull had a single-step planing bottom, with a spray deflecting strake around the nose. Below this was fitted a spray suppressor, which captured water and ducted it along the fuselage chine and ejected it laterally behind the propeller line. This virtually eliminated spray reaching the propellers and engines, which were mounted high on the wing. The T-tail offered good low-speed authority and set the tailplanes high above the turbulence of the fuselage and engines.

Chosen as powerplant for the SS-2 was the General Electric T64-1H1-10 turboprop, which provided 2,850 hp (2126 kW). These were licence-built in Japan by Ishikawajima-Harima, and each drove a three-bladed Hamilton Standard 63E60-15 propeller. These engines provided sufficient power for rapid take-offs when aided by the considerable array of high-lift devices. The outer section of each wing leading edge had powerful slats and there were overwing spoilers. Even the tailplane had leading edge slats. Large flap sections provided considerable lift even without the air blowing system. The inner flap section deflected 80°, while the outer deflected 60°, but could be linked to the ailerons.

The PS-1 was an effective ASW platform, though offering limited range compared to its land-based counterparts. This was a major factor in its replacement by the P-3 Orion.

Above: A PS-1 churns up huge amounts of spray as it alights. Thanks to a novel spray suppression system, the forward part of the aircraft, and especially the engines and propellers, are virtually clear.

Left: For the anti-submarine role, the PS-1 usually carried torpedoes as its principal armament. These were housed in pairs in pods between the engine nacelles.

Right: The cockpit of a PS-1 shows the large tactical plotter display between the pilots' stations. A tactical co-ordinator in the cabin usually controlled an ASW mission.

Blown air for the flaps was provided by a 1,250-shp (932-kW) General Electric T58-GE-6 turboshaft (again built by Ishikawajima) mounted in the fuselage/wing join fairing immediately aft of the rear spar. Intake and exhaust ports were in the upper skin. Air from this unit was ducted through the wings to blow both inner and outer flap sections, and was also ducted along the rear fuselage to blow both rudder and elevators, this to provide greater control authority at very low speeds. The central engine could also act as an auxiliary power unit for the aircraft systems, including engine starting.

Other design features of the SS-2 included a raised flight deck offering excellent visibility, forward of which was a large radome for the search radar. Surprisingly, the stabiliser floats were not retractable but were conventional multi-strutted units and, while the SS-2 remained strictly a flying-boat, beaching wheels were provided in the form of a fully-retractable nosewheel and mainwheels which were carried

semi-recessed on the side of the hull. These hinged down into position to allow the SS-2 to beach under its own power up a slipway, but were not remotely strong enough to effect a normal runway landing. Most of the fuel was carried in tanks between the wing spars, with further tanks located in the area below the main deck.

Maiden flight

Designated PS-1 by the JMSDF, the SS-2 was intended from the outset for anti-submarine warfare. Following the January 1966 go-ahead, Shin Meiwa worked quickly on completing the prototype, and it was moved to Kobe Harbour, from where it made its maiden flight on 5 October 1967. On 31 July 1968 it was delivered to the JMSDF's 51st Kokutai at Iwakuni to begin service trials. These, undertaken by the first and second aircraft through 1969-70, showed the type's enormous potential. Take-off could be accomplished with a sizeable load as slow as 51 mph (83 km/h), and with a fair wind the PS-1

needed only about 260 ft (80 m) to get airborne. Operations in heavy seas were undertaken with ease, and overall it was recognised that the PS-1 had introduced a quantum leap in the capability of the flying-boat.

Type approval was granted in late 1970, prior to which two pre-production PS-1s had been ordered, the first of which was handed over to the 31st Kokutai in late 1971. Twelve production aircraft followed, powered by uprated 3,060-ehp (2282-kW) T64-IHI-10E engines. These joined the pre-series aircraft at Iwakuni with the 31st Kokutai, which began ASW operations with the type. An operational crew consisted of two pilots and flight engineer on the flight deck, and mission operators in the main cabin. These typically comprised a tactical co-ordinator, two sonar operators, MAD operator, navigator, radar operator, radio operator and two observers. Most equipment was along the port side of the cabin, while crew rest bunks were to starboard. A compartment under the flight deck with watertight door accommodated radio equipment and an anchor, and featured a port-side entry hatch. A further hatch was located in the rear fuselage.

ASW equipment included AQA-3 Jezebel acoustic detection equipment with 20 sono-

In common with most maritime aircraft, PS-1s were regularly washed down to prevent salt-water corrosion. Of note is the considerable deflection of the two flap sections.

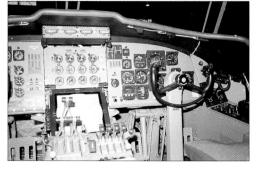

and smoke bombs could be carried in the weapons compartment, which was augmented by underwing pods fitted between the engine nacelles which each carried two torpedoes. A launcher for three 5-in (127-mm) rockets could be fitted under each wingtip for surface attack.

Nine further PS-1s followed the original order, but the continued procurement of the type was halted in 1980 by the announcement that all future ASW requirements would be met by the land-based Lockheed P-3 Orion. This blow to the flying-boat was largely due to steadily-spiralling costs, restricted range compared to its land-based rivals and to a spate of accidents which had befallen the PS-1, although none were attributable to design shortcomings. This attrition, which amounted to six aircraft by 1984, curtailed the establishment of a second squadron (32nd Kokutai), and in 1989 the PS-1 was retired from the inventory, all of its tasks having been passed to the P-3 Orion.

This could have sounded the death-knell for the flying-boat as an anti-submarine platform (although in the 1990s it is seeing a resurgence in the shape of the Beriev A-40), but the mighty Shin Meiwas were set to continue in another vital task: search and rescue. Early in the PS-1 production run, the JMSDF ordered a fully-amphibious

buoys, Julie echo-ranging which employed explosive charges, magnetic anomaly detection and various electronic sensors. Four depth charges

version of the SS-2 to replace its Grumman UF-1 Albatross amphibians in the SAR role. There was to be no prototype as the new aircraft, known by the company as the SS-2A and designated US-1 by the JMSDF, was essentially similar to the ASW 'boat. Providing fully amphibious capability was the only major design change.

Land undercarriage

In fact Dr Kikuhara and his team had been studying the fitment of landing gear for the PS-1 for some time, although the process proved difficult and time consuming. Eventually an arrangement was found whereby the wheels were carried in fuselage-side fairings, with the tyre left exposed. This left the fuselage structure largely unaltered, but resulted in a narrow wheel track. It however did still allow operations in crosswinds up to 25 kt (28 mph; 46 km/h), well above the

With its integral beaching gear deployed, the PS-1 could haul itself out of the water up a slipway without the need for a winch.

role, or 36 in an air ambulance role. Canvas seats were provided for 20 passengers or, as an alternative, the SAR equipment could be removed to allow the US-1 to operate as a troop carrier, carrying over 100. Rescue hatches were provided, with a ramp, and in the port side was a large door for the operation of a rubber dinghy. A hoist was fitted above the door. Searchlights were added, and a loud-hailer for communicating with survivors. Bubbled observation windows were incorporated in the upper cabin area. Further rescue equipment carried in the US-1 consisted of a marker launcher with 10 marine markers, two air-droppable message cylinders, float lights, flare pistol, binoculars and lifebuoys.

US-1 into service

9071 was the first US-1, and it was rolled out at Kohnan on 1 October 1974. It made its first flight on 15 October, and was delivered to the 51st Kokutai for trials on 25 November. A long period ensued for service testing, mostly concerned with the undercarriage and with rescue operations. Joined by the second and third aircraft, 9071 was on hand at Iwakuni on 1 July 1976 when the 71st Kokutai was formed to operate the US-1. From the seventh aircraft, the T64-IHI-10J engine was fitted, offering 3,490 hp (2603 kW) and raising the aircraft's designation to US-1A. All earlier aircraft were subsequently converted to this standard.

Each engine drives a Sumitomo (Hamilton Standard) 63E60-27 constant-speed propeller, with reversible pitch to shorten the landing run. The auxiliary engine is a T58-IHI-10-M2, which provides 31 lb (14 kg) of air per second at a pressure of 27 lb/sq in (1.86 bars) to the flaps and tail surfaces. Fuel is held in five wing tanks holding 3,075 US gal (11640 litres) and two fuselage tanks (below the cabin) holding 2,866 US gal (10849 litres), giving a total usable capacity of 5,941 US gal (22489 litres). A pressure refuelling point is on the port side of the bow.

Two independent hydraulic systems power the control surfaces, high-lift devices and undercarriage, and there is an emergency system which

Above: US-1 flight trials were largely aimed at examining runway operations and its suitability for the SAR role. Wearing 51 Kokutai (the test squadron) markings, the prototype reveals the ease with which it copes with rough seas.

Below: A US-1 rises on to the step as it gathers speed in the take-off run. With flaps blown by the 'fifth engine' the run can be as little as 1,820 ft at maximum weight.

design goal. The undercarriage was built by Sumitomo.

Although the wheeled undercarriage was the primary difference between the PS-1 and US-1, there were many other mission-related changes. All ASW equipment and armament options were removed, and fuel capacity was increased. Provision was made for 12 stretcher cases in the rescue

Above: Although several PS-1s were lost in water accidents, the same fate has not befallen any of the US-1 fleet. The aircraft is unanimously praised by its pilots.

Right: 71st Kokutai US-1s at rest at Iwakuni, with a derelict PS-1 in the background. Of note is the spray suppression system which ejects water behind the propeller line.

operates the inner flaps, undercarriage and brakes driven by a DC motor. A Garrett GTCP85-131J auxiliary power unit is used to start the engines. Oxygen is supplied to all of the crew stations, and to the stretcher positions. A sea anchor is stowed in the bow section.

Search and rescue

A typical SAR crew consists of two pilots and flight engineer on the flight deck, behind which the main cabin houses navigator, radio operator, radar operator and two observers. Up to five medical staff or rescue divers can be added to the crew as required. The main search sensor is the nose-mounted Litton AN/APN-80N radar, backed up by visual searches and beacon locating systems. HPN-101B wave-height measuring equipment provides vital information to the pilots prior to a water landing and, once alighted, there is a drift meter. Further nav/comms equipment includes HRN-101 ADF, ARA-50 UHF/DF, HRN-104 LORAN, HRA-4 LORAN signal processor, HRN-105 TACAN, HRN-106 ILS receiver, APN-171 radio altimeter, APC-187C Doppler, AYK-2 navigation computer, plotting boards, HRC-107 HF, HRC-106 and -110 radios, APX-68N IFF transponder and RRC-15 emergency transmitter.

On a typical rescue mission, the US-1 has a loiter time of six hours at a radius of 690 miles (1110 km), or 2.5 hours at 1,150 miles (1850 km), extending its endurance by flying on two engines only. Once survivors are located, their position is noted with markers, or illuminated with parachute flares. If the sea state precludes a water landing, air-droppable rescue rafts can be delivered, but the aim is usually to land. Again depending on weather and sea state, there are three methods of picking up survivors.

The favourite is to launch the nine-man rescue dinghy, with divers and medical staff to collect the survivors and bring them back to the aircraft. If there are only one or two survivors, a diver will swim from the rescue hatch ramp to them, attached to a lifeline, and bring them in. Alternatively a rescue line can be fired from the ramp to the survivor or his life raft in very rough or difficult conditions, and then winched in to the ramp. Once aboard, the US-1 takes off rapidly and heads for the nearest airfield. Its amphibious capability and excellent STOL performance allow it to use any of Japan's airfields, so that survivors can be ferried to the nearest hospital in the shortest possible time. Loiter time or range can be extended by at-sea refuellings, either from a ship or another US-1A.

The 71st Kokutai has been flying the US-1 since 1976 and has amassed an enviable record of 'saves'. Using forward or seaborne refuelling bases, the US-1 covers a vast area of the Pacific.

Initial production of the US-1 amounted to 12 aircraft, of which eight remain in service with the 71st Kokutai. The squadron made its first rescue in the same month it was formed, taking a seaman off a ship for hospitalisation. Since then it has compiled an exemplary record in the SAR role, saving many lives and performing several rescues that were over 1,000 miles (1600 km) from the Iwakuni base. Both US-1s and PS-1s were very active during the desperate search for survivors following the 1983 shoot-down of the Korean Air Lines Boeing 747 by Soviet fighters in the Sea of Okhotsk. For most of its career, one aircraft has usually been detached to the southern island of Iwo Jima, and since 1981 a three-aircraft detachment has operated from Atsugi.

Civil transport

Foreign interest in the PS-1/US-1 came mainly from Canada and China, with several other nations requesting details or sending technical delegations to the Kohnan works, but nothing came to fruition. Shin Meiwa proposed a civil passenger/cargo transport, and Grumman showed interest in the project. This died inevit-

US-1s are fully equipped for the SAR mission. In the rear cabin is a large double door through which a powered rubber dinghy can be launched once the flying-boat has alighted.

ably as a result of the sheer cost of the Shin Meiwa 'boat. One project which did make it into the air was the fire-fighter version. Taking the prototype PS-1, Shin Meiwa produced a large-capacity (16,200 lb/7348 kg) water bomber which, like the Canadair CL-215, used deployable scoops to ingest water while skimming across the surface. As such the aircraft first flew on 17 May 1976. This was followed by a US-1 fitted with a 30,000-lb (13608-kg) tank developed by Conair. While the prohibitive cost of the aircraft rules out any new purchases of the aircraft for fire-fighting purposes, the prospect remains of converting retired airframes for this task. The type's main use would be against major fires, such as oil installations, forests or metropolitan fires caused by earthquakes.

With any new markets highly unlikely, and production for the 71st Kokutai having ended in 1988, it seemed that the 12th US-1 would be the last big flying-boat built anywhere in the world. Of course, the Beriev concern and the Chinese (with the Harbin SH-5) were later seen to be continuing the trend. Of far greater surprise was the announcement that two further US-1s would be built, one in 1992 and one in 1993, taking the total to 14. These were ordered to bolster the JMSDF SAR fleet as part of a thorough upgrading of Japanese rescue assets. With the prospect of further low-rate production being possible, and the continuing good performance of the type in its role, the Shin Meiwa US-1 is anything but a fading star.

Specification
Shin Meiwa US-1A

Type: long-range search and rescue amphibian
Powerplant: four Ishikawajima-General Electric T64-IHI-10J turboprops, each rated at 3,493 ehp (2605 kW), BLC system powered by one Ishikawajima-General Electric T58-IHI-10-M2 turboshaft providing 1,360 shp (1014 kW)
Dimensions: wing span 108 ft 9 in (33.15 m); length 109 ft 9¼ in (33.46 m); height 32 ft 7¾ in (9.95 m); tailplane span 40 ft 8½ in (12.36 m); wheel track 11 ft 8¼ in (3.56 m); wheelbase 27 ft 4 in (8.33 m); wing area 1,462 sq ft (135.82 m²); tailplane area 248 sq ft (23.04 m)
Weights: empty 51,367 lb (23300 kg); empty equipped 56,218 lb (25500 kg); maximum take-off (water) 94,800 lb (43000 kg), (land) 99,200 lb (45000 kg); maximum usable fuel 40,560 lb (18397 kg)
Performance: maximum speed at 10,000 ft (3050 m) 325 mph (522 km/h); cruising speed at 10,000 ft (3050 m) 265 mph (426 km/h); rate of climb at sea level (at MTOW) 1,600 ft (488 m) per minute, (at 79,365 lb/36000 kg TOW) 2,340 ft (713 m) per minute; service ceiling 28,400 ft (8655 m); take-off run to 50 ft (15 m), 30° flap, BLC on at MTOW on land 2,150 ft (655 m); take-off run, 40° flap, BLC on at MTOW from water 1,820 ft (555 m); landing from 50 ft (15 m), 40° flap, with reverse pitch 2,655 ft (810 m); minimum landing distance on water 722 ft (220 m); maximum range at cruise speed 2,372 miles (3817 km)

Above: Despite its narrow-track undercarriage, the US-1 has good crosswind landing characteristics. All of the fleet is now to US-1A standard, featuring uprated engines compared to the first production machines.

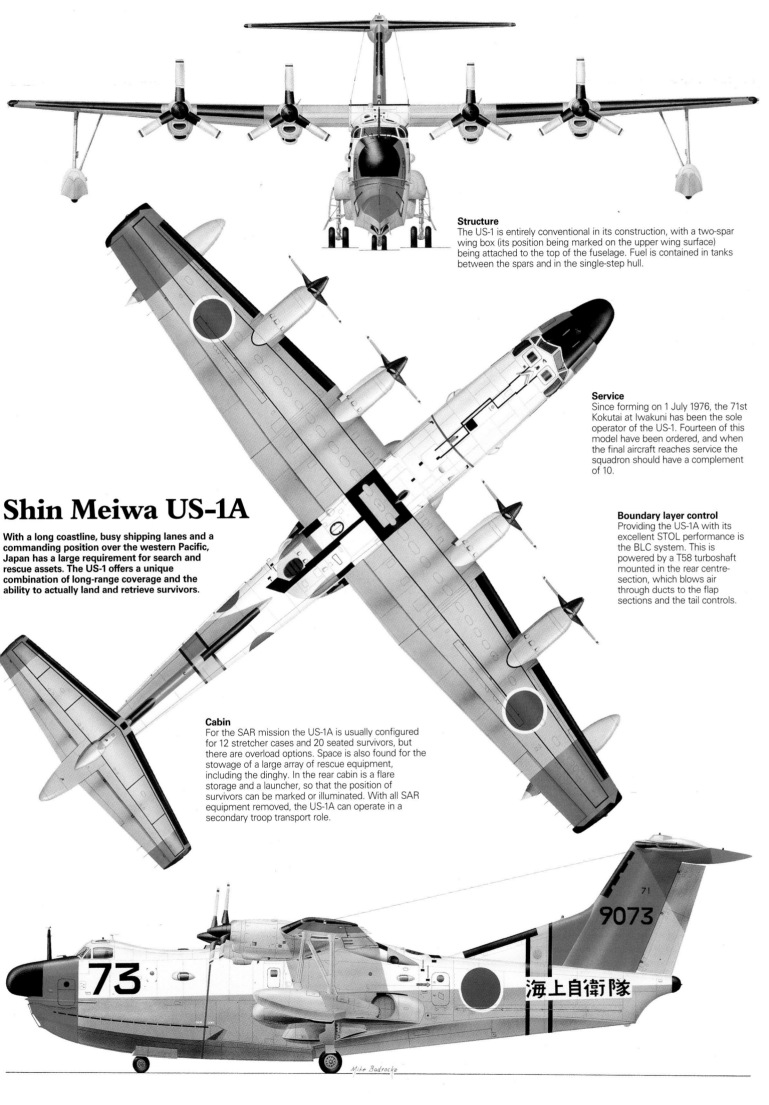

Shin Meiwa US-1A

With a long coastline, busy shipping lanes and a commanding position over the western Pacific, Japan has a large requirement for search and rescue assets. The US-1 offers a unique combination of long-range coverage and the ability to actually land and retrieve survivors.

Structure
The US-1 is entirely conventional in its construction, with a two-spar wing box (its position being marked on the upper wing surface) being attached to the top of the fuselage. Fuel is contained in tanks between the spars and in the single-step hull.

Service
Since forming on 1 July 1976, the 71st Kokutai at Iwakuni has been the sole operator of the US-1. Fourteen of this model have been ordered, and when the final aircraft reaches service the squadron should have a complement of 10.

Boundary layer control
Providing the US-1A with its excellent STOL performance is the BLC system. This is powered by a T58 turboshaft mounted in the rear centre-section, which blows air through ducts to the flap sections and the tail controls.

Cabin
For the SAR mission the US-1A is usually configured for 12 stretcher cases and 20 seated survivors, but there are overload options. Space is also found for the stowage of a large array of rescue equipment, including the dinghy. In the rear cabin is a flare storage and a launcher, so that the position of survivors can be marked or illuminated. With all SAR equipment removed, the US-1A can operate in a secondary troop transport role.

海上自衛隊

Canada

Canadian Armed Forces

Canada comprises the world's second-largest country in terms of area and possesses the world's longest coastline. The nation has a proud military tradition out of proportion to the size of its population, and has long been perched between the massive arsenals of the world's two superpowers: the USA and USSR. It combines intimate involvement in two strategic alliances – the North American Aerospace Defense Command and the North Atlantic Treaty Organization – with a widely respected international reputation as a peacekeeper.

Canada's post-war fighter heritage is represented here by Cold Lake's gate-guards. Lockheed CT-33 and CF-104 are poles, framing the McDonnell CF-101 and Avro Canada CF-1

A limited tanking capability is provided by No. 437 Squadron, which has two of its five Boeing 707s modified accept wingtip refuelling pods.

Latest acquisition for the CF is the tanker version of the Hercules. These will replace the CC-137s in the refuelling role.

One squadron remains of Canadair-built Northrop F-5s, us primarily for fighter training purposes. The majority remaining are CF-116D two-seaters.

Canada's sole tactical asset is the CF-188 Hornet, which serves with four front-line squadrons and a training unit. This example serves with 433 Sqn.

The size of the country is difficult to comprehend. It ranges 2,879 miles (4634 km) from north to south and 3,426 miles (5514 km) from east to west. It has the piece of land closest to the North Pole, Ellesmere Island, at 83°07′ N, but most of its land area is empty of human habitation. It is said that approximately 80 per cent of the Canadian population lives within 100 miles (160 km) of the border with the United States. The close relations between the two countries, separated by the world's longest undefended border, are reinforced by the fact that each is the other's biggest trading partner.

A non-permanent militia organisation, the Canadian Air Force, was created in 1920. Its primary purpose was to provide refresher flying training for some of the thousands of Canadians who had served in the British air forces during World War I. Their success had been impressive by any standards: 10 of the 27 leading Imperial aces were Canadian, all of whom had 30 or more kills to their credit.

The refresher training programme ended on 1 April 1922 and the air force was virtually dormant for some time. On 1 January 1923, the Department of National Defence was created, combining the Department of Militia and Defence, the Department of Naval Service, and the Air Board. All of this had little effect on the CAF's flying hours.

Renamed on 1 April 1924, the Royal Canadian Air Force comprised both permanent and non-permanent components. Three branches were established under the Ministry of Defence: the Royal Canadian Air Force, Civil Government Air Operations, and the Controller of Civil Aviation. Between the wars, the RCAF had a mostly civilian role. The need for aerial transportation throughout the vast area of a country with primitive communications led to the RCAF's roles consisting of such tasks as air and ground photography, mapping, fire fighting, customs patrols, crop dusting and 'mercy' flights over remote northern areas, along with its military duties.

The creation of the Department of Transport in 1936 saw most of these roles transferred from the RCAF, which then embarked on a pro-

gramme of expansion and rearmament. At the beginning of World War II the RCAF possessed only eight permanent and 12 auxiliary squadrons, the combined strength of which totalled just 4,061 officers and men. Three squadrons were sent to Britain in 1940, one of which, No. 1 (later renumbered as 401 by the RAF) took part in the Battle of Britain's later stages.

The remaining squadrons were initially assigned to home defence duties or to the British Commonwealth Air Training Plan. This massive effort produced more than 131,000 aircrew, including 50,000 pilots, before the end of the war. A Home War Establishment had been built up to 39 squadrons by the end of 1943. West Coast units took part in the Alaskan campaign of 1942-43, while East Coast units participated in the battles against enemy submarines throughout the war.

A total of 249,662 men and women served in the RCAF during World War II. Of these, 13,498 became casualties. At the peak of its wartime strength, the Royal Canadian Air Force had no fewer than 46 squadrons overseas. In addition, many thousands of men and women, most of them aircrew, served in the Royal Air Force.

From being the fourth-largest air force in the world at the end of the war, the RCAF underwent a massive reduction in strength immediately afterwards. New roles, such as aerial mapping and surveying of the High Arctic, followed by Canadian commitments to the North Atlantic Treaty Organization and to the United Nations, led to a second, more gradual expansion of the RCAF.

To many people, Canadian military personnel and UN peacekeepers are synonymous. Largely a Canadian creation, for which then-diplomat and subsequent Prime Minister Lester Pearson won the Nobel Peace Prize, peacekeeping has remained a significant feature of Canada's foreign and defence policies. Canadian forces have always stood at the forefront of the United Nations' efforts to keep the peace. Canada has, in fact, been the only country to participate in all of the UN's peacekeeping operations since 1947. Canada has also joined in other peacekeeping missions that were

Canada maintains an active electronic warfare training effort, two squadrons being dedicated to the task. The Challenger and CT-133 are the types in use.

Dedicated to support of Mobile Command, 10 Tactical Air Group is equipped entirely with helicopters. The most numerous type is the CH-136 Kiowa.

The CF-188 is used for both air-to-ground and air defence missions, the latter chiefly in support of NORAD. This is a trials CF-188B in service with the AETE.

not under UN auspices.

These two categories can each be divided into peace-restoring, peacekeeping, peacemaking and truce supervisory operations. Air Command's primary roles have been the transport by air of personnel, support equipment and supplies, and relief supplies. Operation Friction, the name assigned to Canada's involvement in the Gulf War, also included fighter, helicopter, tanker and liaison aircraft. Humanitarian aid, such as the current operations in the former Yugoslavia and in Somalia, are related to peacekeeping in practice but, strictly speaking, are distinct.

A Canadian transport squadron began flying UN supplies across the Pacific during the Korean War, this creating a new long-range transport potential for the peacetime air force. This was developed as new equipment became available and Canada's international commitments expanded.

1958 saw the creation by Canada and the United States of the joint North American Air Defense Command (NORAD) with a US commander and a Canadian deputy commander. The organisation was renamed in 1981 to North American Aerospace Defense Command, to reflect the fact that ballistic and cruise missiles had become the primary threat to North America.

At its peak, Canada's NATO commitment totalled 12 squadrons in an air superiority role. As aircraft became increasingly sophisticated and expensive, this quantity was cut in half, the six squadrons' role changing to that of strike/reconnaissance and strike/attack. The RCAF's maritime patrol organisation was reactivated in the 1950s, conducting long-range sovereignty surveillance flights over the Arctic and anti-submarine operations in the Atlantic. Other RCAF roles included international taskings with the United Nations, routine administrative flights to Canadian bases at home and abroad, search and rescue, air support during natural disasters, and the resupply of Arctic stations.

In February 1968, the 45,000 officers, men and women of the Royal Canadian Air Force, with 19 different aircraft types, were incorporated into the unified Canadian Armed Forces. This new organisation integrated the former RCAF, Canadian Army and Royal Canadian Navy, complete with new green uniforms and

a rank structure based on that of the army. Including the former Army and Navy aircraft and helicopters, the number of types on strength reached 30. Several reorganisations later, the present Canadian Armed Forces consists of three major components, or elements: Mobile Command (the army), Maritime Command (the navy), and Air Command (the air force).

1986 saw a return to separate uniforms for each branch of the forces, and naval personnel again use traditional ranks ashore, having previously gained approval to use them while at sea. The air force revived its own RAF-based rank structure. Many units, whether an Air Command squadron, a Maritime Command ship, or a Mobile Command regiment, have personnel from all three branches. National Defence Headquarters are in Ottawa.

The recession hit Canada hard and, as elsewhere, the military has felt the pinch when budgets were prepared by the government. In his September 1991 statement to Parliament, the Minister of National Defence announced a reduction of military personnel from 84,000 to 76,000 (9.5 per cent) over three years, primarily through attrition. A further reduction of 1,000 in the number of permanent civilian employees to 31,000 was also announced. At the same time, it was announced that the air base at Baden-Soellingen would close in 1994, with the land forces base at Lahr (both in Germany) to follow in 1995. Both dates were later moved forward by one year.

By cutting expenditures on personnel, operations and maintenance, the portion of the defence budget devoted to the procurement of equipment was expected to rise from 22 to 26 per cent within four years, with a target figure of 30 per cent. Recent announced acquisitions include the purchase of three former Canadian Airlines International Airbus A310s with two more to follow in the summer of 1993, 100 Bell Helicopter Textron Canada Model 412HPs and 50 EH.101s.

Following the successful lead of the Americans, Canada has adopted the 'Total Force' concept. The Primary Reserve is to be increased from 29,000 to 40,000. This will be accompanied by better training and equipment. The Supplementary Reserve is also to be increased from 15,000 to nearly 25,000 by 1994.

Maritime Command

Based in Halifax, Nova Scotia, Maritime Command is responsible for ships and related shore establishments. Its aviation component is provided primarily by Maritime Air Group (MAG) with additional support from Fighter Group and Air Transport Group. Further support is provided by Mobile Command. MAG is under the operational control of Maritime Command but it remains part of Air Command.

Mobile Command

The successor to the Canadian Army, Mobile Command (HQ: Valcartier, Quebec) also lacks its own aviation component. It is supported directly by 10 Tactical Air Group and some Air Reserve Group units (all of which come under its operational control), as well as receiving additional support from Air Transport Group and Fighter Group squadrons.

Air Command

Unification combined the three previous services' aviation into the direct successor of the Royal Canadian Air Force, now known as Air Command (HQ: Winnipeg, Manitoba). It is divided into five groups, these being Fighter Group, Maritime Air Group, Air Transport Group, 10 Tactical Air Group, and Air Reserve Group. There are a number of support organisations such as the Aerospace Engineering Test Establishment, Central Flying School, etc. At the time of unification, there was not a distinct air element. Air Command itself only came into being in 1975.

Air Command's role is simply stated as "to provide combat-ready air forces to meet Canada's defence commitment." Its tasks include the surveillance and defence of Canadian air space, the transportation of personnel and equipment, aid to the civil power and peacekeeping support.

Each Group within Air Command has its own headquarters, these being located as follows: **Fighter Group** (including Canadian NORAD Region HQ) – CFB North Bay, Ontario; **Maritime Air Group** – CFB Halifax, Nova Scotia; **Air Transport Group** – CFB Trenton, Ontario; **10 Tactical Air Group** – CFB Montreal, Quebec; **Air Reserve Group** – CFB Winnipeg, Manitoba. Other Air Command components include Training Division, the Aerospace Engineering Test Establishment and Aerospace Maintenance Development Unit, as well as such support elements as air traffic control, fighter weapons controllers, aircraft maintenance and engineering.

The Canadian Coast Guard, unlike its US counterpart, does not transfer to the military from the Department of Transport in time of war. The DoT transferred its VIP passenger role to the Department of National Defence in 1985 and its remaining roles (aside from the Canadian Coast Guard) include airways calibration and inspection. The Royal Canadian Mounted Police and the provincial police forces of Ontario and Quebec also have air branches. The National Research Council maintains a varied fleet of aircraft (including one ex-RCAF and one ex-RCN T-33AN Silver Star Mk 3) for a wide range of test and research programmes. The varying degrees of co-operative efforts between the air force and the Coast Guard, DoT, Royal Canadian Mounted Police, National Research Council and the provincial police, all separate from Canadian military aviation, are beyond the scope of this Air Power Analysis.

Aircraft

Within Air Command, fleet rationalisation (reducing the number of different aircraft types in service) has been underway for some time. By the end of the decade, the Canadian Armed Forces will have gone from seven helicopter types to two (plus the Bell CH-139 JetRangers leased to the Canadian Aviation Training Centre which have civil registrations). Transport types numbered 10 in 1987 and will decline to five; three fighter types are now down to two; maritime patrol types have been cut from two to one. Some types will have as many as four versions in service, but these will be much easier to support than four different types.

Air Command applies local designations to its aircraft, and some types also have official local names rather than those in widespread use. Current types are as follows:

CC-109 Cosmopolitan	Canadair (Convair) CL-66B
CH-113 Labrador	Boeing Vertol 107
CT-114 Tutor	Canadair CL-41A
CC-115 Buffalo	de Havilland Canada DHC-5
CF-116 Freedom Fighter	Canadair (Northrop) CF-5A/D
CH-118 Iroquois	Bell CUH-1H/205
CH-124 Sea King	Sikorsky CHSS-2
CC-130 Hercules	Lockheed C-130E/H
CT-133 Silver Star	Canadair (Lockheed) CL-30/T-33AN
CH-135 Twin Huey	Bell CUH-1N/212
CH-136 Kiowa	Bell COH-58A
CC-137	Boeing 707-347C
CC-138 Twin Otter	de Havilland Canada DHC-6-300
CH-139 JetRanger	Bell 206B
CP-140 Aurora	Lockheed P-3 variant (ASW)
CP-140A Arcturus	Lockheed P-3 variant (MP/OCU)
CC/CT-142 Dash Eight	de Havilland Canada DHC-8M-102
CC/CE/CP-144 Challenger	Canadair CL-600S/601-1A
CH-146 Griffon	Bell 412HP
CH-148 Petrel	Agusta EH.101 (ASW)
CH-149 Chimo	Westland EH.101 (SAR)
CC-150 Polaris	Airbus A310-304
CF-188 Hornet	McDonnell Douglas CF-18

Tight budget restraints have also placed increasing emphasis on life extension and update programmes, delaying the time when various types will have to be replaced. This work is largely carried out by four firms: Northwest Industries (Edmonton, Alberta), Bristol Aerospace (Winnipeg, Manitoba), Canadair (Montreal, Quebec), and IMP Aerospace (Halifax, Nova Scotia).

Other organisational changes are being introduced. In the past, a base commander of an air force installation was little more than the head of a support organisation. That is being changed considerably as wings are reintroduced. Each base will become a numbered wing and the base commander will become the wing commander.

Air Command defines a wing as "a formation of the Canadian Forces comprising two or more units, each with its own Commanding Officer." Under the wing commander will be the wing operations officer, wing logistics officer, wing administration officer and wing comptroller. Coming under the WOpsO will be the flying units and an air maintenance squadron. This system, introduced from 1 April 1993, will see each wing commander continue to report to the parent group commander; for example, 4 Wing at Cold Lake will report to Fighter Group. In those instances where flying squadrons from two or more groups are co-located, the wing commander will report to the group which 'owns' the base.

Other flying units in Air Command will be upgraded to squadron status and numbered accordingly. The first of these will be the CFB Cold Lake Base Flight, which will become 417 Squadron in late June 1993.

The Base Aircraft Maintenance Engineering Organisations (BAMEO), which were part of the old base system, will be replaced by Squadron Air Maintenance Engineering Organisations and/or Air Maintenance Squadrons. Where it was feasible, Air Command has revived wing numbers with historic significance. The introduction of 17 wings has resulted in a significant reorganisation and will improve the way Air Command operates.

With the world's largest coastline bounding huge tracts of inhospitable and uninhabited terrain, Canada requires sizeable search and rescue forces.

Canada is one of the last bastions of the Lockheed T-33, the Canadair-built CT-133 Silver Star serving with Base Flights and EW units.

A vital task of the CF is protecting the sea lanes around Canada. Hard-pressed in this role is the small fleet of CP-140 Auroras, an Orion version unique to Canada.

The indigenous aircraft industry has a proud tradition of supplying the RCAF/CF with its aircraft. Canadair Challengers serve in some numbers in various roles.

In addition to its primary army support role, 10 TAG also supports the police and other civilian agencies. New equipment is expected in the shape of the Bell 412HP.

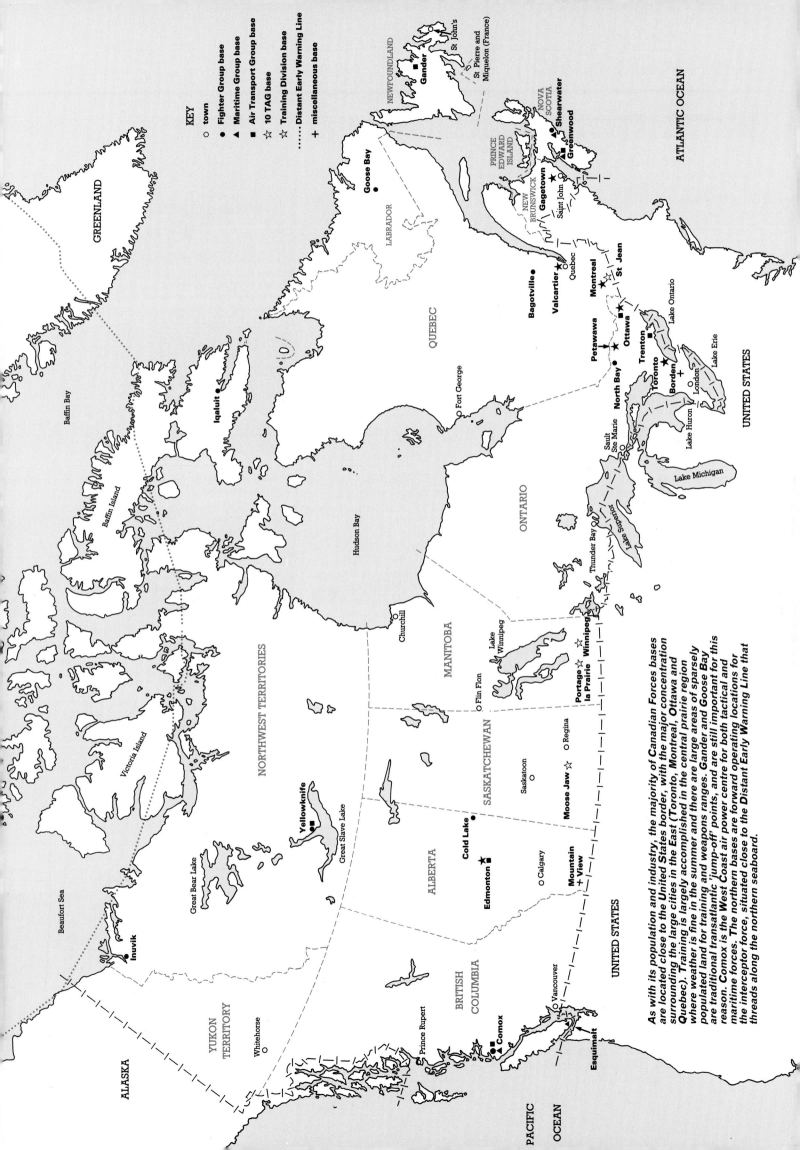

GREENLAND

ALASKA

YUKON
TERRITORY

Whitehorse ○

Inuvik ●

Beaufort Sea

Great Bear Lake

Victoria Island

Baffin Island

Baffin Bay

NORTHWEST TERRITORIES

Yellowknife ●■

Great Slave Lake

Iqaluit ●

Prince Rupert ○

BRITISH
COLUMBIA

Vancouver ○

Comox ●▲

Esquimalt

PACIFIC
OCEAN

Calgary ○

Mountain
View + ●

Cold Lake ★■

Edmonton ●

ALBERTA

SASKATCHEWAN

Saskatoon ○

Regina ○

Moose Jaw ☆

Churchill ○

MANITOBA

Flin Flon ○

Lake
Winnipeg

Portage ☆
la Prairie ○ Winnipeg

Hudson Bay

Fort George ○

QUEBEC

LABRADOR

Goose Bay ●

Bagotville ●
Valcartier ★
Quebec ●

Montreal ★
St Jean ☆

Petawawa →
Ottawa ★■
Trenton ■

North Bay ●
Toronto ★
Borden ★
London +

ONTARIO

Thunder Bay ○

Sault
Ste Marie ○

Lake Superior

Lake Michigan

Lake Huron

Lake Ontario
Lake Erie

UNITED STATES

NEWFOUNDLAND

St John's ○

Gander ■

St Pierre and
Miquelon (France)

PRINCE
EDWARD
ISLAND

NOVA
SCOTIA

Shearwater ▲
Greenwood ■

NEW
BRUNSWICK

Gagetown ★

Saint John ●

ATLANTIC OCEAN

KEY

○ town
● Fighter Group base
▲ Maritime Group base
■ Air Transport Group base
★ 10 TAG base
☆ Training Division base
····· Distant Early Warning Line
+ miscellaneous base

*As with its population and industry, the majority of Canadian Forces bases
are located close to the United States border, with the major concentration
surrounding the large cities in the East (Toronto, Montreal, Ottawa and
Quebec). Training is largely accomplished in the central prairie region
where weather is fine in the summer and there are large areas of sparsely
populated land for training and weapons ranges. Gander and Goose Bay
are traditional transatlantic 'jump-off' points, and are still important for this
reason. Comox is the West Coast air power centre for both tactical and
maritime forces. The northern bases are forward operating locations for
the interceptor force, situated close to the Distant Early Warning Line that
threads along the northern seaboard.*

Fighter Group/Canadian NORAD Region

Fighter Group's role is to provide trained and operationally capable forces to both the North American Aerospace Defense Command and the North Atlantic Treaty Organization.

Prior to Fighter Group's formation in July 1982, Canada's fighter aircraft belonged to different groups. The CF-5s, then front-line fighters, were part of 10 Tactical Air Group, the CF-101s belonged to Air Defence Group, and the CF-104s (all Europe-based except those belonging to the training wing) were assigned to 1 Canadian Air Group (later Air Division). The formation of a single, all-inclusive Fighter Group, headquartered at North Bay, Ontario, paved the way for the introduction of the multi-role CF-18 in 1984.

The other half of the combined headquarters is formed by the command and administrative staff of the Canadian NORAD Region. NORAD was originally divided into areas that were aligned without regard to national boundaries, but they were reconfigured in 1984 resulting in the formation of Canadian NORAD Region (CANR). This allowed the creation of a single command and control structure responsible for all Canadian air space, answering to the Commander-in-Chief NORAD (CINCNORAD). The Canadian NORAD Region is divided into two sectors: Canada East and Canada West. Both are controlled by a Sector Operations Control Centre (SOCC) and are co-located with CANR HQ at North Bay in the underground complex.

Following the formation of Fighter Group and the establishment of CANR, it became apparent that the two organisations were closely linked. Both headquarters were amalgamated with the formation of the combined Fighter Group/Canadian NORAD Region Headquarters in 1987. Members of the Joint Headquarters maintain two roles, as Staff Officers in Fighter Group and as Battle Staff in support of NORAD operations.

The 'Ogdensburg Declaration' of August 1940, issued by Prime Minister Mackenzie King and President Roosevelt, can be considered as the beginning of the present NORAD agreement. It put forth the concept of joint Canadian-American defence. Collective security for continental defence remained of vital concern for both nations after World War II and, in February 1947, the principles of future military co-operation were announced which included consultation on air defence issues. The explosion of the then-Soviet Union's first atomic device in 1949 and the subsequent build-up of their long-range manned bomber and ballistic missile forces led directly to a considerable improvement in Canadian air defence capabilities.

The head of the USAF's Air Defense Command, General Earle E. Partridge, and the RCAF's Chief of Staff, Air Marshal C. Roy Slemon, discussed ways to provide the best defence for North America. Their discussions led to the creation of NORAD in 1954.

On 1 August 1957, the US Secretary of Defense and the Canadian Minister of National Defence announced a bi-national agreement covering a system of centralised operational control of air defence forces under an integrated command to be located at Colorado Springs. General Partridge was named to head the new command. His recommendation to the US Joint Chiefs of Staff and the Canadian Chiefs that operational control of the RCAF's Air Defence Command be transferred to his new headquarters effective 12 September 1957 was quickly approved by both parties, and NORAD was activated on that date. Air Marshal Slemon was appointed as NORAD's deputy commander, and that post has been filled by a Canadian ever since.

Other agreements in the 1950s between Canada and the United States resulted in the building of a series of radar networks to provide early warning and in-depth defence against air attack. NORAD's initial role was to maintain interceptors, warning systems and other installations to detect, track, intercept and destroy all or most bombers before they could reach their targets with free-fall bombs. At that time, NORAD air defence forces included more than 3,000 interceptors, 200 of which were supplied by the RCAF. There were also 90 surface-to-air missile sites, including two Canadian BOMARC sites (one each at North Bay and Lamacaza, Quebec).

Toward the end of the 1960s and into the 1970s, the development of intercontinental and submarine-launched ballistic missiles took precedence in the Soviet Union, and the threat of the manned bomber became a secondary concern. NORAD's defensive posture adapted to meet the new threats and its mission emphasised the warning and assessment of ballistic missile attack, as well as space surveillance. As a result, the number of interceptors declined to about 300, the Mid-Canada Line was abandoned, other radar sites were closed and the BOMARC missiles were withdrawn. At the same time, a number of new systems entered service. These included the Ballistic Missile Early Warning System (BMEWS), the Satellite Early Warning System (SEWS), and the Space Detection and Tracking System (SPADATS), all of which contribute to the present US Space Command sensor network. It provides NORAD with continuous data integrated from BMEWS, SEWS and SPADATS, assuring the detection, categorisation, and assessment of ballistic missile attack with sufficient time to allow retaliatory action. This forms the Mutual Assured Destruction concept which worked for decades.

Canadian personnel are assigned to BMEWS and SEWS. A further contribution is made to the SPADATS with the Satellite Identification and Tracking Unit (SITU), at St Margaret's, New Brunswick. This Fighter Group unit uses the Baker Nunn camera for space surveillance and provides information to the NATO Worldwide SPADATS System which identifies and maintains precise orbital data on all man-made space objects.

New Soviet strategic weapons systems such as the Tu-95 'Bear-H' and Tu-160 'Blackjack' entering service in the early 1980s caused a revision of NORAD thinking. The most significant strategic threat against North America, out

One of two CF-188 squadrons at CFB Bagotville (informally known as 'Bagtown'), 425 Sqn joins 433 in manning the air defence detachment at Goose Bay.

425 Sqn's badge is a lark (alouette) carried on the fin with squadron number.

433 Sqn's fin badge is the cartoon porcupine carrying a missile.

With full-colour Canadian 'Band-Aid' on the fin, this CF-18 flies with No. 433 Sqn, one of two French-Canadian fighter squadrons in the CF.

410 Sqn is known as the 'Cougars', and carry this badge on the fin.

Co-located with the 'Cougars' are the 'Lynxes' of No. 416 Squadron.

No. 410 Sqn celebrated its 50th anniversary in style with this special paint scheme. The squadron was formed on 30 June 1941, initially with Boulton Paul Defiants.

No. 410 Squadron resides at Cold Lake, where it undertakes the **CF-188** OCU/ORTU training roles. As such has a large proportion of two-seat CF-18Bs in its complement. Of the 137 Hornets bought by Canada, 40 were two-seaters. This pair carries ACMI pods for monitoring air combat training.

CFB Cold Lake is the main home of the Hornet in Canada, with three squadrons in residence. The base provides excellent training on ranges nearby.

An important feature of the CF-188 is the nose-mounted searchlight, providing illumination for night-time intercepts.

416 Sqn is a front-line CF-188 operator at Cold Lake which, along with 441, provides aircraft for the alert detachment at Comox, and for deployments to the FOL at Yellowknife. The Cyrillic legend on the LERX strake of this CF-188A translates as 'Check Six'.

of approximately 650 bombers in the Soviet Strategic Aviation Forces, was the 'Bear-H'. This cruise missile-carrying aircraft entered service in 1984. At least 80 were built and could be equipped with six or 16 cruise missiles. The 'Blackjack' became operational in 1989 and was capable of carrying 12 AS15 cruise missiles. This long-range stand-off capability gave the Soviets the capacity to launch nuclear cruise missiles from the periphery of North America.

The cruise missiles represented the first major initiative by the Soviet military to acquire the third element of the nuclear triad: a flexible, effective bomber force. If the bombers were not identified before they could launch their missiles, NORAD would be faced with the overwhelming task of detecting, intercepting and destroying a very large number of small, low-flying targets. When the growing Soviet capability to launch cruise missiles from submarines was added, it became clear that there was a destabilising asymmetry in NORAD's warning capabilities. The ability to detect and track ballistic missiles was excellent but the systems were less effective against cruise missiles.

Based on the evolving Soviet strategic cruise missile attack capability, an air defence master plan was developed in 1982 detailing an overhaul of North American air defence. Specific recommendations included replacing the Distant Early Warning (DEW) Line with a more effective warning system; installing Over-the-Horizon Backscatter (OTHB) radars to cover the Atlantic, Pacific and southern approaches; placing increased reliance on AWACS aircraft; developing new interceptor deployment patterns; and installing gap-filling sensors. The plan also recognised space-based systems as the main elements of NORAD in the future.

On 18 March 1985, the NORAD agreement between Canada and the United States was renewed. This resulted in Canadian participation in a number of programmes for modernising air defence. The most important is Canada's involvement in the North American Air Defense Modernisation Programme (NAADM), which, when fully operational, will replace the detection capabilities of the DEW Line as well as the communications and interceptor control capabilities of the Cadin Pinetree Line. Radar coverage provided by the Alaskan Radar Chain (known as Seek Igloo) to the US Joint Surveillance System (JSS) will increase dramatically with the completion of presently funded programmes.

An additional Canadian coastal radar at Masset, British Columbia, has been improved in principle, although funding 'has not been identified'. Across the north, radar coverage will be provided by the North Warning System Radars. This surveillance is currently being provided by long-range radars and will be augmented by short-range radar now under development. These low-level radars will allow detection of low-altitude, cruise missile-sized targets and are scheduled to be installed over the next few years.

In the east, the coastal radar coverage will overlap that of the North Warning System as well as that of the continental US JSS radars. Two other radar sites will be at Cold Lake, Alberta, and Mont Apica, Quebec. These will replace older radars from the Cadin Pinetree Line and will also support flight training at Fighter Group's two main operating bases (Cold Lake and Bagotville).

The final elements of the updated radar network are the OTHB facilities provided by the United States. This system provides long-range aircraft detection capability at both high and low altitudes, approximately 1,555 miles (2500 km) to the east and west of North America. Aurora borealis activity will prevent Canada from benefitting from this technology and, although not participating in their funding, Canada provides personnel to jointly man them.

Another important component of the NAADM project is the designation and development of forward operating locations in Canada's north. Five locations were selected to undergo development over the next few years. Three of them have already supported deployed fighter operations and are included in current NORAD plans. Full operational capability was reached in the autumn of 1992 at Yellowknife and was scheduled as follows for the remaining four FOLs: Rankin Inlet, Inuvik, and Iqaluit (autumn 1993); Kuujjuaq (autumn 1994). Since that schedule was first announced, it has been decided to delay the work at Iqaluit and Rankin Inlet. No new completion dates have been announced for either of these proposed FOLs. The use of airfields near the periphery of the country, coupled with the improved surveillance systems and newly-developed OTHB radar, will greatly enhance NORAD's knowledge of what is occurring in the air space near the coasts, particularly in the Arctic.

Another significant component of NORAD is that of airborne warning and control aircraft (AWACS). These aircraft conduct random patrols of the North Warning System and can extend NORAD's detection and warning capabilities to the top of the polar ice cap. Canadian air force personnel are in the crews of these aircraft as part of a wider exchange programme with the USAF.

Tanker aircraft comprise an integral part of NORAD, enabling fighters to operate in the harsh northern environment. The introduction of CC-130s with air-to-air refuelling capabilities, able to operate from the FOLs, will enhance NORAD's ability to undertake air defence missions. The CC-137 (Boeing 707) fleet is being replaced by the CC-150 Polaris (Airbus A310). The two CC-137s capable of in-flight refuelling will be the last of the type to be retired. Nothing has been decided regarding the modification of any CC-150s for the inflight refuelling role, although the possibility is receiving strong consideration.

The control of all of these systems is the responsibility of 22 Radar Control Wing. It incorporates two Sector Operations Control Centres (SOCCs) which maintain surveillance of the entire Canadian NORAD Region. The wing is an integral part of Fighter Group, but its main function is orientated strictly towards the NORAD mission. The Radar Control Wing comprises the wing headquarters staff and two operational aerospace control and warning squadrons: Canada East (21 Sqn) and Canada West (51 Sqn). Their personnel staff the SOCCs

24 hours a day, seven days a week. Crews consist of air weapons controllers and air defence technicians. Squadron personnel are responsible for carrying out the functions of air surveillance, identification and interceptor control.

When an aircraft enters the coverage of a coastal or North Warning System radar, it appears on the consoles in the operations centre. The aircraft symbol is tagged as 'pending' by the air surveillance section, which is then required to determine whether the return on the console represents an aircraft, or if it is a system-generated false target. This is accomplished electronically in a few seconds and may be repeated several hundred times per hour during peak air traffic periods. Once an aircraft contact is confirmed, this information is passed to the identification section, which has two minutes in which to classify the aircraft as either 'friendly' or 'unknown'. This process involves cross-referencing the aircraft's position with flight plan data passed by the DoT's air traffic control system; attempting radio contact with the aircraft while communicating with ATC agencies in both Canada and the United States; and contacting Canada's Maritime Air Group and the US Navy to determine if any military maritime patrol aircraft are operating in the area.

In the event that these efforts fail to identify the aircraft, and prior to the expiry of the two-minute time limit, the identification officer will declare the aircraft 'unknown'. If an air intercept is feasible, the senior director will scramble interceptors to determine the identity of the 'unknown'. When it might not be possible to dispatch aircraft to perform an intercept, the control squadron continues its efforts to identify the aircraft by other means.

Once the interceptors have taken off, they come under the control of an air weapons control team in the SOCC. By passing information to the pilot(s), such as the target's position, altitude, heading and airspeed, the weapons control team directs the mission until the interceptor has a confirmed radar contact. The pilot then completes the intercept to a point where he can visually identify the aircraft or, if necessary, destroy it.

Fighter Group bases

Fighter Group's flying operations are centred around squadrons located at the main operating bases. Two of Fighter Group's bases, CFB Cold Lake, Alberta, and CFB Bagotville, Quebec, are CF-18 main operating bases. Cold Lake is the largest fighter base, with approximately 3,400 personnel and four fighter squadrons. Bagotville has about 1,550 personnel and two fighter squadrons.

CFB North Bay, Ontario, is home to Fighter Group/Canadian NORAD Region Headquarters and 22 Radar Control Wing. CFB Goose Bay, elevated to base status from a Canadian Forces Station in 1988, supports NATO tactical fighter training for British, German and Dutch air forces for more than six months each year, and it is used by USAF airlifters year round. Goose Bay is also the site of the Canada East Quick Response Area, a facility to which CF-18s and crews are deployed from both Bagotville CF-18 squadrons to hold NORAD alert 24 hours a day, seven days a week. Similarly, CFB Comox supports the

For most of their Canadian service, the CF-116s wore this green/grey tactical camouflage. Today an air defence grey scheme is worn by most.

416 Sqn sent CF-188s to the Gulf War, supporting those from 1 CAD.

410 Sqn uses the CF-188's LERX strake to carry a likeness of the cougar.

The 'Alouettes' of 425 Sqn are one of two French-speaking CF-188 units.

The checkerboard markings identify No. 441 Squadron at Cold Lake.

441 Tactical Fighter Squadron is the second front-line CF-18 unit at Cold Lake. The unit's nickname is the 'Silver Foxes'.

419 Squadron used this CF-116A to proclaim its patriotism, and also to display its 'Moose' nickname. The unit has 14 single-seat F-5s.

In addition to flying the fighter lead-in training role, 419 Squadron also provides a limited reconnaissance capability. Instructors can fly aircraft fitted with a camera nose containing three 70-mm Vinten cameras. With this kit fitted, the aircraft are known as *CF-116A(R)s*.

One of the missions flown by 419 Squadron is dissimilar air combat training, instructors playing the part of 'red' forces. This CF-116D has a suitable camouflage scheme.

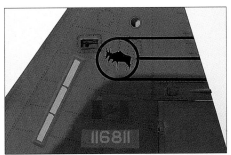

419 Sqn was formed in 1941 as a Wellington unit. Since the war it has operated nothing but fighters.

Advanced training remains 419's most important role, for which the CF-116D is the most important variant. Adding another variation to the list of 419's colour schemes is this example in natural metal with red conspicuity panels on wingtips and tailplanes.

Canada West NORAD alert force and 414 Squadron, although Comox is a Maritime Air Group base rather than a Fighter Group base.

At Cold Lake, 419 Squadron is equipped with approximately 23 CF-5Ds and 14 CF-5As and conducts two basic fighter courses per year, each lasting seven months. The number of students, formerly 24, was reduced to 20 and is now being further reduced to 16. Most BFPC students arrive directly from the advanced flying training course at CFB Moose Jaw, where they received their wings. Known as 'pipeliners', the students receive 81 hours of ground instruction, 48 hours of mission briefings and flight planning, and 38 hours of flying in the CF-5 conversion phase. In the tactical phase, students have 184 hours of ground school, 81 hours of briefings and 41 hours' flight time. The tactical phase includes ACM, air-to-air gunnery, air-to-ground weapons delivery, air-to-air refuelling and low-level navigation.

A few of the instructors maintain an aerial reconnaissance qualification, using CF-5s with three nose-mounted Vinten 70-mm cameras. When so equipped, the aircraft are temporarily designated as CF-5A(R) so as to identify them for maintenance and scheduling purposes. (CF-5Ds cannot be fitted with either the recce nose or the inflight-refuelling probe.) Instructors also use the CF-5s of 419 Squadron in the aggressor role, not only during the annual Maple Flag exercises but also at other Canadian and US bases.

The CF-5s with the Avionics Upgrade Programme (AUP) have not yet entered service with 419. The first are due to arrive by June/July 1993 for instructor training and the first student course should begin by late 1993. Once the AUP is complete, it is not expected that any non-upgraded CF-5s will remain in service.

Graduates of 419's lead-in fighter course move on to 410 Squadron, also at Cold Lake, to begin their conversion to the CF-18. Two courses per year are conducted, the number of students having recently been reduced to 12 per course. About 60 per cent are 'pipeliners', with the remainder coming from other aircraft types. Pilots returning to the CF-18 after a ground posting usually receive 'customised' refresher courses. The basic course includes 124 hours of ground school, 30 to 35 hours in the simulator, and 105 to 111 hours of flying. Instructor pilots maintain their operational efficiency and, when 1 Canadian Air Division was in Europe, 410's instructors were tasked with augmenting the Germany-based squadrons during times of tension.

Forward operating locations

Previously, one CF-18 squadron at each of the main operating bases (425 at Bagotville and 441 at Cold Lake) were assigned to NORAD duties, while the other two (433 and 416) were to reinforce NATO if needed. Currently, each of the four squadrons spends half the year assigned to NORAD and concentrates its training on air-to-air; during the other six months the unit emphasises air-to-ground training, during which time the unit can be deployed anywhere in the world. The four operational CF-18 squadrons are required to be dual-role capable but this semi-annual changeover enables them to devote their full attention to a specific role while training.

The Cold Lake squadrons deploy to CFB Comox to hold alert, and also deploy to two FOLs: Yellowknife and Inuvik. The Bagotville squadrons deploy to Goose Bay for alert duties and also to the (still-unfinished) FOL at Iqaluit. Two aircraft are kept armed and on alert at Comox and Goose Bay and are backed up by others at the respective home bases. Deployments to the FOLs have brought attention to the difficulties associated with operating in that region of Canada and are an excellent test of a squadron's ability to operate away from its main base in a very harsh climate.

The construction of new facilities at the FOLs has helped, but other factors remain beyond the control of those attempting to work in such an environment. The long Arctic night, bitter cold and extreme weather are compounded by the lack of nearby diversion airfields. In all of Canada, there are fewer than 90 airfields with runways 6,000 ft (1830 m) or longer and only 12 of these are above 55°N, of which five have already been selected as FOLs. The flexibility normally associated with fighter operations is greatly restricted. The combination of weather and light conditions with the distances involved, and the other dangers that go with flying in the North, reinforce the need for inflight refuelling.

The disbandment of the Germany-based CF-18 squadrons has resulted in those in Canada receiving additional aircraft. Some of the extra aircrew assigned to the squadrons will be Regular Force personnel, but others will be Air Reservists. These will be former Regular Force personnel with CF-18 experience who have recently left the air force, rather than Reservists trained to fly the type.

Fighter Group's other two squadrons are 414 (CFB Comox) and 434 (CFB Shearwater). 414 was previously based at CFB North Bay and was the air force's sole electronic warfare training squadron, flying versions of the CT-133 Silver Star and CE-144 Challenger. In July 1991, 414 split into two portions. One moved west to Comox, absorbing the personnel and equipment of VU 33, a MAG unit employed in the maritime training and support role, also retaining the 414 number and the 'T-bird' OTU role for the air force. 414 will receive some of the Challengers at a later date.

The other part of the North Bay-based 414 moved to the East Coast, absorbing MAG's VU 32 and being renumbered as 434 Squadron. It took all of the Challengers. Three of the Challengers have been earmarked to become CP-144s for the maritime patrol mission but funding for the modifications needed has not yet been approved. Patrol missions are being flown, but no CP-144s exist yet. 434 Squadron is also the EW Challenger OTU.

Three of the Challengers are CE-144s, fitted to an interim EST (Electronic Support Trainer) standard. Three other CC-144s have been designated to become definitive EST aircraft but, again, funding has not been released.

Reference is often made to 'ET-133s', but this is inaccurate. When in North Bay, half of 414's CT-133s were fitted with underwing pylons to carry jamming pods and with a few related switches in the rear cockpit. The differences compared with standard CT-133s were con-

sidered too slight to warrant a new designation (which would be 'CE-133' in any event), but the squadron referred to these aircraft as 'ET-133s' so as to be able to distinguish between the two versions for scheduling and maintenance purposes.

At Shearwater, 434 is supported by 420 Air Reserve Squadron, which had been 'twinned' with MR 880 prior to its disbandment at CFB Summerside when the CP-121 Trackers were retired in 1990. It should be noted that 420 remains assigned to MAG and did not switch to Fighter Group when VU 32 disbanded. 409, previously a CF-18 squadron in Germany, will be returned to service as an Air Reserve unit at CFB Comox and will support 414 Squadron. 409 will belong to Maritime Air Group rather than Fighter Group when it is reformed.

414 and 434, as previously mentioned, assumed the maritime support roles of VU 32 and VU 33. These include target towing for naval gunnery training as well as simulating sea-skimming missiles using a nose-mounted DPT-1 threat emitter. Both squadrons also take their EW training aircraft as far afield as Florida and Nevada, as well as across Canada. Other duties include calibrating radars by flying at known courses and altitudes.

Fighter Group's remaining flying units are the Base Flights at Cold Lake, Bagotville and Goose Bay. 'Cool Pool' and 'Bagtown' each have three CH-118 Iroquois and a number of CT-133s which are used for several roles including adversaries during ACM training, weather checks and high-speed priority passenger transport, and are also used by rated pilots currently assigned to non-flying jobs. The venerable CT-133s can hold their own against the CF-18 in-close and often present a considerable challenge to the fighters. At least one of the CT-133s at Cold Lake has had its tip tanks removed to improve its turn rate.

The Base Flight helicopters can be used for SAR in the area, but this is mainly used as an interim while waiting for a dedicated SAR unit to arrive. Their primary focus remains to support the flying operations of the base. The CAF's nine CH-118s, 42 CH-135s and 64 CH-136s will all be replaced by Bell 412HP helicopters, to be designated CH-146 Griffon, between 1994 and 1997. After the training unit (403), the Base Flights will probably be the next to receive the new aircraft.

Note: Some units (especially Air Reserve and Air Transport Group squadrons) are based at airfields which come under the operational control of other groups. Such lodger units are listed below under their wing assignment, and not under their parent group.

Fighter Group

UNIT	EQUIPMENT	ROLE
3 Wing, CFB Bagotville, Quebec		
425 'Alouette' Tactical Fighter Squadron	18 × CF-188A/B	NORAD/NATO
433 'Porcupine' Escadron d'Appui Tactique	18 × CF-188A/B	NORAD/NATO
439 'Tiger' Squadron	3 x CH-118, 2 x CT-133, CH-146*	Base Flight
3 Field Technical Training Squadron	various ground instructional airframes	
(rotational QRA detachment from 425 or 433 to Goose Bay; FOL at Iqaluit)		

A pair of CT-133s is assigned to Bagotville's Base Flight (now known as 439 Sqn), which flies them on a variety of duties including liaison and air combat training.

Cold Lake's Base Flight (417 Sqn) has no less than eight CT-133s assigned, these being used intensively by the base's training units for adversary work.

For utility transport and local rescue, 417 Sqn has three CH-118s. These are Bell 205s, and are shortly to be replaced by the CH-146 Griffon (Bell 412HP).

'Cool Pool' BF CH-118s wear this badge over the high-conspicuity yellow.

The 'Honkers' of the Goose Bay BF (444 Sqn) feature the silhouette of Labrador.

Goose Bay differs from the other Fighter Group Base Flight by having the CH-135 Twin Huey, providing greater lifting power and twin-engined reliability.

CF-188 launches from Bagotville as the Base Flight CH-118 ...ts on the apron. During flying operations a rescue crew is ...ways on alert.

'Bagtown's' rescue flight has a bilingual patch featuring the CH-118.

Three of 434 Squadron's Challengers are equipped to CE-144 standard, able to create an ECM environment for realistic training for other units.

CT-133s are currently flown by 414 Squadron in the EW role and for target facilities. The squadron should receive CE-144 Challengers in due course.

...or the EW training role, 414's CT-133s carry pods under wing pylons. Only some of the ...rcraft are so equipped, but to call them 'ET-133s' or 'CE-133s' is erroneous, although the ...rmer has some unofficial currency. Other aircraft fly target facilities missions.

414 is the 'Black Knight' squadron, and its aircraft wear this badge.

The Challengers of 434 'Bluenose' Sqn wear a ship badge on the fuselage.

...nly three examples of the 434 Sqn Challenger fleet are to CE-144 standard, three others flying target ...cilities missions as standard CC-144s although these are planned to have a full electronic warfare ...pgrade. Further airframes are due for conversion to patrol aircraft as CP-144s.

4 Wing, CFB Cold Lake, Alberta

410 'Cougar' Tactical Fighter Operational Training Squadron	23 × CF-188A/B	CF-188 OCU/ORTU
416 'Lynx' Tactical Fighter Squadron	18 × CF-188A/B	NORAD/NATO
419 'Moose' Tactical Fighter Training Squadron	14 × CF-116A/A(R), 23 × CF-116D	CF-188 lead-in; recce and aggressor
441 'Silver Fox' Tactical Fighter Squadron	18 × CF-188A/B	NORAD/NATO
417 Combat Support Squadron	3 × CH-118, 8 × CT-133	Base Flight
AETE (Aerospace Engineering Test Establishment)	5 × CF-5A/D, 3 × CF-188A/B, 2 × CT-114, 5 × CT-133, 2 × CH-135, 3 × CH-136, 1 × CX-144 (wfu?)	test and evaluation
10 Field Technical Training Squadron	various ground instructional airframes	

(rotational QRA detachment from 416 and 441 to Comox, BC; FOLs at Yellow-knife and Inuvik, NWT)

5 Wing, CFB Goose Bay, Labrador

444 Combat Support Squadron	3 × CH-135, CH-146*	Base Flight

(Canada East QRA – CF-188s deployed from Bagotville)
(RAF/KLu/Luftwaffe low-level training area)

22 Wing, CFB North Bay, Ontario

(HQ: Fighter Group/Canadian NORAD)

(414 Sqn, see 19 Wing, Maritime Air Group)
(434 Sqn, see 12 Wing, Maritime Air Group)

* not yet in service	wfu = withdrawn from use

1 Canadian Air Division

Canadian military aviation in Europe ended on 19 January 1993 with the departure of 24 CF-18s of 439 Squadron, the last flying unit in 1 Canadian Air Division.

1 CAD began as the RCAF's 1 Air Division in 1951, consisting of 12 squadrons in four wings. After the Sabre, the all-weather Avro Canada CF-100 Canuck was added. The Canadair CF-104 Starfighter arrived in 1962, accompanied by a change of role from air defence to nuclear strike/reconnaissance.

Following France's departure from NATO's military structure, the Canadian units based at Marville and Grostenquin, France, relocated to Germany. The Zweibrücken unit also moved and all fighter squadrons were consolidated at the other German air base, Baden-Soellingen. The Canadian Forces air element was further reorganised in 1970 with 1 Air Division being superseded by 1 Canadian Air Group. Its headquarters were at Lahr, the other Canadian base in Germany. In 1972, the Canadian government announced that the three remaining CAF squadrons in Germany would switch to a conventional attack role, relinquishing their nuclear strike and reconnaissance capabilities.

1 Canadian Air Group entered a new era with the arrival of the first CF-18 aircraft in June 1985. 409 Squadron moved to Germany in July 1985 with its new CF-18s, joined by 439 Squadron in November 1985 and 421 Squadron in July 1986, both having converted from CF-104s. The CF-18s were pooled, officially belonging to 1 Air Maintenance Squadron. The flying units applied their badges to some aircraft, but this was usually done for air shows, exchange visits, exercises and the like and did not indicate ownership.

A change of government policy resulted in the end of Canada's commitment to the ACE Mobile Force (Air) in northern Norway at the end of May 1988 and, coincidentally, the rapid reinforcement role of two Canada-based units, 416 and 433 Squadrons, shifted to NATO's Central Region. 1 Canadian Air Group was replaced by a reactivated 1 Canadian Air Division with two wings of five CF-18 squadrons: 3 (Fighter) Wing at Lahr and 4 (Fighter) Wing at Baden-Soellingen. Of the five squadrons, three were based in Germany (409, 421, and 439) with the other two (416 and 433) in Canada.

409 Squadron was deployed to Qatar in October 1990 as part of the Canadian contribution to the coalition effort in the Gulf War. In December 1990, it rotated home and was replaced by 439 Squadron which was augmented by 416 Squadron, as well as by aircraft and pilots from the other CF-18 units.

409 was disbanded on 24 June 1991 as part of the government's reduction of Canadian Forces in Europe. At the same time, 3 Wing disbanded. 421 Sqn was disbanded on 1 June 1992, leaving 439 Sqn to carry on, supported by 1 Air Maintenance Squadron. Both continued to be part of 4 Wing.

1 Canadian Air Division and 4 Wing disbanded on 1 September 1992. On 31 December 1992, 439 ceased operational flying and its CF-18s were returned to Canada beginning on 19 January 1993. 439's official disbandment was scheduled for 15 May 1993. When 409 disbanded, its aircraft and most of its personnel were reassigned to 421 and 439 Squadrons. 421's disbandment resulted in the transfer of its aircraft and personnel back to Canada.

While no Canadian aircraft will be permanently based in Europe, both 416 and 433 Squadrons retain the reinforcement assignment and the other CF-18 units can be deployed across the Atlantic. In addition, the squadrons will participate in exercises in Europe to maintain proficiency in that operating environment.

NATO's Airborne Early Warning Component, based at Geilenkirchen, Germany, operates 18 rapidly deployable E-3A Sentry aircraft and three Boeing 707 trainers with 29 multinational crews. Its principal mission is the air surveillance of NATO sovereign territory. Of the 11 member nations involved, the Canadian contingent ranks third in terms of financial contribution and manpower participation, with 137 officers and NCOs representing 30 different classifications and trades.

409 Squadron was a 1 CAD stalwart, and saw action in the Gulf War. Disbanded as a fighter squadron, the number has been transferred to a Reserve unit at Comox.

Auroras from the Greenwood BAMEO wear the station badge.

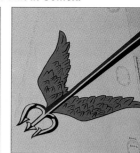

The winged trident is the badge of CP-140 operator 407 Sqn at Comox.

The CP-140 combines the airframe of the P-3 Orion with an ASW suite derived from that fitted to the S-3 Viking. This example serves with 407 Sqn at Comox.

Auroras rarely wear squadron badges as they are centrally maintained by Greenwood BAMEO. This base houses two front-line squadrons and a training unit.

Maritime Air Group

The role of Maritime Air Group (MAG) is to provide combat-ready maritime air forces to support North American and NATO defence commitments. These include anti-submarine warfare (ASW), sovereignty surveillance, open-ocean reconnaissance, and direct support of fleet operations. MAG's duties include the provision of a presence and control in the areas over and under Canada's sea approaches, along its coastal waters and in the Arctic. Maritime Air Group aircraft also have a secondary search and rescue role.

With the transfer of the aircraft of VU 32 and VU 33 to Fighter Group's 414 and 434 Squadrons, Maritime Air Group was reduced to just two basic types of aircraft. MAG's CP-140 Aurora fleet of 18 aircraft is in the process of being increased by three with the addition of the CP-140A Arcturus. These are 'austere' versions, lacking an ASW suite, but with enhanced search radar capabilities. They will have two roles: 'front end' crew training, and Arctic sovereignty patrols. Because they lack the expensive and sensitive avionics, they will be much better suited for use as trainers. Their presence at Greenwood will enable MAG to send a fifth Aurora to the West Coast unit (407), this coinciding with Maritime Command's shift of assets there to bring the Atlantic and Pacific fleets more in line with each other. (Canada's NATO role had always placed an emphasis on helping to keep the sea lanes to Europe open.)

CFB Greenwood is home to three squadrons. 404 is the CP-140 OCU, while 405 and 415 Squadrons are the operational units. The Maritime Proving and Evaluation Unit is also located at Greenwood, as is the Aurora Soft-

Like the CP-140s, the CH-124 Sea Kings are centrally maintained, by the Shearwater BAMEO. The unit supports two front-line squadrons, one training unit and the HOTEF

Above: HS 423 is the operational CH-124 squadron at Shearwater.

Left: Three CH-124As deploy to Somalia. The two trailing aircraft are both in (Gulf Mod) configuration, with nose-mounted thermal imagers.

ea Kings regularly operate from warships of Maritime Command, in this case HMCS Nipigon. Of the total of 28 ea Kings, eight have been given the 'Gulf' modification, which substitutes FLIR, door-guns and self-defence equipment for ASW gear. Six are CH-124Bs with uprated systems to provide CH-148 lead-in support.

Maritime Air Group has 18 regular CP-140 Auroras for ASW work, augmented by three 'austere' CP-140A Arcturus airframes which are used for training and patrols.

equipment from the oldest Auroras, and then store the early CP-140s until the average airframe hours of the new aircraft matched the old. It was hoped that by then funds would be available to put the latest equipment into the empty airframes and then to upgrade the rest on a regular basis. With the virtual disappearance of the former Soviet Union's submarines from the North Atlantic, it is certain that such a programme will not proceed.

Near-shore patrol was previously performed by the CP-121 Tracker but the type was withdrawn in 1990. Consideration had been given to re-engining the Trackers with turboprops and IMP had a contract to temporarily convert one aircraft but, in the end, the decision was made not to proceed. Aside from a few which were set aside for preservation, the fleet went into storage. Many have since been sold to forest fire-fighting operators, one of which, Conair, is converting them to turboprops. The Tracker's fishery and environmental patrol mission was taken over by a pair of civilian Beech King Airs under contract to the federal government. CP-140s also are used in support of the Department of Fisheries and Oceans. Other Aurora missions support the Royal Canadian Mounted Police and the Defence Research Establishment (Atlantic).

The second aircraft type operated by MAG is the CH-124 Sea King, most of the improved CH-124A version. An initial batch of six, followed by two more, were modified for service in Operation Friction. The ASW gear was removed and a 'Gulf mods' package installed. This included a FLIR turret, chaff and flare dispensers, anti-IR missile devices, and a light machine-gun in the cargo door. Initially designated as CH-124C, this was soon changed back to CH-124A. Many of the modifications have been retained and they are now known as 'surveillance mods' and are used with considerable success during anti-smuggling patrols.

The CH-124B designation has been assigned to six modified Sea Kings that will serve as a lead-in to the EH.101. Equipped with HELTAS (Helicopter Towed Array Support), these Sea

ware Development Unit. The CP-140s and CP-140As at Greenwood are 'owned' by the Base Aircraft Maintenance Engineering Organisation and are assigned to the flying units on an as-required basis. As they are pooled, they only wear squadron insignia when participating in major exercises and competitions such as Fincastle.

The first CP-140A Arcturus entered service on 30 November 1992, and all three will be carrying out operational patrols by early summer 1993. Internally the CP-140 is quite different to the P-3 Orion and the Canadian aircraft has perhaps been best described as being 'two S-3s in a P-3 airframe'. The CP-140As were delivered in very basic condition to IMP Aerospace, the subcontractor to Lockheed.

Had Lockheed switched to producing the P-7, as was then expected, the third Arcturus would have been the very last P-3 airframe to come off the assembly line. With the cancellation of the P-7, the P-3 line was moved from California to Georgia, keeping open the possibility of more aircraft being purchased for MAG. There was a strong push at one point to buy perhaps a dozen more aircraft, transfer the

Kings will also have updated mission systems to provide lead-in training and better mission capability prior to the EH.101 service introduction. A total of 50 EH.101s has been ordered, but 15 of these will be assigned to SAR duties and will have the rear loading ramp. The 35 ASW variants will be deployed on the new frigates. As with the Sea Kings before them, the EH.101s will be large helicopters on small ships. They will be fitted with the 'bear trap' haul-down system which permits flying operations in rough seas. In this procedure, the helicopter enters a hover above the landing deck and lowers a cable which is locked into the device. The pilot then maintains tension against the pull of the 'bear trap' which is constantly and rapidly adjusted to the rise and fall of the deck.

The first EH.101 is currently scheduled to be delivered in 1998. The first examples in service will be the Westland-built SAR variant with rear loading ramps, radar and FLIR, and will have the Canadian designation of CH-149 Chimo (an Inuit word for 'welcome'). It is not yet known if all of the SAR versions will be delivered before any of the ASW helicopters. The Sea King replacements will have the designation of CH-148 Petrel.

The ASW version will be equipped with AN/APS-137 surface search radar, FLIR, Thomson-CSF dipping sonar, AQS-503 sonics processor, AN/ALR-76C ECM, sonobuoys, torpedoes and the haul-down system described above. CH-148s will be built by Agusta in Italy.

The programme cost is approximately $4.4 billion (Cdn) but, of that, only about $1.5 billion will be paid to Agusta and Westland for 'green' aircraft. A $100 million contract with General Electric Canada covers the T700 engines (three per helicopter), and Paramax Systems Canada in conjunction with IMP Aerospace will design and integrate the avionics packages. (Spending estimates announced in February 1993 included approximately $5.5 billion for the EH.101 acquisition.)

The Sea Kings all belong to the CFB Shearwater BAMEO (Base Aircraft Maintenance Engineering Organisation), including those on ships and those based on the West Coast at CFB Esquimalt with HS 443. HT 406 also trains AESOPs (Airborne Electronic Sensor Operators) for the CT-133 and Challengers. In practice, the Sea Kings are assigned to the Shearwater units for varying periods of time, rather than just for the duration of the mission, although there is a degree of swapping between the two squadrons and the Helicopter Operational Test and Evaluation Flight (HOTEF). Given the geographical separation, the Sea Kings based

on the West Coast tend to stay there, but they still belong to the Shearwater BAMEO, whose detachment maintains them.

One Sea King is known as the 'water bird' and is designated as the helicopter to be used for practising water landings. While any Sea King is theoretically capable of doing this, this example has had some of the equipment removed and its water proofing receives extra care and attention.

Maritime Air Group

UNIT	EQUIPMENT	ROLE
12 Wing, CFB Shearwater, Nova Scotia		
HT 406 (406 Maritime Operational Training Squadron)	uses BAMEO CH-124	CH-124 OCU/ORTU
HS 423 (423 'Eagle' Helicopter Anti-Submarine Squadron)	uses BAMEO CH-124	ASW; SAR; anti-smuggling
HOTEF	uses BAMEO CH-124	
BAMEO	22 × CH-124A, 6 × CH-124B	
434 'Bluenose' Composite Squadron (Fighter Group)	3 × CC-144, 3 × CE-144, CP-144*	EW; patrol; support; FRU; calibration
420 'Snowy Owl' Composite Squadron (Air Reserve/Maritime Air Group)		twinned with 434
14 Wing, CFB Greenwood, Nova Scotia		
404 Maritime Patrol and Training Squadron	uses BAMEO CP-140/140A	CP-140 OCU/ORTU
405 Maritime Patrol Squadron	uses BAMEO CP-140/140A	MP/MR surveillance
415 Maritime Patrol Squadron	uses BAMEO CP-140/140A	MP/MR surveillance
BAMEO	13 × CP-140, 3 × CP-140A	
413 'Tusker' Transport and Rescue Squadron (Air Transport Group)	2 × CH-113/113A, 3 × CC-130E, CH-149*	SAR and transport
19 Wing, CFB Comox, British Columbia		
407 Maritime Patrol	5 × CP-140	MP/MR surveillance Squadron
414 'Black Knight' Composite Squadron (Fighter Group)	14 × CT-133	CT-133 OCU; FRU; DACT
409 'Nighthawk' Composite Squadron (Air Reserve/Maritime Air Group)		twinned with 414
442 Transport and Rescue Squadron (Air Transport Group)	5 × CH-113/113A, 6 × CC-115	CH-113/CC-115 OCU/ORTU; SAR; light transport
(Canada West QRA – CF-18s deployed from Cold Lake)		
CFB Esquimalt, British Columbia		
HS 443 (443 Helicopter Anti Submarine Squadron)	5 × CH-124A from Shearwater BAMEO, CH-148*	ASW and SAR

Air Transport Group's badge depicts an albatross flying over the globe.

412 Squadron has a peregrine falcon as its badge.

Six CC-109 Cosmopolitans remain on charge with 412 Sqn, used for staff transport. Originally fitted with Eland turboprops, the aircraft now have Allisons.

One of 412's CC-109s is detached to Colorado Springs in the US to provide support for the Canadian contingent at NORAD headquarters.

412's main mission type for the staff/VIP transport role is the CC-144 Challenger. Seven are in service, either CL-600S or CL-601-1A variants.

Air Transport Group

Air Transport Group provides the Canadian Armed Forces' strategic, tactical, utility, aeromedical evacuation and VIP airlift for both domestic and international missions. ATG is also responsible for the co-ordination of search and rescue (SAR) across Canada and its near-shore waters, SAR satellite control, and the warning and provision of air resources for SAR response. No longer involved in the daily trans-Canada passenger flights which have been contracted out, ATG's primary mission re-

mains the development and maintenance of an airlift force capable of responding to national or international emergencies requiring Canadian military participation.

Air Transport Group crews must be proficient in both strategic and tactical airlift, in-flight refuelling, scheduled and VIP airlift, and aeromedical evacuation. SAR responsibilities include both land and sea, mercy flights, major air disaster response, and civilian SAR training through the Civilian Search and Rescue Asso-

424 Sqn has the nickname 'Tiger'. This badge is on a CH-113.

The CC-130s of 429 and 436 Squadrons wear the Trenton base badge.

424 Squadron at Trenton is a SAR unit, flying three CH-113s and borrowing a single CC-130 from Trenton AMEO for the 'search' part of its mission. During World War II it was a distinguished bomber unit flying Wellingtons, Halifaxes and Lancasters.

The buffalo is the badge of 429 Sqn, flying CC-130s from Trenton.

Partnering 429 is 436 Sqn, whose badge is an elephant holding a log.

424 Sqn personnel practise rescue techniques from one of the squadron's CH-113 Labradors.

Approaching the end of its CF career is the CC-137, of which five served with 437 'Husky' Squadron. Two of the quintet are equipped for aerial refuelling and a third has a VIP transport interior. Replacement by the Airbus A310 is under way.

ciation (CASARA). Aircrew training is conducted to the highest standards to ensure a capability to respond safely and effectively anywhere in the world. Many such missions are often tasked on very short notice and ATG crews live up to their motto, 'Versatile and Ready', on a daily basis.

On 1 June 1991, the scheduled trans-Canada and transatlantic passenger flights using 437 Squadron's Boeing CC-137s were taken over by Air Canada and Nationair under a three-year contract. Rather than using the military bases, the flights now connect the nearest major cities, using existing airline facilities such as check-in and baggage handling. Between 1 October 1991 and 30 September 1992, these flights carried 273,794 passengers. Nationair assumed responsibility for the transatlantic flights (Ottawa-Lahr), while Air Canada handles the domestic services (Halifax-Ottawa-Toronto-Winnipeg-Edmonton-Vancouver). Other flights, such as trooping flights taking Canadian personnel to UN duties, are also contracted out occasionally.

Aircraft types

Canadian Airlines International owned several ex-Wardair A310s (acquired through its take-over of that airline) and sold three for $150 million to the Department of National Defence. This was accompanied by the cancellation of the five-year, $111-million contract with CAI covering the maintenance and overhaul of the Boeing CC-137s (707s). The normal useful life of the CC-137 was expected to come to an end by 1996. A five-year life extension programme would have cost at least $150 million and the problems that are associated with ageing aircraft would have also arisen.

Designated CC-150 Polaris by the air force, the A310s can carry 24 more passengers than the CC-137s' 170, plus additional freight, for a fuel burn two-thirds that of the older aircraft. They are also quieter, a fact no doubt appreciated by CFB Trenton's neighbours. It is also expected that one of the three aircraft will receive a VIP interior, although this will be readily convertible to a standard interior (as was the case with the CC-137s). Inflight-refuelling equipment is the subject of serious study for installation on at least two of the CC-150s. It is also planned to acquire a further two ex-airline A310s, replacing the CC-137s on a one-for-one basis in 437 Squadron.

The aircraft will be operated in a role and configuration similar to that of an airliner and virtually no changes were made to the CC-150s beyond the installation of a TCAS (traffic alert, and collision avoidance system) and the application of a gloss grey colour scheme. It is expected that at least two of the aircraft will eventually be modified to have a cargo door to permit the carriage of freight on the upper deck, but this will involve additional work to strengthen the floor. The capacity of the lower compartment is sufficiently greater than that of the CC-137 that it may prove unnecessary to use the upper deck for cargo. The air force will need to acquire motorised container loading systems at its bases to take full advantage of the CC-150's ability to carry the LD-3 containers.

Two of the five CC-137s can be fitted with wingtip-mounted Beech inflight-refuelling pods and these will be the last two of the type to remain with 437 Squadron. The fleet was obtained from a cancelled Western Airlines order beginning in 1970. Until the contract was let to the private sector, the aircraft were used for six flights per week across Canada. The Shearwater-Ottawa-Trenton-Winnipeg-Edmonton (Namao)-Victoria flights were operated three days a week, with the reverse being flown on alternate days. Further flights were operated across the Atlantic to the two German bases and still others were in support of UN peacekeeper trooping flights, VIP operations, etc. Of the five aircraft, one was always in Calgary with CAI for a major overhaul, this lasting approximately one year and effectively limiting the fleet to four serviceable aircraft.

The first CC-137 (13702) was scheduled to be retired in March 1993, followed by 13701 in September. The two tankers (13703 and 13704), along with 13705, will be retired following the CC-150s' cargo conversion.

Most of the de Havilland Canada CC-115 Buffalo aircraft have been withdrawn. Only those with 442 Squadron, a SAR unit based at Comox, remain, this aircraft being better suited than CC-130s to the mountainous terrain in 442's area of responsibility. (When the SAR version of the EH.101 [the CH-149 Chimo] enters service, replacing the CH-113 and CH-113A, 442 is expected to operate only helicopters.)

The CC-115s had a secondary light transport role and, at one time, were also used for maritime patrol. 413 Squadron replaced its four Buffaloes with two Hercules, greatly extending their unrefuelled range and shortening transit times. 424 draws from the pool of CC-130s (a mix of E and H models) belonging to the CFB Trenton BAMEO (as do 429 and 436 Squadrons), but two CC-130s are normally 'semi-assigned' to 424. The SAR equipment containers can be quickly transferred to another aircraft in the event of mechanical problems. The rear doors normally used by paratroops can be opened and replaced by a large, clear panel which improves visibility during search operations.

The CC-130 fleet is a varied one, comprising both E and H models (three survivors of the first four Bs having been sold) and there are several sub-types of both models in service. All are now camouflaged in shades of green and grey (a pattern adopted by the Royal New Zealand Air Force as well) but consideration is being given to an overall grey. A darker grey than that selected by the USAF, both gloss and matt versions have been tried.

Considerable confusion exists concerning the official designations for the Hercules in Canadian service. 'CC-130' is the official designation, regardless of variant, but 'CC-130E' and 'CC-130H' are used frequently. This is probably to simplify things for scheduling, maintenance, and aircrew. According to ATG's public affairs office, the tanker versions are currently known as 'CC-130H(T)' but there is some thought to changing this to 'KCC-130'.

Northwest Industries, in Edmonton, has several contracts relating to the CC-130 fleet. One calls for the aircraft to be cycled through a progressive structural inspection programme every 3,200 flying hours. Each such inspection takes about 35 working days. Another programme covers the conversion of the newest five CC-130s to tanker configuration, and NWI is the only company anywhere approved by Lockheed to perform this work. Flight Refuelling Mk 32B pods, a 3,600-Imp gal (16365-litre) fuselage tank, and flight deck controls are part of the programme, due for completion in April 1993.

A third NWI programme covered the detailed inspection and investigation of two E model Hercules in order to determine the structural condition of the aircraft, some of the air force's E models having reached 32,000 flying hours. The data obtained will contribute to the development of maintenance and inspection requirements for the remainder of the E models in the inventory.

Another NWI CC-130 programme covers the overhaul of the Quick Change Engine Unit. QCEUs are processed at the rate of approximately 25 per year. NWI also handles the CC-130 Publications Management Services.

Other ATG missions

The Canadian Mission Control Centre (CMCC) is located at CFB Trenton and it is part of the growing international SAR Satellite Aided Tracking (SARSAT) programme. Founded by Canada, the United States, the then-Soviet Union and France, the programme dates back to 1979. SARSAT uses satellites to detect emergency locator transmitters (ELTs, also known as 'beacons'), which are designed to be activated at the time of an aircraft crash or a ship sinking.

CMCC processes information received from three satellite tracking stations (Edmonton, Churchill and Goose Bay) as well as from foreign MCCs. The resulting information is transmitted to the Canadian Rescue Co-ordination Centres (RCCs) or foreign MCCs. Since the programme's inception it has saved more than 1,500 lives and the first worldwide SARSAT-initiated rescue occurred in Canada in late 1982.

The implementation of SARSAT has drastically reduced the number of major searches conducted by the air force's SAR squadrons and has reduced the alerting time to a matter of hours. Under most circumstances, a beacon is detected within two hours and its position determined within several kilometres. A 'constellation' of four satellites in polar orbits provides adequate coverage for the vast Canadian territory.

Air Transport Group is Air Command's major contributor to UN and other peacekeeping missions. It conducts trooping flights to transport CAF personnel to and from the overseas locations, as well as carrying humanitarian relief supplies.

Other duties include the handling of passengers, cargo and mail to support airlift in Canada and around the world. 1 Air Movements Unit (CFB Edmonton), 2 AMU (Trenton), 3 AMU (Ottawa), and 1 Air Transport Unit (Lahr) have been assigned this mission. The commander of ATG exercises direct operational control over 1 ATU. In the case of the three AMUs, their respective base commanders occupy an intermediate position.

437 Sqn's husky badge adorned CC-137s for many years.

442 Sqn is a rescue unit based at Comox as part of 19 Wing, MAG.

Looking suitably military, the CC-150 Polaris (Airbus A310) is ATG's latest acquisition. Three have been purchased, with a further two likely.

Standard tactical transport for the CF is the Hercules, most of which are assigned to the Trenton BAMEO for use by 426 (training), 424 (rescue), 429 and 436 Sqns.

Significantly enhancing the tanker capabilities of the CF are five CC-130Hs converted to CC-130H(T) status, with underwing FR Mk 32 HDUs.

435 Squadron is based at Edmonton, flying transport and tanker Hercs.

The badge of the 103 Rescue Unit features a universal symbol of salvation!

0 Squadron's nickname
'Bats'. It was a wartime
ghter-bomber unit.

From its Greenwood base, 413 Transport and Rescue Squadron flies three CC-130s (above) on long-range SAR patrols, and two CH-113s (below) on short range.

In common with many other nations, Canada is adopting an anonymous mid-grey colour scheme for its CC-130s. The Hercules fleet is heavily involved in humanitarian work.

he 'Bats' of 440 Sqn are equipped with five CC-138 Twin
tters, two of which are detached to Yellowknife. The type
most useful in mountainous terrain.

ying from Comox, 442 Sqn still uses the CC-115 Buffalo,
is aircraft proving far better-suited to the mountain
gions than the Hercules.

ander's dedicated SAR mission is handled by the 103
escue Unit with CH-113s. The ancient Labrador also equips
3 Sqn (above right) at Greenwood.

The AMUs are responsible for providing Mobile Air Movements teams (MAMs) in support of airlift operations on a global basis. 1 and 2 AMUs can each provide up to three MAMs and 3 AMU can provide one. Each team consists of 10 people. MAMs personnel are regularly involved in the resupply of remote facilities such as CFS Alert (the world's most northern settlement) and in various relief aid programmes. During Operation Friction, MAMs personnel were stationed in Germany, Cyprus and throughout the Middle East, airlifting 9 million lb of cargo and 4,000 passengers.

426 Squadron is based at CFB Trenton, where ATG itself is headquartered, and it conducts training for aircrew and technical support personnel for the CC-109 Cosmopolitan, CC-130 Hercules and, until recently, the CC-137. (No decision has been announced yet concerning the training of future crews for the CC-150s, which is being conducted at the Airbus training centre in Miami at present.) 426's aircraft are provided by trainee squadrons.

Air Transport Group operates a variety of scheduled services to connect its bases, such as the CC-130 run from Trenton to Bagotville and Goose Bay and return one or two times a week. Other commitments include providing aircraft support to the Canadian Airborne Regiment, the jump school and to various land forces units. Finally, ATG participates in a variety of international and domestic military exercises and competitions, such as Airlift Rodeo, Bullseye and TALEX.

Air Transport Group

UNIT	EQUIPMENT	ROLE
7 Wing, CFB Ottawa, Ontario		
412 Transport and Rescue Squadron	6 × CC-109, 7 × CC-144	VIP transport
(detachment at NORAD HQ, Colorado Springs, with one of the CC-109s)		
8 Wing, CFB Trenton, Ontario		
424 'Tiger' Transport and Rescue Squadron	3 × CH-113/113A, 1 × BAMEO CC-130, CH-149*	SAR and transport
426 Transport Training Squadron	borrows CC-109, CC-130	CC-109/130 OCU/ ORTU
429 Transport Squadron	uses BAMEO CC-130E/H	transport
436 Transport Squadron	uses BAMEO CC-130E/H	transport
437 'Husky' Transport and Tanker Squadron	5 × CC-137, 3 × CC-130	passenger, VIP and cargo transport; inflight refuelling
BAMEO AMDU	17 CC-130E/H; various ground instructional airframes	
9 Wing, CFS Gander, Newfoundland		
103 Rescue Unit	3 × CH-113/113A	SAR
18 Wing, CFB Edmonton, Alberta		
435 Transport Squadron	12 × CC-130E/H/T	transport; tanker
418 Transport Squadron (Air Reserve)		twinned with 435
440 'Bat' Transport and Rescue Squadron	5 × CC-138	SAR
(+ two-aircraft detachment at Yellowknife, Northwest Territory)		
CFB Lahr, Germany		
1 Air Transport Unit		
	1 × CC-109	transport
(413 Sqn, see 14 Wing, Maritime Air Group)		
(442 Sqn, see 19 Wing, Maritime Air Group)		

401 Sqn is an Air Reserve unit providing CH-136 training at Montreal.

438 Sqn is based alongside 401 but has a front-line role

At Montreal the two Air Reserve squadrons form 1 Tactical Aviation Wing, equipped solely with the Bell CH-136 Kiowa. Both observation and VIP transport work is undertaken.

The 2nd TAW is located at Toronto, comprising 400 and 41. Sqns. Illustrating the waterborne capability of the CH-136 this float-equipped example.

11 Wing comprises five squadrons, four of which are locate at Mobile Command bases. 408 Sqn is one of these, flying from Edmonton.

10 Tactical Air Group

10 Tactical Air Group provides the land forces with an aviation component. It also supports other national and international commitments of the Canadian Armed Forces, such as peace-keeping and observer missions, and 10 TAG aircraft fly missions involving support to the Royal Canadian Mounted Police (RCMP) and other federal agencies. Aircraft are additionally used for the transport of VIPs throughout Canada.

These tasks are accomplished by three tactical helicopter squadrons and one helicopter operational training squadron from the Regular Force in Canada. 10 TAG exercises operational control over two Air Reserve wings, each with two squadrons. Until mid-1991, 10 TAG had two squadrons (447 and 450) equipped with a total of seven CH-147 Chinooks, but the aircraft were withdrawn due to their high operating costs. 447 Squadron was disbanded, while 450 retained its CH-135 Utility Tactical Transport Helicopter (UTTH) Flight and added a second flight. This was known as the SAH Flight, or SERT Assault Helicopter Flight. The flight supported the RCMP's Special Emergency Response Team, whose mission is being taken over by the military. The Chinooks have reportedly been sold to the Netherlands.

403 Squadron, located at CFB Gagetown, New Brunswick, is responsible for training helicopter crews for the Regular Force. Equipped with eight CH-136 Kiowas and nine CH-135 Twin Hueys, the unit trains students who have graduated from the basic helicopter course at the former CFB Portage, now Southport Aerospace Centre.

Night vision goggles were introduced into 10 Tactical Air Group during 1991, with all squadrons carrying out an intensive training programme. When complete, the operational effectiveness and capability of 10 TAG's helicopters and crews will be significantly enhanced.

Observers for the Kiowas which serve in the LOH role come mostly from land force units, such as armour or artillery. Pilots frequently spend time 'in the field' with the ground troops to ensure that both components understand the needs of the other.

Except for 450 Squadron, the other Regular Force 10 TAG units are located at major 'army' bases and exercise with their counterparts.

In April 1992, a deal was announced for the purchase of 100 Bell 412HP helicopters, which are produced in Montreal, as are the Pratt & Whitney Canada PT6T engines. These are to replace the CH-135s and CH-136s of 10 TAG, Air Reserve Group and the Fighter Group Base Flights. Deliveries are to commence in 1994 (to 403 Sqn) and will be completed by mid-1997. Early reports indicate that the Base Flights will likely be early recipients of the new aircraft. It is not yet known if AETE will replace its helicopters with the 412s, which are to be designated CH-146, but this is most likely. The deal is worth about $1 billion.

10 Tactical Air Group

UNIT	EQUIPMENT	ROLE
1 Wing, CFB Montreal, Quebec		
401 Helicopter Operational Training Squadron (Air Reserve)	10 × CH-136	OCU; LOH; VIP
438 Tactical Helicopter Squadron (Air Reserve)	10 × CH-136	LOH; VIP; etc.
1 Tactical Aviation Support Squadron		
2 Wing, CFB Toronto, Ontario		
400 Helicopter Operational Training Squadron (Air Reserve)	10 × CH-136	OCU; LOH; VIP
411 Tactical Helicopter Squadron (Air Reserve)	10 × CH-136	LOH; VIP; etc.
2 Tactical Aviation Support Squadron		
11 Wing (at various 'army' bases)		
CFB Gagetown, New Brunswick		
403 Helicopter Operational Training Squadron	9 × CH-135, 8 × CH-136, CH-146*	advanced helo OCU
CFB Edmonton, Alberta		
408 Tactical Helicopter Squadron	6 × CH-135, 10 × CH-136, CH-146*	LOH; UTTH
CFB Petawawa, Ontario		
427 Tactical Helicopter Squadron	16 × CH-135, CH-146*	LOH; UTTH
CFB Valcartier, Quebec		
430 Tactical Transport Squadron	16 × CH-136, CH-146*	LOH; UTTH
CFB Ottawa, Ontario		
450 Composite Helicopter Squadron	7 × CH-135	UTTH; VIP; and RCMP Special Emergency Response Team support

The 11 Wing squadrons all feature a mix of CH-136 Kiowas for observation work, and CH-135 Twin Hueys (illustrated) for assault transport.

TAG has over 70 CH-136 Kiowas on charge, used for liaison, utility transport, observation and training. The fleet is fitted with wire-cutter protection above and below the cockpit, and night-vision goggles are available to the pilots. Along with the CH-135s which partner the Kiowa on army support, the CH-136 is scheduled for replacement by the Bell 412HP, which will be known as the CH-146 Griffon in CF service.

00 Sqn's eagle and rossed axe badge was arried by Lysanders in 940.

For 403 Sqn's 50th anniversary, this CH-136 was adorned in D-Day invasion stripes and the unit's wartime 'KH' code. At the time it was flying Spitfire Mk IXs.

A squad of troops rides in the doors of this 403 Sqn CH-135, ready for immediate action. The unit acts as the OCU for both Kiowa and Twin Huey.

he Canada Goose badge f 408 Squadron is worn by H-135s and CH-136s.

Kiowas have a weapons capability in the form of small rocket launchers. These are principally used for marking targets.

427 Squadron at Petawawa is equipped solely with the CH-135. Like the Kiowas, these also have wire-cutting blades installed.

27 Sqn formed in ovember 1942 and has lways used this badge.

450 Sqn flies from Ottawa with the CH-135 (right) on RCMP support.

Training

It is in the area of training that Air Command has seen one of its biggest changes recently. 14 Training Group was responsible until 1990, but upon the disbandment of this organisation the administration of training was assumed by Air Command Headquarters through its Training and Reserve Branch, specifically the Operations and Training Cell. This branch is responsible for all undergraduate pilot training up to wings standard.

The operational groups then take over the responsibility for operational training, examples including 410 Squadron and 426 Squadron in Air Transport Group. Other units serve as operational training units for specific types, such as Moose Jaw Base Flight for the CH-118.

Cuts resulting from the 1989 federal budget led to the consideration of privatising primary flying training then being conducted at CFB Portage, which was to be closed. (The question of civilian contractor support for the helicopter and multi-engine schools was also examined and found to be feasible.) A Request For Proposals was issued in March 1991. Of the three bidders, the Canadair-led consortium was selected as the winner. (The other two bidders were Northwest Industries, a subsidiary of CAE Industries, and British Aerospace Canada teamed with Canadian Helicopters.)

The RFP did not contain any stipulation that Portage be retained as the site, but the government decided that training should stay there under civilian contract. The former CFB Portage was taken over by a newly formed, community-based, non-profit group known as Southport Aerospace Centre, Inc. (SACI) in September 1992. It is responsible for the site and attempts are being made to attract aviation-related and dependent industries to the location.

Canadair, as the lead contractor, is responsible for the contract as a whole, and is specifically concerned with the conduct of primary flying training. The sub-contractors who are responsible to Canadair include:
Field Aviation: They are responsible for maintenance of all aircraft used for flying training. These are the Slingsby T67C3 Firefly for primary flying training, the Beech King Air C90A for multi-engine training, and the Bell CH-139 JetRanger for basic helicopter training.
Midwest Helicopters: Canadair sub-contracted the helicopter maintenance. The CH-139s were basically off-the-shelf Model 206Bs. They have been leased to the contractor by the air force and are being given civilian registrations, although military serials will continue to be worn. As of late March 1993, five of the helicopters had received civilian certification and work was proceeding on the remainder. The helicopter instructor pilots are CAF personnel who are assigned to 3 CFFTS (No. 3 Canadian Forces Flying Training School).
Atlantis Aerospace: This company provides all ground-based training systems.

All ground support from ATC to runway clearing and catering is provided by contractors.

Canadian Aviation Training Centre is the name used by the consortium. CFB Portage closed as a military base on 1 September 1992

and was turned over to SACI. The same month, CATC started a 'small group tryout' of 10 primary flying students who subsequently finished a month ahead of schedule with a 100 per cent graduation rate. The first full course was scheduled to begin on 4 January 1993. It was to consist of 26 students and the contract calls for an annual rate of about 150.

By March 1993, all of the King Air C90As were in service and 10 of the T67C3s were flying at Southport. The other two were on hand but were still being reassembled. The King Airs wear a three-digit number (901-908) in addition to their civilian registrations, while the Firefly fleet has numbers from 201 to 212.

As with the JetRangers, air force instructors cover the multi-engine flying training course. Because they are no longer located at a military base, 3 CFFTS is, technically, a detachment from Winnipeg.

In May 1992, the Flying Instructors School (FIS) moved with its Canadair CT-114 Tutors to CFB Moose Jaw, joining 2 CFFTS and the 'Snowbirds' (431 Sqn) there. All of the Tutors at Moose Jaw actually belong to the BAMEO, although all wear unit markings as the aircraft are allocated on a fairly permanent basis. (When the FIS was at CFB Portage, its Tutors also belonged to the Moose Jaw BAMEO.)

2 CFFTS and the FIS have a total of 89 Tutors between them, including those undergoing major servicing in the BAMEO. The 'Snowbirds' have a further 14. Due to the higher stresses resulting from their air show performances, the display team's Tutors are all carefully monitored. The aircraft are moved to different parts of the formation (e.g. inner to outer) and are rotated in and out of the team from time to time. Northwest Industries in Edmonton has a contract covering the modification/demodification and refinishing requirements of an average four such aircraft per year. NWI also has a contract covering the design, installation, testing and documentation of a prototype rewiring of a CT-114 and it is expected that a fleet-wide rewiring will take place.

The expected date for replacing the Tutor is 2005. Several possibilities are being considered, including the Tucano, PC-9, Hawk and the type eventually selected for the US JPATS. There is an extensive liaison on a regular basis between the Air Command Pilot Training Cell and their US and NATO counterparts.

The contract covering privatised flying training at Southport runs for five years and is valued at approximately $165 million. The government has the option of up to two one-year extensions. If it is found to be successful, consideration will be given to extending the privatisation to Moose Jaw. If that happens, it is most likely that it would not extend beyond a contract for maintenance support on the Tutor or on a contractor-supplied replacement aircraft type and that the instructors would still be military personnel. This all remains in the conceptual stages and a final decision will depend on many factors, including the savings incurred through privatising the flying training at Portage la Prairie.

Backbone of the CF training syllabus is the CT-114 Tutor. Of 190 originally purchased, 124 were still flying in mid-1992, with 21 stored.

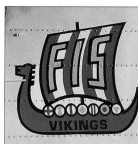

This is the badge of the Central Flying School, located at Winnipeg.

The Flying Instructor School proclaims itself as the 'Vikings'.

The FIS is based at Moose Jaw, and uses the CT-114 to teach instructors. Another important task is to return 'desk jockeys' to flight status after ground tours.

2 CFFTS is the principal training unit, operating the majority of the CT-114s on charge. All of the Tutors are actually maintained by Moose Jaw BAMEO.

The Central Flying School is responsible for standardising the CF training syllabus, and for producing instrument check pilots. Seven CT-114s are assigned to the unit.